ALGEBRA 1
RESCUE!

Teacher's Guide

SOPRIS
WEST
EDUCATIONAL SERVICES

ISBN 1-57035-932-6

Developmental editing by Sandy Rusch
Copy editing by Beverly Rokes
Editorial assistance by Annette Reaves
Text layout by Kathy Bone and Sopris West
Cover design by Maria Coccaro
Production assistance by Scott Harmon

08 07   6 5 4 3

Printed in the United States of America

Published and Distributed by

SOPRIS
WEST™
EDUCATIONAL SERVICES

A Cambium Learning™ Company

4093 Specialty Place • Longmont, CO 80504
(303) 651-2829 • www.sopriswest.com

169ALG/169TG/10-05

Acknowledgments

In addition to the contributing authors who shared ideas and activities for *Algebra 1 Rescue!*, the following people deserve recognition and appreciation for their contributions to the program: Kate Gallaway, educational therapist specializing in mathematics, who reviewed materials and contributed ideas and strategies from the point of view of special needs students; Martha Cantrell, middle school math teacher, who used activities with her students to validate their usefulness and reviewed other activities; Sandy Rusch, math editor, who reviewed activities with regard to correct mathematical use and language; Lynda McKelvey, project director, who reviewed activities and mathematical tests and served as a resource for ideas and suggestions; and, finally, Shirley Bradsby, special education teacher/consultant, who for reviewed materials to determine their appropriateness for special needs students and has spent many years helping Larry understand the type of strategies and classroom management techniques that are necessary for a teacher to reach all students.

About the Authors

Larry Bradsby, senior author

Larry Bradsby, a past president of the National Council of Supervisors of Mathematics, is currently a mathematics consultant and curriculum writer. His consulting work has included projects with the National Association of Educational Progress, school curriculum design, and national curriculum design. In the capacity of curriculum writer, he has developed and directed a nationally validated mathematics program as well as co-authoring the *Math Rescue Series: Resources for Computation,* which provides both special and general education teachers with alternative methods for teaching math computation skills. Prior to his role as consultant and curriculum writer, Larry's math experience included serving as math coordinator in Jefferson County, Colorado, as well as many years of teaching. Despite his numerous projects and commitments, Larry's greatest love is still teaching!

Contributing Authors

Tom Botkin, M.A.: Math and science teacher specializing in working with the low-achieving student. *Major Interest:* Finding a way to reach all students.

Richard "Dick" Bradsby, M.A.: Math teacher, department chair, inservice leader; school award for outstanding teaching. *Major Interest:* Helping students through careful monitoring of progress.

Gene Collins, M.A.: Math and science teacher, computer consultant, curriculum developer. *Major Interest:* Using computers as a modeling device for the classroom.

George Dinwiddie, M.A.: Math teacher, coach, and volunteer tutor. *Major Interest:* Modeling concepts and rules to make mathematics meaningful.

Dean Larsen, Ed.D.: Math and science teacher, city supervisor of mathematics, principal, professor of math education. *Major Interest:* Educational strategies that allow students to be actively involved in formulating rules and concepts.

Hope Law, M.A.: Teacher of mathematics and many other subjects in both the United States and Africa; Colorado Teacher of the Year Finalist. *Major Interest:* Using effective classroom management techniques to maximize learning opportunities.

Jane Walker, M.S.: Math teacher at all grade levels including the International Baccalaureate program; Outstanding Secondary Mathematics Teacher Award, Distinguished Teaching Awards. *Major Interest:* Using a variety of teaching strategies to maximize learning, no matter how difficult the concept.

Art Wilson, Ed.D.: Math teacher, Presidential Award Recipient for Mathematics, city supervisor of mathematics. *Major Interest:* Making mathematics "come alive" using models and applications.

Algebra Readiness Assessment and *Classroom Management for Algebra 1 Rescue!*

Joe Witt, Ph.D., has, throughout his professional career, been actively pursuing answers to questions about how professionals in schools can work together to prevent and remediate problems. This pursuit has led him to publish over 100 papers and 12 books. Through collaboration with teachers and other professionals, he has worked to develop strategies that have face validity, are practical for use in classrooms, and are connected to the effective schools literature. Joe has received numerous awards and national recognition for his work.

Algebra One-Minute Fluency Skill Builders

Ray Beck, Ed.D., co-developer, is currently senior consultant for Sopris West Educational Services, where he trains and consults in the development and dissemination of both positive discipline and fluency programs. As a school psychologist and former director of special education, Ray directed the development of two U.S. Department of Education Validated Projects, "Project RIDE (Responding to Individual Differences in Education)" and "Basic Skill Builders."

Denise Conrad, Ed.D., co-developer, is director of special education in Great Falls, Montana. She has past experience as a teacher and administrator in both general and special education. A primary focus of her work has been to train educators to provide effective educational programs and services to children and adolescents with various types of disabilities. She is a co-developer of the U.S. Department of Education Validated Project "Basic Skill Builders," and she most recently co-authored *Cool Kids: A Proactive Approach to Social Responsibility.*

Peggy Anderson, Ph.D., co-developer, is the superintendent of schools in Frenchtown, Montana. She was an elementary principal for 14 years in Florida and Montana prior to becoming the superintendent of schools. An educator for the past 36 years, Peggy has been an elementary classroom teacher, a special education resource room teacher, and the coordinator of the U.S. Department of Education Validated Project "Basic Skill Builders."

Objectives and Contents

Chapter 1 Variables and Expressions

Chapter 2 Exploring Rational Numbers

Chapter 3 Solving Linear Equations

Chapter 4 Graphing Relations and Functions

Chapter 5 Analyzing Linear Equations

Chapter 6 Solving Linear Inequalities

Chapter 7 Solving Systems of Linear Equations and Inequalities

Chapter 8 Exploring Polynomials

Chapter 9 Using Factoring

Chapter 10 Exploring Quadratic and Exponential Functions

Chapter 11 Exploring Rational Expressions and Equations

Chapter 12 Exploring Radical Expressions and Equations

No DataAnalysis + Probability

Foreword

E ducational reform such as the No Child Left Behind Act needs to address not only the literacy issues in our schools but our educational crisis in math as well. More and more states are implementing higher math standards for students, including the requirement of completing an algebra course prior to graduation. "Algebra for All" has become a frequently stated goal in school reform literature and is supported by the National Council of Teachers of Mathematics (Chambers, 1994). **But, will all students succeed in algebra if it continues to be taught using the current methods?** According to the states that track algebra proficiency levels, on average, 48% of students fail to meet algebra standards. When schools mandate algebra for graduation, this requirement creates a roadblock, particularly for those students who struggle with basic mathematical concepts and skills. How schools address this roadblock is critical to our youths' success in math.

Current Methods

Basal mathematics programs are frequently used to guide instruction. But, these curricula use a spiraling approach that introduces numerous skills at a rapid pace. In order to "get through the book," new skills are introduced quickly without ensuring students' mastery of each concept presented. The primary concerns regarding basal mathematics programs include the following:

- Lack of adequate practice and review
- Inadequate sequencing of problems
- Absence of strategy teaching and step-by-step procedures for teaching problem solving (Wilson & Sindilar, 1991)

In response to these concerns, many districts have spread algebra over two years, with the idea that the same basal program will be used over the two years, allowing for a slower pace. This is not providing intervention, however; it is simply prolonging the inevitable struggle these students will now face over a two-year period rather than one.

Another strategy that some districts have implemented is to introduce algebra at much earlier grades, in the hope that students will "catch on" to these algebraic thinking skills with earlier and repeated exposure. But, how can students who continually struggle with the basic operations of mathematics (addition, subtraction, multiplication, and division) and math concepts in general be expected to master the abstract symbolic representation of algebra?

Diverse classrooms require diverse instructional strategies. When faced with the difficult decision of whether to cover the full curriculum or to spend sufficient instructional time on selected parts of the curriculum to address these diverse needs, many teachers are not sure what to do. If teachers must now ensure that **all** students successfully complete algebra to satisfy new graduation requirements, this issue becomes even more critical.

How Can *Algebra 1 Rescue!* Help?

Successful intervention requires a change in instructional strategies and approaches. For students to apply skills and problem-solving strategies in an algebraic situation, the **concepts** behind the skills must be taught first. *Algebra 1 Rescue!* provides the necessary resources to effectively teach students the concepts and skills required to pass an algebra course. Through the explanation of concepts, students learn not only how to solve problems but also why to use specific techniques. Learning why techniques work helps students generalize what they have learned for future encounters. Engaging students in conversations both with the teacher as well as with peers promotes reflective thinking and develops student-generated problem-solving strategies (Witzel, Smith, & Brownell, 2001).

The lessons in *Algebra 1 Rescue!* follow a three-step process: **concept development**, then **practice**, and finally the application of **problem-solving** skills. Students will be more likely to remember the steps to apply for problem-solving skills and techniques if they first understand and then can fully explain the concepts behind the skills.

The explicit instruction in *Algebra 1 Rescue!* along with the prescriptive pre- and posttest assessments target individual student needs. Teachers may choose from the variety of activities and lessons provided for every objective in each of the twelve chapters. Included are:

- cooperative group activities;
- hands-on activities requiring manipulatives;
- student investigation and problem-solving situations; and
- independent practice activities.

While the No Child Left Behind Act remains at the forefront of our country's educational focus, we must not ignore the fact that we, as math educators, are faced with issues just as critical—bringing our students to the level required to meet higher math standards. To meet these standards, we must realize the importance of intervention. The incorporation of sound, effective approaches into our current instructional strategies **can** make a significant difference, enabling us to fulfill the necessary standards while impacting each and every math student's performance.

—Sopris West Math Consultants

Algebra 1 Rescue!—Introduction

The materials in *Algebra 1 Rescue!* were written to answer the question, "How do I meet the needs of all my students so they experience success in algebra?" With the increased mathematics requirements for graduation, teachers are faced with a different population of students taking higher-level mathematics. With higher curriculum standards being required, students are asked to acquire and master a multitude of concepts. Many secondary students are disadvantaged by this approach to curriculum, and students with disabilities are placed at an even greater disadvantage because of difficulties they experience in acquiring and retaining knowledge (Miller & Mercer, 1997).

Algebra 1 Rescue! is written with a focus on the mastery of objectives rather than using a classroom lesson approach. Crawley, Parma, Yan, and Miller (1996) found that many students acquire skills in a broken sequence and have lower retention rates, which decrease even further as the concepts become more difficult. A lesson approach will not address this problem. Teaching specific skills and using a variety of activities until mastery is achieved will better guarantee student success. With this approach, individualized, small group, or large group instruction can be used depending on the needs of the students and the teaching situation. The *Algebra 1 Rescue!* flexible design allows teachers to design instruction based on student needs and to carefully monitor student progress.

Organization

The *Algebra 1 Rescue!* curriculum is based on the NCTM Algebra Standards. The objectives, or outcomes, are specified for each chapter, with approximately five objectives for each chapter. The activities are designed so that students can be successful regardless of their modality strengths: auditory, visual, or kinesthetic. The program provides teachers with curriculum resources to help students discuss and write about mathematics, model mathematical concepts, and make mathematical connections. The activities are categorized to help teachers with conceptual modeling, practice, and problem solving.

The program's design follows a well-researched nationally validated program, Project STAMM (National Diffusion Network). This design has led to high levels of student success.

Key Components

Management System

The success of *Algebra 1 Rescue!* is based on objectives, diagnosis, activities, evaluation, and records. Students are pretested to determine their needs for the various objectives. The teacher can then select from the concept development, practice, and problem-solving activities provided to support mastery of the objectives. A variety of activities is included so teachers can most effectively match the needs of their students. The concept development activities are particularly important, as research has shown that these activities lead to improvements in acquisition and retention of mathematical concepts (Miller & Mercer, 1993).

At the end of each objective, the students are posttested to determine mastery, and student data are recorded to help guarantee that all students are successful. If mastery has not been achieved, students are given opportunities for further instruction.

Teacher Support

The *Algebra 1 Rescue!* program has been packaged to be user-friendly. Included in the program are a Teacher's Guide, a Teacher's Resource Manual, two Student Books, and a Teacher's Solution Book.

Teacher's Guide:

- Classroom Management for *Algebra 1 Rescue!*

- Listing of all objectives for each chapter

- Sample test for each objective

- Concept development activities for each objective

- Practice activities for each objective

- Problem-solving activities for each objective

- Glossary

Teacher's Resource Manual:

- Blackline masters for activities
- General algebra blackline masters (Appendix materials)
- Readiness test
- Record-keeping masters

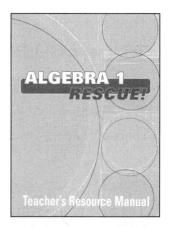

Student Books:

- Pretest for each objective
- Practice worksheets for each objective
- Posttest for each objective
- Chapter tests
- Glossary of algebra terms

Teacher's Solution Book:

- Answer key for the Student Books
- Algebra Fluency CD
- Activity card masters CD

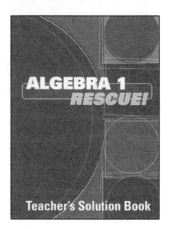

Special Features

Teacher's Guide

Objective Statement

The objective defines the skill or concept that the student is to learn.

Code Number

The code number identifies all the resources from the various products that support the objective.

Sample Test

The sample test illustrates how the objective will be assessed.

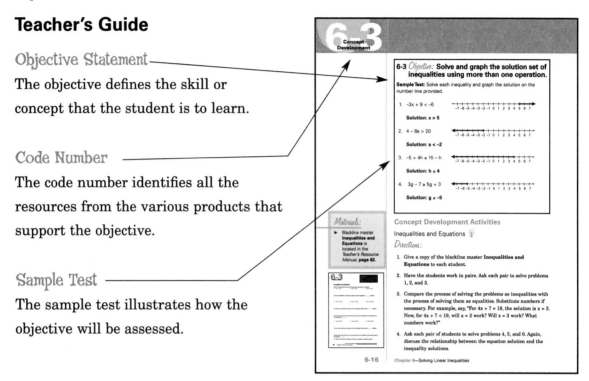

Concept Development Activities

Concept development activities utilize manipulatives as well as other models to give students concrete modeling experiences. Witzel, Smith, and Brownell (2001) stated that explaining concepts helps students learn not only how to solve the problem at hand but also why to use a specific technique. Included with each objective is a variety of activities to match student needs.

Title

Materials

Description

Teacher's Tips

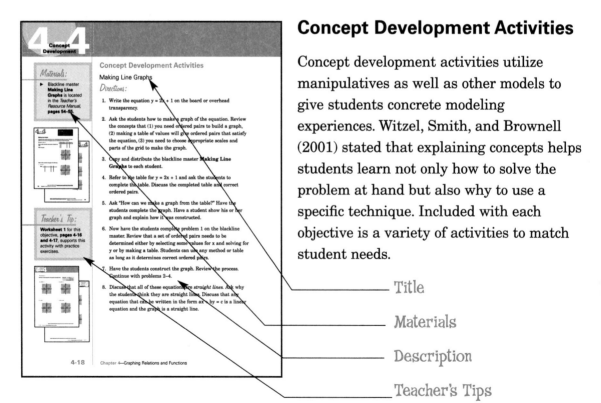

Practice Activities

Designed to reinforce the concept the student has just learned, practice activities build understanding and relevance as well as motivation through personal success. These activities include games, projects, sharing, and problem-solving strategies along with worksheets for additional independent practice.

Title ——————————————

Materials ——————————————

Description ——————————————

Teacher's Tips ——————————————

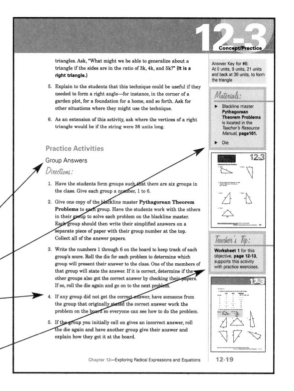

Problem-Solving Activities

The problem-solving activities require students to apply a variety of skills to solve problems related to the specific objective. **A problem-solving logo identifies other activities in the book that require the use of problem-solving skills.** All students participate in problem-solving activities. This experience engages students in the development of student-generated problem-solving strategies and reflective thinking.

Title ——————————————

Materials ——————————————

Description ——————————————

Teacher's Resource Manual

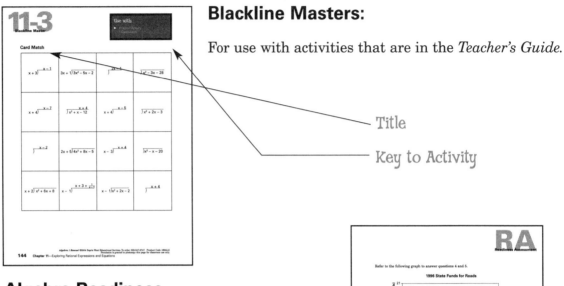

Blackline Masters:

For use with activities that are in the *Teacher's Guide.*

Title

Key to Activity

Algebra Readiness Assessment/Appendix Materials:

Readiness Assessment along with additional blackline masters for students (e.g., graph paper, coordinate grids).

Record-keeping Masters

Class List

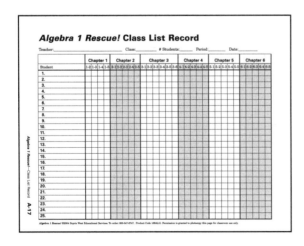

Individual Student Card

Student Books

Contains practice worksheets for each objective. Each worksheet deals with only one concept so the students can develop step-by-step solution strategies. Each objective has multiple practice worksheets.

Worksheet

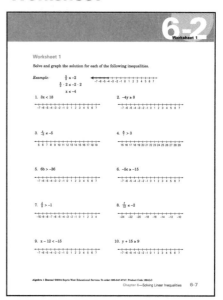

Pre- and Posttests

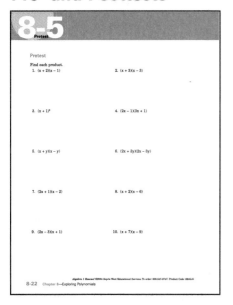

Glossary

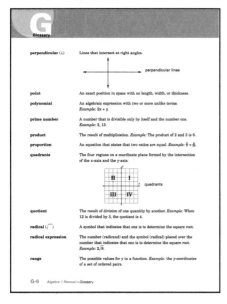

Chapter Tests

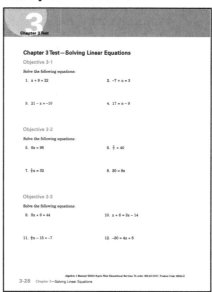

Teacher's Solution Book

Contains answer keys for student worksheets and blackline master activities.

Solutions —————————————————————————⟶

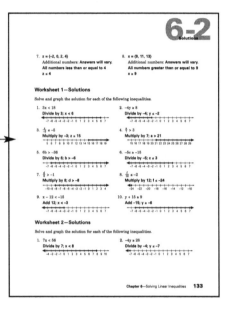

CD-ROM for Blackline Masters: 💿

Many of the lesson activities require the use of teacher/student created materials. This handy CD contains printable PDF files of these materials.

Algebra Fluency CD:

These fluency-building skill sheets were originally validated by the U.S. Department of Education and approved for dissemination through the National Diffusion Network. Research has shown that providing students with opportunities to practice skills and reach proficiency levels, setting clear expectations, and measuring learning help ensure student success. The skill sheets on this CD correlate with the 12 *Algebra 1 Rescue!* chapters.

Classroom Management
for *Algebra 1 Rescue!*

Joe Witt, Ph.D.
Department of Psychology
Louisiana State University

Most teachers will use *Algebra 1 Rescue!* with students who have not been successful in learning math. Students are unsuccessful in math for a variety of reasons. With some, the problem is that they lack the learning strategies that will unlock the door and enable them to be successful. These children want to learn, but they can't, and the techniques in *Algebra 1 Rescue!* will help you address their needs. For other children, behavioral and emotional issues directly interfere with their ability to learn and your ability to teach them. These children may have problems with paying attention, with behavior, or with day-to-day social interactions. Even the best teaching strategies can be defeated by a child who is behaviorally resistant to teaching. For example, a child who continues to talk throughout a well-planned lesson will not benefit from the lesson and may detract from the learning of other children. *Algebra 1 Rescue!* is designed to help you teach the whole child, including the struggling at-risk learner.

This little primer is dedicated to bringing about higher achievement for your students and greater success and happiness for you. In the perfect world, you would not need this information. Children would enter your classroom eager and ready to learn and listen, and you could devote all your energies to delivering world-class instruction. The self-motivated eager student, especially in "remedial" classes, is increasingly difficult to find. And, this comes at a time when the teacher's world is increasingly pressured by the move toward greater accountability and higher test scores.

So, the crux of the situation is this: The children are more difficult to teach, and you are supposed to take them to a higher level. This situation represents a new kind of math in which you have 10 minus 20 and the answer is *supposed* to be 100. Factor in

the lack of prerequisite skills for some students and the "situation" becomes even harder to resolve. How are you supposed to teach factoring when a student cannot multiply or divide? On top of that, when you try to teach children something they cannot do, some would rather disrupt the class than look "stupid" in front of their friends.

The apathy and behavior you may see in your class obviously did not start when the children came through your door. Rather, these behaviors are part of a long chain of events starting, in most cases, years ago in the home and in the primary school. Some children have been carefully trained over the years to annoy you, disrupt your class, and generally ruin day after day.

There is probably nothing you can do about who is in your class, what their problems are, and how much they know. You have this group and you have to teach them. There is hope, however. In most schools, there are teachers who are successful with this group of children and there are teachers who are not successful. What is the key to success? Are the successful teachers more strict? Are they nicer? Do they have a certain kind of personality that children listen to?

Prevention: The key to solving classroom management and discipline problems

The key to teaching success is actually quite simple. One of the most interesting pieces of research over the past 20 years studied effective and ineffective teachers. Effective teachers were defined as those who produced the largest achievement gains in their students. Amazingly, the researchers found that there were no differences between how effective and ineffective teachers *responded to* problems. The difference was in terms of what these two groups of teachers did to *prevent* problems from occurring. The effective teachers did much more up front. They established rules and procedures in their classroom, they taught those rules and procedures, and then they monitored compliance with the rules. The goal for these teachers was to achieve a level of automaticity with how the classroom operated and to free up more time for learning and creative teaching.

Motive and opportunity

We all face decisions. Which should we eat first at dinner, carrots or cake? Should we rent a movie or work in the yard? Should we go to our job at school today or take off for the islands? As adults, we have some appreciation of the consequences of one choice over another. The adolescent mind, in many cases, has not yet developed this respect for consequences, especially those consequences that reside in some uncertain future. If you understand this simple fact, you know 80 percent of what you need to know about adolescent behavior as it pertains to successfully negotiating a 50-minute math period with 25 or more energetic adolescents. Many adolescents will be *choosing* on a moment-by-moment basis what they will do next, and they will be making those *choices* based upon short-term gain rather than long-term consequences.

So, you have 25 or more individuals who will be continually making up their mind in your class about what to do next. Your wish is that they do what *you* want them to do; however, some will opt to do other things.

Two ingredients are required for students to misbehave: motive and opportunity. To prevent behavior problems, you must remove both of these key ingredients. Similar to a firecracker that needs a match to blow up, children need motive and opportunity.

The terms "motive" and "opportunity" should be familiar from crime stories. The police are always searching for the villain's motive and opportunity. This simply means that someone has the time or the occasion and they require some motivation.

Let's examine opportunity first. Put yourself inside the head of a student in your class. When is the best time to get off track or to have a behavior problem? When is the teacher most vulnerable and least likely to notice? If the teacher is kind enough to provide an opportunity, some student will seize that moment. The teacher who is not prepared to get started right from the first second of class is doing two things wrong: He or she is providing an opportunity for students to *choose* what they want to do and wasting valuable instructional time. The teacher who is not prepared to get started right at the beginning of class and who allows students to "sit quietly" is providing a golden opportunity. Likewise, the teacher who has not given explicit instructions on how to work in small groups is providing an opportunity for students to choose how they wish to behave in that setting.

The goal is to keep instruction moving at a fast pace, to bring daily routines to a quick automatic level, and to use that momentum to remove the idle time, which can set the occasion for problematic behaviors to emerge.

Opportunity is only half of the picture, however. If you leave your car unlocked with your purse or wallet visible, you are providing the opportunity for a crime. However, most people who see the purse or wallet will not touch it. They lack a motive, or, at least, they are motivated to avoid being caught and put in jail. In the classroom, you control some, but not all, of the motive part of the equation. Some children will be motivated by the attention they receive from peers. Others will be motivated to get a negative reaction from you.

The best you can do is set up a situation that "helps" students make good choices. That is, you can create a situation where the payoff is more certain and perhaps larger for doing the right thing than the wrong thing. If the consequences for doing the right thing and the wrong thing are so far apart, then the decision by the student becomes a test: One would be "not smart" to choose to behave badly because you have made it very clear what the correct choice is.

Getting ready for success with good planning and preparation

Your job is to engage students in productive learning activities for the entire class period with the goal of helping students to achieve to the fullest. Some students may need to learn the content in order to pass a state mandated test and move on to the next grade. Further, your class may be a prerequisite for students to enter the next class. In that situation, both the students and the teacher of the next class need you to do a good job.

To the extent that some students are not engaged, they are not learning to the fullest and they are perhaps interfering with the learning of others. How do you get them engaged? Even more important, how do you get them engaged from the first minute and keep them engaged? This requires careful planning and meticulous preparation. The teacher who is an effective classroom manager attends to two key aspects for getting off to a good start:

- Planning and implementing procedures to make the best use of the 50-minute class period

- Planning and implementing procedures to hold students accountable for their behavior

These aspects are discussed separately below, but they are very much related. They form a total package. The package must also include lesson planning and delivery.

Planning and implementing procedures to make the best use of the 50-minute class period

How would you feel if you were the first customer to go into a restaurant after it opened for the day, and you noticed that the tables had not been cleaned from the evening before and the floor had not been swept? Then someone came out from the back room and greeted you in a friendly manner, saying, "We are not quite ready. Please be seated and I will be with you in a few minutes." What would your impression be? By analogy, what is the impression of students the first day of class? Perhaps in one class the teacher met them at the door, finger to lips indicating, "Be quiet as you enter my class—it is a place for learning." A student information sheet is handed out immediately. This is followed by a highly structured get-acquainted icebreaker. In another class, the teacher is visiting with a colleague in the hall and enters the classroom late. He then fumbles around for a while attempting to locate something and then says, "Pardon me. I am just not ready for the year to start. We'll do better tomorrow." What would be the difference in perception of students in those two classes? Does it really matter if you, as a teacher, are not quite prepared? You bet it does! Does it matter to you if there are dirty dishes on your table at a restaurant? Certainly.

The next section describes perhaps the most critical of all issues pertaining to classroom management: procedures to get students to do things correctly the first time and every time so you don't have to waste precious instructional time being a disciplinarian.

Defining and teaching expected behavior

Here is a four-step process that will take you through the process of defining and teaching expected behavior.

Step 1: Plan the class period.

This step is easy and should occur well before school begins. During July, lay out by the pool or on the sofa. *(Can you handle this so far?)* Close your eyes and imagine how you will spend the 50 minutes of class time. What do you want to accomplish? A typical sequence might be:

1. Students take their seats.

2. Students turn in their completed homework.

3. Teacher presents new material.

4. Students practice new skills.

5. Students break into cooperative learning groups.

6. Homework assignment is given.

7. Dismissal.

Make your own sequence. Perhaps your Tuesday/Thursday sequence will differ slightly from your Monday/Wednesday/Friday sequence.

Step 2: State explicitly what you expect students to do and not do.

Now, again well before school begins, think about what you expect students to do and, correspondingly, what you expect them not to do for each segment of the class period. What are the trouble areas likely to be? When might the class start to get off track? In the sequence above, how long do students have to take their seats after entering your classroom? What are they supposed to be doing after they get seated? When they turn in their homework, do you expect them to have their names on their papers? Of course you do. How do you want the papers passed in? Is it okay for students to bonk the student in front of them on the head as they pass in their papers? It is important for you to state, explicitly, what you expect students to do and not do for every segment of your class.

Step 3: Teach expected behaviors, rules, and routines.

For each behavior, rule, and routine you expect, you will need to be prepared to teach children what to do and what not to do. Merely stating what you expect is probably not sufficient. You must teach students how to enter the room, take a seat, and wait. You must teach your *particular* way of passing in papers. You must teach students how to transition and move around the room. The idea is to take a little time during the first few days of class to systematically teach the children what you expect. The first few times you have the class transition to cooperative learning groups, you should teach/review the process of transitioning. Think about it as a mini-lesson, but instead of teaching your usual subject matter, you are teaching *behavior.* To teach this lesson *in behavior,* you should have overheads or printed materials. This lesson should be taught as seriously as anything else you teach.

To teach a behavior lesson on, for example, passing in papers, conduct the lesson on one of the first days of class, when students are passing in papers. Divide the lesson into three parts: Tell, Show, and Do. In the *Tell* phase, describe each of the steps. Also specify behaviors you do not want to see, such as touching other students. In the *Show* phase, have a good student demonstrate your way of passing in papers as you talk the student through the steps. Finally, in the *Do* phase, have the students do what is expected slowly while you observe and provide feedback and correct errors. Then, have them practice the behavior two to three times. The goal is to take the routine and make it *automatic.* Within two weeks, when you give the signal to pass in papers, the routine will be done quickly and fluently and no one will have to think about it.

Something very important happens when you get expected behaviors to the automatic level. When something is automatic, you do not have to think about it. This means students will just do it. They are taking a very deep and well-worn path, and the momentum of the routine carries them quickly through it. *This means students are not thinking of other options.* If there are infinite ways to pass in papers, some student will opt to do it some way that is annoying. Make the process automatic, and do not give the students time to think about it.

Step 4: Monitor and reteach.

You can expect to very quickly reduce your involvement in these basic routines. In no time at all, you will need to explain and remind less. Perhaps, for a while, you will put the steps on an overhead to guide the students, but your role will shift from teaching to monitoring and reteaching. It is important to monitor carefully. For some classes of

children, close monitoring of every step will be needed throughout the year. Close monitoring is one of your most effective tools for preventing problems. Monitoring should be active. Walk around the room. Look at all the children. Make frequent comments. Talk about what students are doing. If you notice students doing something incorrectly, reteaching may be needed. In such cases, simply repeat the lesson.

At some point, you will need to decide that you have taught the expected behaviors and that errors made by students are related more to "won't do" than to "can't do." That is, there are only two reasons why children do not perform an expected behavior: Either they cannot do it because they do not know how, or they will not do it because they prefer not to. A major advantage of teaching explicitly what you want is that it removes the excuse of not knowing the rules. What do you do with someone who consistently continues to do things wrong?

The best thing to do is to apply a consequence to the child. And, the best type of consequence is a logical consequence. In this case, an excellent consequence would be to have the child practice the problem area at a time that is inconvenient to him or her. The logic goes like this: As a teacher, your major goal is to engage students in learning activities that maximize their learning and achievement. You take a little bit of valuable class time to teach basic routines and procedures so that, in the long run, you conserve class time. If a student is taking *your* class time by continuing to do simple things the wrong way, a logical consequence would be to take some of that student's time for reteaching. Hence, you might require the student to cut lunch short or to cut a free period short in order to return to your classroom and practice the skill. Ideally, this practice is done at a time when peers are not present, so that student receives no attention from his or her peers. Might this be inconvenient for you? Yes. Does it take some of your time? Yes. Is it worth it? Yes, because you will need to do this only a couple of times with one or two students and the word will get out that you are serious about students doing things correctly in your class and the problems will disappear. Occasionally, you may have a problem that persists. Such problems should be treated as more serious behavior problems and might require consultation with administration. Also see the section below on holding students accountable for their behavior.

Routines and procedures for algebra

This section contains specific proven practices for getting organized for teaching algebra and for teaching students how to meet *your* expectations. Because *Algebra 1 Rescue!* utilizes small group interaction, presented first in this section are strategies for making small group sessions more successful. Following that discusson, the common classroom routine of transitioning is presented. This routine is included for two reasons. First, transitioning is one of the most common routines in the typical algebra classroom. Second, providing some detail about this routine illustrates how it is possible to teach any routine. Using the same general model, you can develop your own routines and teach them at the beginning of the year. The information is adapted from Witt, LaFluer, Naquin, and Gilbertson (1999), *Teaching Effective Classroom Routines,* which can be consulted for procedures for teaching a variety of common classroom routines.

Teaching algebra in small cooperative learning groups

Many of the instructional activities contained in *Algebra 1 Rescue!* rely on dividing the class into small groups in which students interact with one another in various instructionally relevant ways. Obviously, this mode of instruction is effective in assisting students to find a deeper understanding of algebra. However, these groups also bring with them some special classroom management considerations. For example, students will be talking to one another. In fact, they should be *encouraged* to talk with one another. Because these student-to-student interactions are less structured than teacher-directed activities, it is more difficult for students to maintain a learning focus. How can you help to ensure that the student discussions remain instructionally relevant? How do you keep these discussions down to a dull roar?

To be successful, you will need to pay careful attention to the following four phases.

Phase 1: Select the groups and teach the students how to be a group.

The teacher should assemble the groups and include in each a range of abilities and possibly a range of social interaction skills.

How loudly students may talk is of critical importance, so demonstrate the level you expect and have the students practice talking and *listening* when someone else is talking quietly.

Explain group roles, such as how to be a leader and get the group moving, how to provide feedback and how to take and benefit from feedback, and how to get your point across without aggression and other inappropriate strategies.

Phase 2: Start with baby steps.

With certain groups of at-risk students, you may need to start small and gradually increase the amount that students can handle at a group level.

Ways to do this include starting with two-person groups and building gradually to four persons. It is also helpful to provide very structured tasks at first that require very little interaction between group members. In addition, keep group sessions short and gradually lengthen them. From two-person groups working for five minutes on a very structured task, you can gradually increase to four- to five-person groups that can work for longer periods.

Phase 3: Be active during group activities.

Actively *monitor* each group. Group time is *not* the time for preparing your next lesson; rather, it is the time to be extraordinarily vigilant.

Reteach group interaction skills if you notice students interacting too loudly or in a manner that is disrespectful or is not task related.

Set the tone and use your own higher-order thinking skills to jump in and out of groups and elevate the discussion by asking questions that occasion critical thinking.

Phase 4: Build in careful monitoring and evaluation.

The real key to getting the group performance you want is to set up each group activity with the following end in mind: a specific product that can be evaluated. When you evaluate this product, you will connect the group work to evaluation and grading.

Ideally grading for group activities will involve not only a group grade but also grading for group activities at the individual level. Parents and students can become justifiably upset when a good student's grade is affected by a bad group. To prevent this problem, individual grading can be divided into grading on group participation

and on the individual's contribution to the product. The grading of group participation requires meticulous monitoring and note-taking during the group activities.

For very difficult classes, it might be necessary to build in group rewards, which can be very powerful motivators. The general notion is that everyone in the group is rewarded if the group's project is of a certain quality. A good twist on this is to make the reward for the group contingent upon the test performance of the academically weakest member. This needs to be done with care because it can backfire; however, it usually has the effect of motivating the stronger members to mentor and teach the weaker members.

These strategies combined will help to enhance the quality of using the excellent *Algebra 1 Rescue!* activities.

Next, sample classroom routines are presented. The same basic format can be adopted for teaching any of your own unique routines.

Teaching classroom routines: The example of transitioning

Transitioning refers to changing, usually by moving, from one activity to another. A transition occurs, for example, when students move from the typical seating plan to working at computer stations or other learning stations. When transitions take too long, valuable instructional time is lost. Also, because transition periods are frequently less structured than instructional time, they provide students with the opportunity to engage in inappropriate behaviors such as talking and touching.

Getting ready

When teaching a transitioning routine, you will need two things. First, you will need a kitchen timer, preferably a digital timer that beeps loudly at the end of a user-determined time limit. Second, you will need to have the steps involved in transitioning written on an overhead or on the board so that you may review the steps with the students.

Training the children to transition

In introducing a lesson on transitioning to students, begin by explaining what a transition is (i.e., moving from one activity to another in a timely and efficient manner) and describing occasions when the transitioning routine might be used. Tell the students that you will use a particular signal, such as blinking the lights, to get their attention. Following that, you will give them specific directions about what to do and how much time they will have to do it. When you signal, they are to listen closely to you and then immediately move from one activity to another in the manner prescribed by the transition. The training for this, as for other routines, proceeds in a tell-show-do fashion. First, you explain the steps of the transition (i.e., the tell phase). Next, you show the students how to appropriately transition. Finally, you have them *do* the transition while you observe and provide feedback.

Steps

The steps involved in the transitioning routine are as follows:

1. **Signal.** Begin with a signal to get the students' attention.

2. **Tell.** Tell the students exactly what you expect them to do and how you expect them to behave during the transition. For example, "I want you to put away your math workbook and quietly move to your first learning center."

3. **Time limit.** Specify how much time they will have to complete the transition. Typically, in a high school classroom, a transition can be completed within a two-minute time limit. Immediately after you give your instruction for the children to transition, start the timer.

4. **Monitor.** As the students begin to transition, you should actively supervise them as they move from one place to another. This will involve actively scanning the room, walking around the room, and prompting students who are off task.

5. **Feedback.** If the students are able to complete the transition before the time limit is up, give them positive feedback. If all of the students were not able to complete the transition before the two minutes were up, provide positive feedback to those students who did complete the transition and tell the students who did not accomplish the transition in the allotted time that they will need to do better next time. If the problems with the transition are chronic, have the students who are having difficulty come in at a time inconvenient for them to practice the transitioning routine a few times.

6. **Next activity.** Following your feedback to the students, you are ready to begin the next activity.

Again, the transitioning routine is a sample. It is critical for you to identify problem areas in your own classroom and ask yourself the question, "Do my students really know what they are supposed *to do* in this situation?" If the answer is no or maybe not, then ensure that they know what to do by teaching the routines.

Other common classroom routines

Teacher Routines

Giving Directions

Providing Feedback

Providing Correction

Ensuring Student Compliance

Transition Routines

Breaking Into Learning Groups

Bathroom Break

Lining Up and Walking

Entering the Room

Basic Student Routines

Sharpening Pencils

Independent Seatwork

Student Grading

Putting Everything in Its Place

Making Up Missed Work

Special Routines

Welcoming Visitors

Using Free Time

Lunchroom Behavior

Behaving With Substitute Teachers

From: Witt, J.C., LaFluer, L., Naquin, G., & Gilbertson, D. (1999). *Teaching Effective Classroom Routines*. Longmont, CO: Sopris West.

Planning and delivering the lesson

When planning and delivering a lesson, the following issues related to student behavior and discipline should be kept in mind. First, what you expect children to learn and how you teach it are directly related to student behavior. It is not possible to separate teaching and student behavior. It is possible to help yourself a great deal with behavior problems by careful planning and delivery of the lesson. (This book will help you a great deal in that regard.) Your teaching and student behavior are closely related.

Second, the lesson should be at the right level of difficulty for your students. It is very important that lessons be planned such that students are very likely to be successful.

If a lesson is too difficult, you will lose student interest during class presentation and particularly during seatwork. There are two ways to ensure that students are with you. One is to make sure they have the prerequisite skills needed to be in your class. If students cannot multiply or divide, they should not be in an algebra class. Unfortunately, in many schools, teachers have to teach the students they are given. It is worth working within your math department to develop placement tests that assess prerequisite skills. If the math department is organized into a sequence, then you can place the child at the right stage in the sequence so that he or she has the background knowledge to learn the concepts expected in the class. If this is not feasible, you may need to spend additional time working with a student on prerequisite skills or provide an alternative assignment for the student who is unprepared for the class assignment. It cannot be overemphasized that if students cannot do their main job of school work, then they will do other things that potentially mean trouble for you. If students start out being able to do the work, then the second aspect of ensuring that they are with you is to use frequent assessment to make sure they stay with you. If you are losing some students, it might be necessary to reteach a skill, especially those skills that are foundational to subsequent skills.

Third, you must be thoroughly prepared and know your subject matter. Being prepared means having every second of the class period planned. You might write the daily schedule on the board and then stick to it. Being unprepared means that you use some class time to get your thoughts and materials together. And, what are the students supposed to do during that time? Idle? Wait patiently? Adolescents do not idle well. They need structure—moment by moment. Frequently, they view your being unprepared as a sign of weakness and some will seize the moment.

Relatedly, if you do not know what you are talking about and make mistakes about the content, students can quickly lose respect for you as a teacher, and conditions in your classroom can deteriorate. If you do not know the subject matter, then learn it. Study. Get mentoring. You owe it to the students to know the material well enough to explain it to them and assist them in gaining understanding.

Finally, it is immensely helpful if the lesson maintains student interest. An interesting lesson makes it easier for students to choose to pay attention. The wise teacher learns about the interests of students and connects the lesson to those interests. Students are rarely interested in obscure mathematical theories and

proofs. Instead, they are interested in themselves. Involve students in the lesson. Put them on the spot. Regularly and randomly ask open-ended questions or questions to keep students tuned in.

Managing behavior problems

The effective classroom manager does everything possible to help students be more responsible and to make good decisions about how to behave in the classroom. Despite all those efforts, behavior problems may still occur. As teachers, we must work with an increasingly diverse group of students. Disorders such as attention deficit-hyperactivity disorder have increased dramatically. Some children suffer from parental neglect and do not really care about pleasing you or any other adult. Many other children get everything they want at home and are just plain spoiled. Despite your best efforts to *prevent* problems, students will test you by talking back, by walking around without permission, by pushing the limits, and so forth. The well-prepared teacher must be ready for these inevitable challenges. Below is a step-by-step process for reducing behavior problems. It is similar in format to the process discussed earlier for teaching classroom routines, but it focuses on the prevention of behavior problems.

Step 1: Make sure students know what to do.

If you ask students what they have to do to stay out of trouble in class, many will say, "Don't hit, don't swear, don't talk" or, in other words, don't do this and don't do that! Most have a very good idea of some *general* things they are *not* supposed to do. For you to be effective in preventing behavior problems you need to prepare a very specific list of acceptable behaviors so that you know, and your students know, when students are getting off track. If there is a gray area, then students will exploit it and you will be more tentative in your response. For many students, a teacher being tentative or delaying his or her response to a problem provides an open invitation to continue the problem behavior, argue with the teacher, or escalate the behavior.

To solve this problem, you need some rules for behavior. Although it is tempting to make a long list of what *not* to do, this is often ineffective. First, there are simply too many possible things not to do, and, hence, it is impossible to list all of them. Would you think to have a rule that no student should cut his or her hair during class?

Probably not, but that is exactly what happened in a classroom in Louisiana. Second, you want to set a tone that you have high positive expectations for students to act like responsible young adults. A laundry list of bad behaviors sets the opposite tone.

Consider having a short list stating your expectations for what students are supposed *to do*. By being a little bit creative, you can develop a list such that if students are not doing these things, then what they *are* doing is potentially a problem behavior. Take, for example, this rule: "Follow instructions." This is an all-purpose rule that indicates it is a rule to do what *you* say. This covers a lot of different areas and can include following written instructions for assignments, and so forth.

With a little thought, you can come up with a simple, understandable list of four to six "rules" or expectations. Most teachers address general areas, such as working cooperatively with others, working independently, and listening attentively during presentations. Most of all, you want your students to do what you tell them to do.

As you develop classroom rules, bear the following in mind: Never make a rule you won't enforce. The key to good behavior is being consistent. Say what you mean—mean what you say.

Step 2: Teach the rules.

As with classroom routines and procedures, it is important to spend a little time at the beginning of the year reviewing classroom rules and talking about what they mean. This is a good time to talk about misbehavior, because some students may not "get it" that problem behaviors are covered by the rules.

Step 3: Monitor and provide consequences.

Consequences should be provided for both following the rules and not following the rules, even during the first few weeks of school. Remember, if there is more payoff for not following the rules than for following the rules, then you have set up a "test" that many students will "pass" by choosing options you will not like. So, find every opportunity to be positive. Sometimes it is better to provide positive or negative feedback privately. Some children feel it makes them look like the "teacher's pet" if they are praised in front of their peers, and these feelings turn a positive experience into a negative one. As with many other teacher situations, you need to read the situation.

Developing effective consequences

Effective classroom managers select a handful of consequences that they use sparingly in response to behavior problems. Consequences must meet some relatively stringent criteria. First, your primary goal is for the students to learn as much as possible. Hence, consequences should ideally be applied quickly in the classroom causing minimum interference or delay of ongoing instruction. Second, the consequence must be easily available to you. The consequence of moving close to a talking child is almost always available to you, whereas having a child stay after school is not available in many cases. If a consequence may not be available, do not put it on the list you will use because consistency is the key to discipline. Further, when you dole out a consequence, make sure the children experience the consequence 100 percent of the time they carry out the behavior. Say what you mean—mean what you say. Always.

There are three basic types of consequences: changing the environment to make the behavior less desirable, removing something positive, and applying something negative.

Changing the environment to make the behavior less desirable. The first type of consequence, making an environmental change, is often the easiest and most appropriate for mild problems. A prime example is proximity, where you move closer to the student who is misbehaving and do nothing else. Your presence will make it less desirable for the student to talk to others, make noises, daydream, and so on. And, the lesson continues without interruption. A second example of teacher response in this category, often used when several students start to lose touch with the lecture or task at hand, is to redirect the group focus by asking some questions or making the lesson more personal to the students.

Removing something positive. The second general category of consequences is the removal of something positive. This means that when an inappropriate behavior occurs, you take away something that the child values. Usually this involves removing free time or removing access to the group. For example, you may require that lost learning time be made up during lunchtime or some other free period. In essence, this is taking away the free time the student already has. Access to the group and participating with the group are privileges, often ones that students don't realize they enjoy! Isolating a student from the group by asking him or her to move

to the side of the room or sending the student out of the room, then, represents a loss to some students who value being with the group.

Applying something negative. The third category of consequences to reduce inappropriate behavior is to apply or give the student something negative in response to a behavior problem. This category is often the most common in schools. When a child breaks a rule, then the teacher dishes out something punishing as a consequence. Some "negatives" commonly employed by teachers include assigning a fine or penalty, assigning detention, assigning a mediation essay, or referring the student to an administrator.

Using consequences for rule violations

Once you have in place some rules and consequences for breaking the rules, then your focus, with regard to inappropriate behavior, should turn to applying consequences and rules consistently. A good idea is to divide rule violations into three broad categories: mild problems, moderate problems, and severe problems. Consequences should then be applied based upon the severity of the problem such that the punishment fits the crime. You have to decide for yourself what behaviors go into each of the categories.

It is strongly recommended that you commit firmly to memory a list of negative consequences for specific behavior problems. By doing so, you will be able to make quick automatic decisions, and this will help you notice behaviors and respond immediately. Sometimes we do not respond because we are not sure what to do (or we are too busy teaching to notice the behaviors!). It would not be too extreme to make yourself a set of flashcards with a behavior on the front and a consequence on the back. For *talking,* you might write *proximity*. After the note cards are developed, study them and memorize them to the point that you can do 15 cards correctly in 15 seconds. This means you can make discipline decisions in a split second!

Responding to specific discipline issues

This section addresses how to deal with specific discipline issues. The topics include some of the common, and not so common, behaviors that are challenging to teachers. Although this section is organized in somewhat of a cookbook manner, it is important to keep in mind that for most discipline problems, one size does not fit all. Different

children may engage in the same behavior for different reasons. One child may cause a disruption to get attention from peers, whereas another may cause a disruption in order to be sent to the office to avoid work. For each discipline issue discussed below, some possible reasons for why this problem may be occurring are presented. Effective classroom managers closely observe their students to try to determine what they are getting out of the problem behaviors in which they engage, for they know that is the key to solving the discipline problem. One does not need to look too deep into the child psyche. It is usually sufficient for the teacher to examine what is happening immediately after the behavior. This tells you what the child is getting out of the behavior or what the pay-off is. If you find no clues in what is happening immediately after the behavior, then examine what was happening at the time the behavior started. Was the task at hand boring? Did the behavior occur during a transition or other more unstructured activity? These types of information provide further data about what might be contributing to the problem.

Talking without permission

What is it? Talking without permission usually occurs when a student engages in dialogue with another student, but it could involve a student talking to himself or herself.

Why does it occur? Students may talk to peers to get their attention. Students find talk interesting. Gossip about who did what at the football game last Friday night is fun. Hence, students sometimes talk to get the attention of their peers. Students who use talking to get out of something may be doing it to avoid the boredom of independent seatwork or the boredom of a lecture.

What to do about it. The reasons for this behavior occurring can be viewed as opposite sides of a coin. That is, a student who talks because he or she is bored may also be getting peer attention. Hence, the two reasons are sometimes related. If you believe that the primary reason a student is talking is to get peer attention, then the obvious solution is to remove the peer attention. This can be done by applying a consequence of moving the student or temporarily isolating the student within the room. The latter is most effective if there is a small area of classroom in which the student can sit and not face his or her peers. If you believe the primary reason that a child is talking is to get out of or avoid work, then a logical consequence of this

behavior is to make sure that the student does not get out of the work. The basic philosophy is that if a student takes some of your time then you will take his or her time. This may mean that the student has to return to your classroom after school or before school the next day to make up the time. Another alternative is for the student to return to your classroom during a free period or at lunch. Some teachers are reluctant to give up "their time" in order to impose a consequence such as this. However, most children, after experiencing this consequence, will be very motivated to avoid experiencing it in the future. Hence, it will not be necessary to use this type of consequence very often. Students will get the idea very quickly and will respect "your time."

What makes these strategies effective? These strategies are effective because they attempt to remove the desired consequence for talking. The child who talks to get peer attention is less likely to talk if access to peer attention is denied. The child who talks to get out of work will be less likely to do so if work has to be made up at a time that is inconvenient for the child.

Disrespect for teacher authority

What is it? Defiance of teacher authority is a situation in which the teacher tells a student either to stop doing something or to do something and the student makes an outright refusal, often in a loud and disrespectful manner. This is understandably a very serious concern for most teachers. In most schools, fortunately, it occurs infrequently.

Why does it occur? A lot of research has gone into understanding the type of child who would defy teacher, parent, or adult authority. Such defiance is a surprising and bold move to many middle-class teachers who are unaccustomed to confrontation. However, the student who engages in this type of interaction often is extremely comfortable with it. The student has practiced the interaction, usually in his or her home, many, many times over a period of years. Frequently, the child has learned at home that this method of interacting with adults "works." Some children merely find it enjoyable to be mean and obnoxious. Occasionally, children will exhibit this kind of behavior in order to be removed from the classroom and sent to the office. These children want to be removed from the classroom, sometimes because they want to avoid what is happening or is about to happen in the classroom. A student who

cannot read in the ninth grade may, for example, engage in this type of behavior in order to be sent to the office so that she does not have to demonstrate that she cannot read in front of her peers.

What to do about it. The student who demonstrates disrespect needs to know that he or she has clearly "crossed the line" and that this behavior is unacceptable. When discussing classroom rules early in the year, many teachers review instances of rule violations, as mentioned earlier. At that time, it is a good idea to review behaviors such as disrespect for teacher authority to indicate when the student has in fact crossed the line. Some teachers use another strategy to indicate when a student has crossed the line. They use a special phrase to denote that the student is engaging in an inappropriate behavior. One such special phrase is, "I need you to." In this case, the teacher may say, "I need you to stop talking now and return to your seat." Whenever the teacher uses the special phrase, "I need you to," it tells the student that the teacher means business and that it is time to stop whatever is occurring. Ideally, this conversation occurs privately so that other students do not hear the conversation and the noncompliant student is not worried about "saving face." The teacher should remain neutral and try to avoid becoming angry. Becoming angry and/or losing neutrality can cause the situation to escalate.

If a student fails to respond to your requests beginning with "I need you to," then it may be necessary to impose a small penalty. For example, the student may lose some participation points for the day or may have to spend some additional time with you at the end of the day. After imposing the penalty, the student should be sent to the office. If the student fails to accept this consequence and leaves the classroom, then you will need to call the office or send another student to the office for assistance. Most schools have clear policies for major problems such as defiance of teacher authority. If your school does not have such a policy, work with your administration to form one. Situations like this are potentially explosive because they can escalate from verbal confrontation to physical confrontation, so they need to be dealt with swiftly and calmly, and every attempt should be made to defuse rather than escalate the situation.

Absolute apathy about everything

What is it? At the opposite end of the behavior continuum, although equally frustrating, is the student who lacks the interest or motivation to do anything. This type of student seldom displays negative behaviors, but rather sits quietly and does absolutely nothing all the time. Attempts to get the child engaged or interested generally go nowhere.

Why does it occur? This situation can occur for many reasons, and it is often difficult to determine the true cause. Sometimes an individual conference with a child or a parent-child conference may help you to understand why it is occurring and give you some clues about how to solve it. The child may be severely depressed. Perhaps the behavior has occurred in reaction to a traumatic event, such as the death of a parent. This type of behavior may also occur when a student cannot do the academic work. He or she prefers to sit quietly rather than to show you and possibly everyone else how "stupid" he or she is. Other children may engage in this type of behavior because they see that it frustrates you and gives them "power" over you. You cannot make them do anything that they do not want to do.

What to do about it. Often, this is one of the most difficult problems to respond to effectively for the simple reason that the child seems unmotivated by everything. This is in contrast to most children with discipline problems, who respond to some type of motivational or incentive-based intervention. With some patience, you can go through a series of "rule outs" in an attempt to get down to whether the child's problem is truly a motivational issue or whether it is something else. The first thing to rule out is the possibility that the child has some serious emotional concerns. Children with clinical depression are often unmotivated even to engage in simple life processes such as eating. Perhaps the child did experience some traumatic event. To rule out this possibility, an assessment by a counselor or a psychologist may be helpful.

The second area to rule out is the possibility that the child has serious academic deficits. To rule out this possibility, you can conduct a simple test referred to as a "can't do/won't do" assessment. (See *One Minute Functional Assessment* by Witt and Beck for a full description of this procedure.) To conduct this test, ask the child along with all the other children to complete a normal classroom assignment. Then collect the papers. The assignment should be one that takes 10 minutes or less to complete. After the child has completed the assignment under "normal" circumstances, talk to

the child privately and ask the child to repeat the assignment. Tell the child that he had gotten "x" number correct and that if he can get more correct then he will receive a reward. The reward should be something small, easily accessible, and affordable to you. If the child dramatically increases his score during this assessment, then he has a "won't do" problem, which means that he can do the work, but simply prefers not to. Based upon the results of the "can't do/won't do" assessment, you will have two options. If the student does not improve on the assignment, then the student may actually have a skill problem and not be able to do the work. There is also the possibility that the child was unmotivated by whatever reward was offered and additional assessment may be warranted. If the child did improve dramatically on the "can't do/won't do" assessment, then the child has a motivational problem.

What to do about it. Depending upon what you determined by going through the various "rule outs," you can decide upon a strategy for dealing with the problem. If a counselor discovers that the child has been through some traumatic events and has emotional problems, additional counseling may be warranted. If you discover that the child lacks basic academic skills, placement in your classroom may be inappropriate. If the child must remain in your classroom, then providing work at a different level may be necessary. If the child is apathetic and lacks motivation, then the key will be to try to find something that might address the problem. One strategy here would be to involve the parents and make a contract with the student. The contract would entail setting some goals for the student to accomplish. You might include some simple goals such as bringing materials to class, completing assigned work, participating in class discussions, and performance on tests. These goals should be put onto a sheet of paper, and every day you should indicate with a check mark or a numerical rating how the child did with respect to the goals. The child should be required to take the paper home, review it with his or her parents, and receive something desirable if the goals were accomplished at a pre-specified level. The reason to involve the parents is that your normal motivational schemes have not worked with the student and parents typically know a wider range of things that can motivate the child, such as outings, special meals, and so forth.

What makes these strategies effective? The strategies are more likely to be effective if you can discern the cause of the problem. The utterly apathetic child is most

difficult to deal with, and if the child is not motivated by anything, he or she is going to be extremely difficult to reach even with parent cooperation.

Summary

Although consequences and other techniques described here often come quickly to mind for most teachers when thinking about "classroom management," they should be the last resort. Your goal should be to never use them. Instead, it is far better to begin with two key ingredients:

- Teach an interesting lesson in which there is a high likelihood that the students will succeed.

- Use proactive classroom management techniques, such as teaching routines and procedures.

Focusing on these two guidelines will prevent all but a few "discipline" problems. Those problems can then be handled swiftly and your teaching can proceed.

Variables and Expressions

1-1 Translate verbal expressions into mathematical expressions and vice versa.

1-2 Evaluate expressions by using the order of operations.

1-3 Solve open sentences by performing arithmetic operations.

1-4 Use mathematical properties to evaluate expressions.

1-1 *Objective:* Translate verbal expressions into mathematical expressions and vice versa.

Sample Test: Write a mathematical expression that is equivalent to the given verbal expression.

1. Three times nineteen decreased by twenty-seven

   Solution: 3 × 19 − 27

2. Nine times the quantity seven minus five

   Solution: 9 × (7 − 5)

Write a verbal expression that is equivalent to the given mathematical expression.

3. 29 − 3 × 7

   Solution: Twenty-nine minus three times seven

4. 3% × (55 − 7)

   Solution: Three percent of the quantity fifty-five minus seven

Concept Development Activities

Different Verbal Expressions for One Mathematical Expression ☼

Directions:

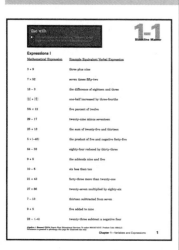

Materials:

▶ Blackline master **Expressions I** is located in the *Teacher's Resource Manual,* **page 1.**

1. Give each student a copy of the blackline master **Expressions I** for this activity.

2. Call on different students to read aloud the verbal expressions for the mathematical expressions. Some problems may have to be repeated, depending on class size.

3. For maximum inductive reasoning practice, skip now to step 6. If the class seems to need more help, do steps 4 and 5.

4. Based on the information on the blackline master **Expressions I**, identify five or six different ways that the addition of two numbers, such as the mathematical expression 5 + 2, could be represented verbally.

5. Do not identify the different ways of stating multiplication and subtraction. Let the students discover them while performing steps 6 through 8.

6. On the board or overhead transparency, write a new mathematical expression that uses multiplication.

7. Ask the students to come to the board one at a time to write a different verbal expression for this new mathematical expression. Continue this process until four or five different but equivalent verbal expressions have been written for the new mathematical expression. Allow the students to use the blackline master as a guide.

8. Repeat the process in steps 6 and 7 using a new expression each time that involves addition, multiplication, or subtraction. The expressions should involve only one operation. See the following expressions for examples:

Do in small grps with a large class. + give different expressions

a. $9 + 7$

(1) nine plus seven

(2) nine increased by seven

(3) the sum of nine and seven

(4) seven more than nine

(5) nine added to seven

b. 13×6

(1) thirteen times six

(2) thirteen by six

(3) the product of thirteen and six

(4) thirteen multiplied by six

c. $27 - 9$

(1) the difference of twenty-seven and nine

(2) twenty-seven minus nine

(3) twenty-seven reduced by nine

(4) nine less than twenty-seven

(5) nine subtracted from twenty-seven

(6) twenty-seven subtract nine

Different Verbal Expressions for One Mathematical Expression Involving Two Operations and Symbols of Grouping

Directions:

1. Give each student a copy of the blackline master **Expressions II** for this activity.

2. Discuss the terms "variables" and "algebraic expression" with the students.

3. Call on different students to read aloud the verbal expressions for the mathematical expressions. Some problems may have to be repeated, depending on class size.

4. Divide the class into groups of four.

5. Assign each group a mathematical expression involving at least

Materials:

▶ Blackline master **Expressions II** is located in the *Teacher's Resource Manual*, **page 2.**

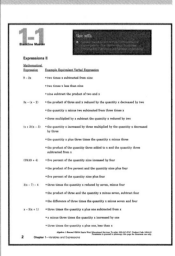

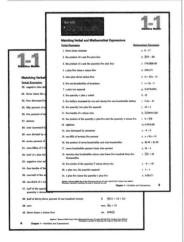

two operations and at least one pair of grouping symbols. For example,

$$3(x - 7) - 19 \qquad 5x - 3x \qquad 2(8 - 6) \qquad (2 + 15) - 9 \times 3$$

Variation: Ask the groups to make up their own expressions.

6. Ask each group to write at least three differently worded verbal expressions for their mathematical expression.

7. Ask one member of the group, one group at a time, to write the mathematical expression and the three differently worded verbal expressions on the board.

8. Ask the other groups to evaluate the work of the group at the board. Offer extra credit points to each group that finds errors in the work on the board; offer extra credit points to the group at the board if there are no errors.

Practice Activities

Matching Verbal and Mathematical Expressions

Directions:

1. Have the students work in groups of two to match as many verbal and mathematical expressions as possible on the blackline master **Matching Verbal and Mathematical Expressions**.

2. Discuss the mathematical terms "powers," "squared," and "cubed" with the students.

3. Call on various groups and list their answers on the board.

4. Encourage the other students to raise their hands and object if they disagree with the answer given by the group responding.

5. For the rest of this activity, use only those expressions on the blackline master **Matching Verbal and Mathematical Expressions** for which there is a major disagreement. Ask pairs of students to discuss the problems for which there are major disagreements.

6. Call on pairs of students to verbally justify the answer they think is correct. Discuss related examples until there is class agreement.

7. **Variation:** Cut out the mathematical expressions on the blackline master and put the slips of paper in a container. Have students take turns drawing one slip and finding on the blackline master the verbal expression that matches it.

Writing Equivalent Verbal and Mathematical Expressions

Directions:

1. Have the students form pairs.

2. Give each student pair one copy of the blackline master **Writing Equivalent Verbal and Mathematical Expressions**.

3. Ask each student pair to complete the blackline master by filling in the missing verbal and mathematical expressions.

4. When the student pairs are finished, ask each pair to exchange papers with another pair and ask them to check each other's work.

5. When all student pairs are finished with their checking, ask one pair to write an incorrect example, if they found one, and their correction on the board.

6. Discuss as many examples as possible in this way, using data generated by the students.

7. Have the class reach consensus on the correct answer for each example presented.

Teacher's Tip:

Worksheet 2 for this objective, **page 1-3**, supports this activity with practice exercises.

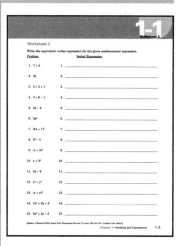

Materials:

▶ Blackline master **Writing Equivalent Verbal and Mathematical Expressions** is located in the *Teacher's Resource Manual,* **page 5.**

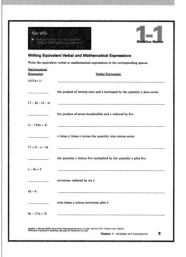

Materials:

▶ Large sheets of newsprint

▶ Marking pens

▶ Blank 3 × 5 cards

Teacher's Tip:

Worksheet 3 for this objective, **page 1-4**, supports this activity with practice exercises.

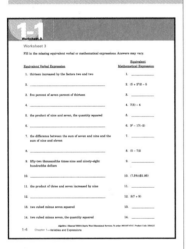

Teacher's Tip:

This activity should be done after a complete discussion of the examples in the preceding Practice Activity, **Writing Equivalent Verbal and Mathematical Expressions.**

Problem-Solving Activity

Creating Closely Related Verbal and Mathematical Expressions ☼

Directions:

1. Divide the class into groups of three.

2. Give each group one sheet of newsprint and a marking pen.

3. Direct each group to write two closely related mathematical expressions on the newsprint, one at the top and one in the middle. Examples of such expressions include $(x + 5)(x - 5)$ and $(x + 5x - 5)$; or $3(x + 3) - 3(x - 3)$ and $3x + 3 - 3x - 3$.

4. Post each group's newsprint on the wall.

5. Ask each group to study another group's newsprint and write an equivalent verbal expression for each mathematical expression on separate 3 × 5 cards. Have the groups tape the cards on the newsprint below the corresponding mathematical expression.

6. Have the groups move on to another group's newsprint and repeat step 5.

7. Ask each group to check the cards on their own newsprint. The groups should mark a large "C" by each correct 3 × 5 card. They should mark a large "X" by each incorrect 3 × 5 card.

8. For those cards identified as incorrect, all of the students involved should discuss the differences and come to consensus about the correct answer. They should then, if necessary, post a new card with the correct verbal expression. Ask all students to check the work on all charts.

9. **Variation:** Reverse the process on another day, starting with student-generated verbal expressions and moving to mathematical expressions.

1-2 *Objective:* **Evaluate expressions by using the order of operations.**

Sample Test: Find the values of the given mathematical expressions.

1. $14 - 6 \times 2 + 8 - 10$

   Solution: 0

2. $5 \times 5 - 3 - 7 \times 2$

   Solution: 8

Find the values of the algebraic expressions with the given variables.

3. $ab - c$, when $a = 5$, $b = 3$, and $c = 6$

   Solution: 9

4. $(x + 5)(x - 5)$, when $x = 7$

   Solution: 24

Concept Development Activities

Student Concept Attainment for Order of the Operations Addition and Multiplication ☀

Directions:

1. Define the concept as determining the order of operations in numerical expressions involving only addition and multiplication without grouping symbols.

2. The goal for this activity is to identify the critical attributes (rules) of the concept. ***Do not give these rules to the students.***

   The rules are:

   a. First, perform all multiplications in order from left to right.

   b. Second, go back and perform all additions or subtractions in order from left to right.

3. Create as many examples as possible, both positive (correct examples that contain all of the attributes of correct calculation) and negative (incorrect examples that contain some but not all of the attributes of correct calculation). Use the examples given below and make up additional examples if needed. Write two lists on the board, one labeled "Positive or Correct Examples" and the other labeled "Negative or Incorrect Examples."

Materials:

► At least one sheet of newsprint for each example (10 or more)

► Markers

► Tape

Positive or Correct Examples	Negative or Incorrect Examples
$3 \times 5 - 4 + 2 \times 3 = 17$	$2 \times 7 + 1 + 3 \times 3 = 54$
$2 + 3 \times 5 - 6 + 1 - 5 + 2 \times 8 = 23$	$1 + 2 \times 5 - 10 + 6 + 3 \times 4 - 10 = 46$
$9 - 7 + 3 \times 2 \times 3 - 14 + 5 \times 2 = 16$	$11 - 7 + 5 \times 3 - 1 - 2 \times 4 = 96$
$5 \times 5 + 2 \times 7 - 20 + 2 \times 3 = 25$	$2 \times 2 + 3 \times 4 - 15 + 3 \times 4 = 64$
$2 \times 3 + 3 \times 4 + 4 \times 5 = 38$	$2 + 3 \times 3 + 4 \times 4 + 5 = 65$

4. Introduce the process to the students: Ask the students to study
    each example separately and to list the exact steps taken to get
    the answer shown. The goal is for the students to identify what is
    essential for correct calculation (the rules for order of operations
    for addition and multiplication).

5. Present each of the examples separately to the students, working
    with the class to make a clearly labeled chart, like the ones below,
    for each problem. Do this on newsprint or on the board, having
    the students fill in the mathematical and verbal expressions.
    Examples are given next. Keep all charts available on the walls
    or the board so the students can examine them simultaneously
    when they are finished.

Positive or Correct Example: $3 \times 5 - 4 + 2 \times 3 = 17$

Mathematical Evaluation Process	Verbal Statement of Evaluation Process
$3 \times 5 - 4 + 2 \times 3 = 15 - 4 + 2 \times 3$	Multiply 3 times 5 and replace that operation with 15.
$= 15 - 4 + 6$	Multiply 2 times 3 and replace that operation with 6.
$= 11 + 6$	Add 15 and negative 4 and replace that operation with 11.
$= 17$	Add 11 and 6 and replace that operation with 17.

Negative or Incorrect Example: $2 \times 7 + 1 + 3 \times 3 = 54$

Mathematical Evaluation Process	Verbal Statement of Evaluation Process
$2 \times 7 + 1 + 3 \times 3 = 14 + 1 + 3 \times 3$	Multiply 2 times 7 and replace that operation with 14.
$= 15 + 3 \times 3$	Add 14 and 1 and replace that operation with 15.
$= 18 \times 3$	Add 15 and 3 and replace that operation with 18.
$= 54$	Multiply 18 by 3 and replace that operation with 54.

How one got the incorrect answer!

Positive or Correct Example: $2 + 3 \times 5 - 6 + 1 - 5 + 2 \times 8 = 23$

Mathematical Evaluation Process	Verbal Statement of Evaluation Process
$2 + 3 \times 5 - 6 + 1 - 5 + 2 \times 8$ $= 2 + 15 - 6 + 1 - 5 + 2 \times 8$	Multiply 3 times 5 and replace that operation with 15.
$= 2 + 15 - 6 + 1 - 5 + 16$	Multiply 2 times 8 and replace that operation with 16.
$= 17 - 6 + 1 - 5 + 16$	Add 2 and 15 and replace that operation with 17.
$= 11 + 1 - 5 + 16$	Add 17 and negative 6 and replace that operation with 11.
$= 12 - 5 + 16$	Add 11 and 1 and replace that operation with 12.
$= 7 + 16$	Add 12 and negative 5 and replace that operation with 7.
$= 23$	Add 7 and 16 and replace that operation with 23.

6. Develop a concept definition: After the students have studied all of the charts, ask the students to write a definition or rule for the correct calculation of an expression involving addition and multiplication. By studying all of the charts together, the students should be able to "induce" the rule stated in step 2.

Powers and Division as Forms of Multiplication

Directions:

1. Divide the class into pairs of students.

2. Write the first problem (see #8 below) on the board or on a transparency.

3. Have one student in each pair rewrite the expression in an equivalent form using only multiplication and addition.

4. Have the other student in the pair evaluate the expression activity to the knowledge gained in the previous Concept Development Activity, **Student Concept Attainment for Order of the Operations Addition and Multiplication**.

5. Choose a student pair at random to show their work on the board, with each student showing his or her own part.

6. Ask the class for corrections if necessary.

7. Repeat steps 3 through 6 using another problem from the list in step 8.

8. *Example:* Problem: $3^2 \times 5 + 2 \times 3 + 7 + 20 \div 5$

    Equivalent Expression: $3 \times 3 \times 5 + 2 \times 3 + 7 + 20\left(\frac{1}{5}\right)$

    Evaluation: $45 + 6 + 7 + 4 = 62$

Answer Key for #8:

a. 19	b. 21	c. 21
d. 21	e. 25	f. 2
g. 1	h. 3	i. 2
j. 1	k. 47	l. 20
m. 24		

Problems:

a. $3 + 6 \times 2^3 \div 3$
b. $17 + 3 \times 2^3 \div 6$
c. $5^2 \times 3 \div 5 + 6$
d. $16 \div 8 \times 2^3 + 5$
e. $2^3 + 3^2 + 4 \times 2$
f. $5 \div 5 + 2^2 \div 4$
g. $21 \times 3 \div 7 \div 9$
h. $24 \div 6 \times 6 \div 8$
i. $3^2 \times 2^2 \div 36 + 1$
j. $3 \times 5^2 \times 2 \div 5 \div 30$
k. $2^2 + 3^2 \times 2 + 5^2$
l. $5^2 \times 4 \div 10 \times 2$
m. $2^3 \times 3^2 \div 3$

Inserting Grouping Symbols in an Incorrect Expression to Correctly Yield an Identified Value

Directions:

1. Review the rule for the order of operations: (1) inside grouping symbols first; (2) exponents left to right; (3) multiplications and divisions left to right; (4) additions and subtractions left to right.

2. Present the following eight incorrect problems and have the students insert grouping symbols to make the equations correct. Remind the students that the order of the grouping symbols, when they are embedded, is { [( )] }.

Negative or Incorrect Example	Example Corrected
$3 \times 6 + 4 = 30$	$3 \times (6 + 4) = 30$
$5 + 2 \times 3 = 21$	$(5 + 2) \times 3 = 21$
$2 + 3 \times 4 + 5 = 45$	$(2 + 3) \times (4 + 5) = 45$
$2(3 + 4) + 2 \times 3 = 48$	$[2(3 + 4) + 2] \times 3 = 48$
$2 + 3 \times 6 - 5 \times 4 = 100$	$\{[(2 + 3) \times 6] - 5\} \times 4 = 100$
$6 \times 5 - 3 + 3 \times 2 = 30$	$[6 \times (5 - 3) + 3] \times 2 = 30$
$2 \times 2 + 3 \times 4 - 15 + 3 \times 4 = 64$	$\{[(2 \times 2 + 3) \times 4 - 15] + 3\} \times 4 = 64$
$2 + 3 \times 3 + 4 \times 4 + 5 = 65$	$[2 + (3 \times 3) + 4] \times 4 + 5 = 65$

Substitute and Solve ☀️

Directions:

1. Review some formulas that students have had previously in mathematics, such as $A = lw$, $A = s^2$, $A = \frac{1}{2}bh$, $P = 2l + 2w$, $D = rt$, etc.

2. Discuss the fact that to find the solution (example: $A = lw$), we need to substitute values for the variables. For example, to find the area of a rectangle, we need to know the length (l) and the width (w). Suppose our classroom has the dimensions 40 feet by 30 feet, that is, $l = 40$ ft. and $w = 30$ ft. Then, since $A = lw$, the area is $A = 40$ ft. $\times 30$ ft. $= 1,200$ square feet.

3. Ask, "What is the perimeter of the same classroom?" $P = 2l + 2w$. For $l = 40$ feet and $w = 30$ feet, $P = 2(40) + 2(30) = 140$ feet.

4. Present another example, such as finding the value of A if $A = s^2$ and $s = 7$ feet.

5. Discuss finding the value of an expression by substitution. If a variable is repeated in an expression, the same value is used each time. For example, in evaluating the expression $3x + yx$ when $x = 6$ and $y = 2$, we get $3(6) + (2)(6) = 30$. We must substitute the value 6 for both x's.

6. Present other examples if the students seem confused.

Practice Activities

Operation Bingo

Directions:

1. Give each student a blank 4×4 bingo card.

2. Ask the students to write the following numbers in any squares they choose at random: 0, 1, 2, 9, 11, 12, 15, 18, 21, 24, 27, 32, 41, 43, 49, 68.

3. Write the following problems one at a time on an overhead transparency or the board. Each student should use a marker to cover the square with the number that is the correct answer to each problem. The first student to get four markers in a row says "Bingo!" Check the answers to determine if the four in a row is a bingo. Problems **(with answers)**—do *not* write answers on the board:

   1. $4 \times (2 + 6) =$ **(32)**
   2. $7 \times (8 - 5) + 3 =$ **(24)**
   3. $(12 - 8) \times 3 =$ **(12)**
   4. $5 \times 7 - 6 \times 4 =$ **(11)**
   5. $(8 - 3) \times 2 \div 5 =$ **(2)**
   6. $9 \div 3 \times 1 + 6 =$ **(9)**
   7. $9 \div 3 \times (1 + 6) =$ **(21)**
   8. $20 - 10 \div 2 =$ **(15)**
   9. $12 \div 4 - 21 \div 7 =$ **(0)**
   10. $3 + 4 \times 6 =$ **(27)**
   11. $39 + 74 - 16 \times 4 =$ **(49)**
   12. $(8 - 2) \times (7 - 4) =$ **(18)**
   13. $17 - 6 \times 2 - 4 =$ **(1)**
   14. $26 + 5 \times 4 - 3 =$ **(43)**
   15. $10 \times 10 - 4 \times 8 =$ **(68)**
   16. $[(6 - 4) \times 3] + 5 \times 7 =$ **(41)**

4. Repeat, using the remaining problems or make new ones with the answers from step 2.

Materials:

▶ Blackline master for a **4 × 4 bingo card** is in the Appendix.

▶ Game markers to cover squares

▶ Overhead projector or board

Calculating Correctly When There Are No Parentheses

Directions:

1. Give each student a copy of the blackline master **No Parentheses**.

2. Ask the students to individually complete the problems on the master.

3. Work the problems on the board or overhead that are unclear to the students.

4. Have each student make up two problems that involve at least two different operations and no parentheses. Have them work the problems that they made up following the order of operations.

5. Exchange the problems in the class with other students. Have the students work the problems to see if the given answer is correct.

Materials:

► Blackline master **No Parentheses** is located in the *Teacher's Resource Manual,* **page 6.**

Inserting Grouping Symbols

Directions:

1. Give each student a copy of the blackline master **Inserting Grouping Symbols**. Note that some of the problems are the same as those in the preceding practice activity, but the instructions are different.

2. Review the order of parentheses with the students: {[( )]}.

3. Ask the students to individually complete the problems on the master.

4. Choose students to place corrected problems on the board.

5. Have each student make up five problems using parentheses and at least two different operations. Have the students work the problems they made up.

6. Have the students then rewrite their five problems, leaving out the parentheses.

7. Have the students exchange papers to see if they can put in parentheses to get the given answer.

Materials:

► Blackline master **Inserting Grouping Symbols** is located in the *Teacher's Resource Manual,* **page 7.**

Problem-Solving Activity

Inserting Parentheses in Different Ways in the Same Expression to Get Different Values 💡

Directions:

1. Divide the class into pairs of students.

2. Give the class an expression such as $3 - 2 \times 4 + 7 \times 3$.

3. Ask each pair to find the value of the expression. **(16)**

4. Challenge the student pairs to insert one or more pairs of parentheses in such a way that the value of the expression changes.

5. Call on one student pair to put their new expression on the board along with the correct value. **[Many answers are possible. For example, $(3 - 2) \times 4 + (7 \times 3) = 25$, and $3 - 2(4 + 7) \times 3 = -63$.]**

6. Ask the class to check the value to see if it is correct.

7. If the value that the pair found is correct, leave it on the board. If the value that the pair found is incorrect, have the class agree on the correct solution.

8. Move to a new spot on the board and repeat steps 4 through 7 as long as student pairs come up with new expressions. Be sure to leave each example on the board. For example,

   a. $3 - 2 \times 4 + 7 \times 3 = 16$

   b. $(3 - 2) \times 4 + 7 \times 3 = 25$

   c. $3 - 2 \times (4 + 7) \times 3 = -63$

   d. $3 - 2 \times [4 + (7 \times 3)] = -47$

   e. $3 - [2 \times (4 + 7)] \times 3 = -63$

   f. $\{3 - [2 \times (4 + 7)]\} \times 3 = -57$

9. When the class can find no new ways of writing the expression, start this activity over with a new expression.

10. **Variation:** Give the students five different numbers (e.g., 2 through 6). Have the students write as many different problems (different answers) as they can using all five numbers without using parentheses. The order of the numbers and operations may change.

Teacher's Tip:

At this point, student-generated expressions may require use of calculation with negative numbers. Allow such expressions and require correct calculation. Formal review of integer arithmetic is presented in Chapter 2.

Chapter 1—Variables and Expressions

1-3 *Objective:* **Solve open sentences by performing arithmetic operations.**

Sample Test: Solve each problem.

1. True or false: $x - 17 = 23$ if $x = 40$.

    Solution: True

2. What is the value of x if $x = \dfrac{19 - 7 \times 3}{2}$?

    Solution: x = –1

3. $y = 2x - 7$. If $x = 3$, find y.

    Solution: y = –1

Concept Development Activities

Determining If a Mathematical Statement Is True, False, or Open—I

Directions:

1. Divide the class into groups of three to five, with as many groups the same size as possible.

2. Ask each member of each group to write his or her name on a small piece of paper.

3. Collect the names and keep them separated by group.

4. Distribute one copy of the blackline master **Determining If a Statement Is True, False, or Open—I** to each group.

5. Explain to the class that each group must come to consensus on their answer to each problem on the blackline master. Ask the groups to complete the blackline master.

6. After the groups are finished, review the problems in the following way:

    a. For each problem, draw a name at random from a given group.

Materials:

► Blackline master **Determining If a Statement Is True, False, or Open—I** is located in the *Teacher's Resource Manual*, **page 8.**

► Small pieces of paper for students' names

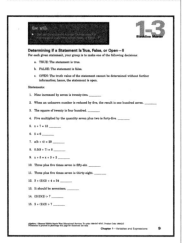

b. The student whose name is drawn must come to the front of the class and give the group's answer and the rationale for the answer.

c. If the group's answer is correct, each member of the group gets five points. If the group's answer is incorrect, each member of the group loses five points. *Note:* This structure keeps the group interdependent during the group discussion because no one knows who will have to give the answer for the group. All of the group members must be prepared.

7. Repeat the process for each problem, each time drawing a name from a different group. When every group has had a chance to answer, draw names at random and continue, this time awarding one point for each correct response.

Determining If a Mathematical Statement Is True, False, or Open—II

Directions:

1. Divide the class into groups of three to five, with as many groups the same size as possible.

2. Ask each member of each group to write his or her name on a small piece of paper.

3. Collect the names and keep them separated by group.

4. Distribute one copy of the blackline master **Determining If a Statement Is True, False, or Open—II** to each group.

5. Explain to the class that each group must come to consensus on their answer to each problem on the blackline master. Ask the groups to complete the blackline master.

6. After the groups are finished, review the problems in the following way:

a. For each problem, draw a name at random from a given group.

b. The student whose name is drawn must come to the front of the class and give the group's answer and the rationale for the answer.

c. If the group's answer is correct, each member of the group gets five points. If the group's answer is incorrect, each member of the group loses five points. *Note:* This structure keeps the group interdependent during the group discussion because no one knows who will have to give the answer for the group. All of the group members must be prepared.

7. Repeat the process for each problem, each time drawing a name from a different group. When every group has had a chance to answer, draw names at random and continue, this time awarding one point for each correct response.

Evaluate It

Directions:

1. Explain to the class that a sentence such as x + 3 = 12 is an open sentence. It is not true or false until a value is substituted for x. Ask, "If x is 4, is the sentence true or false?" **(False)** "Why?" "What value makes the sentence true?"

2. Discuss that some open sentences have more than one variable. To illustrate this point, say, "Suppose the cost of a telephone call is 75¢ plus 7¢ per minute. This can be represented by C = 75 + 7m." Write this statement on the board. Explain that you can find the cost (C) if you know the minutes (m). With the class, figure out the cost of a 20-minute telephone call, substituting 20 for m. Continue with other values for m, such as 60 minutes and 10 minutes.

3. Work some other examples on the board, such as those listed below.

   a. Which of the following values makes the sentence 2x + 4 = 14 true? x = {3, 4, 5, 6}

   b. Evaluate: x = $\dfrac{3 \times 8 - 4}{2}$.

   c. Find d when r is 60 and d = 14r.

   d. Evaluate 2x − 7 + 3y if x = 2 and y = 3.

Teacher's Tip:

Worksheets 1 and 2 for this objective, **pages 1-13 and 1-14**, support this activity with practice exercises.

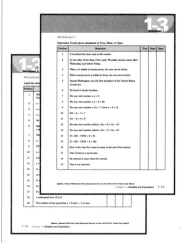

Teacher's Tip:

Worksheet 3 for this objective, **page 1-15**, supports this activity with practice exercises.

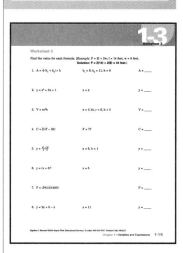

Materials:

► Dice

► Blank cards or 💿

Practice Activities

Roll the Value for Equations

Directions:

1. Divide the class into groups of five. Give each group six blank cards and one die.

2. Ask the students to write the following equations on the blank cards, one equation per card:

   a. $5x - 7 = 3$ b. $3x - 17 = 1$ c. $33 = 42 + 2x - 15$

   d. $x - 1 + 2x = x + 1$ e. $3x + 2 = 7 + 2x$ f. $3x - 2 = 6 - x$

3. Have each group shuffle their cards, place them face down, and turn the first card over.

4. In each group, each person should, in turn, roll the die and remember the number he or she rolled. If the number was already rolled by someone else in the group, the player should continue rolling until he or she has a number that no one else in the group has.

5. Have each player substitute his or her number in the open sentence showing on the card and determine if the resulting statement is true or false. Each person in the group should report his or her result, and the group should record the number that makes the sentence true.

6. The next card is turned over, and step 5 is repeated. The activity continues until all six cards are used.

7. Conduct a class discussion about the equations and what makes an equation true. Ask, "How many numbers do you think will make the equation true?"

Roll the Value for Inequalities

Directions:

1. Divide the class into groups of five. Give each group six blank cards and one die.

2. Ask the students to write the following inequalities on the blank cards, one equation per card:

   a. $5x - 7 < 5$ b. $3x - 13 > 1$ c. $50 > 42 + 2x$

   d. $2x - 5 > 3$ e. $3x - 2 < x + 7$ f. $2x < x + 3$

3. Review inequalities such as $2x - 1 > 4$ with the class. Ask the students, "If you substitute 2 for x and solve the inequality, is it still true? What about if you substitute 4 for x?"

4. Have a student from each group shuffle the cards, place them face down, and turn the first card over.

5. In each group, each person should, in turn, roll the die and remember the number he or she rolled. If the number was already rolled by someone else in the group, the player should continue rolling until he or she has a number that no one else in the group has.

6. Have each player substitute his or her number in the open sentence showing on the card and determine if the resulting statement is true or false. Each person in the group should report his or her result, and the group should record the number that makes the sentence true.

7. The next card is turned over, and step 6 is repeated. The activity continues until all six cards are used.

8. Conduct a class discussion about the inequalities and what numbers make them true. Ask, "Are there other numbers that would make the inequality true?"

Problem-Solving Activity

Developing a Formula by Using "Yes/No" Questioning

Directions:

1. Write on the overhead or board:

	x	y	z	A
Case 1	2	4	7	21

2. Explain that the value of A was calculated by using the values of x, y, and z and that a method of calculation (formula) was used. Tell the class that they are to find the method of calculation (formula) used in this case by following this procedure:

   a. Any student may raise his or her hand and ask any question about the formula as long as it can be answered "yes" or "no."

   b. The rest of the class members may not talk during this process but must listen to the questions and answers. You will call on as many students as want to ask questions until the class indicates it wants to caucus (talk as a group). This must be a class discussion.

   c. During the caucus, you will accept no more questions, but the class members may discuss what they know. This discussion process must be managed by the class with you being silent.

   d. If the class discovers it wants to ask more questions, the caucus will be stopped and the "yes/no" questioning resumed.

   e. The process in steps a–d will continue until the class can state how the calculation was made by stating a rule in the form of a "yes/no" question.

   f. Once this point is reached, you will ask someone in the class to present the verbal rule as an algebraic formula.

3. Have the class use this procedure to find the formula for case 1.

4. Repeat the process for other cases, as shown below:

	x	y	z	A
Case 2	4	3	5	7
Case 3	9	3	8	48
Case 4	0.5	3.5	7	11
Case 5	13	17	5	75
Case 6	2	6	7	9

5. Cases 1, 3, and 5 can be solved with the same formula. See if the students can find it by using the "yes/no" questions.

1-4 *Objective:* Use mathematical properties to evaluate expressions.

Sample Test: Evaluate the following expressions:

1. $\dfrac{3(9 + 7)}{5} \times \dfrac{5(9 + 7)}{3}$

   Solution: 256

2. $6 \times \left[\dfrac{1}{2}(5 + 7)\right]$

   Solution: 36

Concept Development Activities

Identifying Simple Instances of Mathematical Properties

Directions:

1. List the following formulas and properties on a transparency master and project it. Discuss and review the properties, giving an example of each:

Formula	Property
a. $a + 0 = a$	Additive Identity
b. $a \times 1 = a$	Multiplicative Identity
c. $a \times 0 = 0$	Multiplicative Property of Zero
d. $\frac{a}{b} \times \frac{b}{a} = 1, (a \neq 0, b \neq 0)$	Multiplicative Inverse
e. $a \times (b + c) = a \times b + a \times c$	Distributive Property
f. $a + b = b + a$	Commutative Property of Addition
g. $a \times b = b \times a$	Commutative Property of Multiplication
h. $(a + b) + c = a + (b + c)$	Associative Property of Addition
i. $(a \times b) \times c = a \times (b \times c)$	Associative Property of Multiplication

2. Write the formula and property on blank cards, one per card.

3. Have the students work in groups of four. Distribute a copy of the blackline master **Identifying Properties** to each group and ask the group members to complete the table.

4. Choose a group at random and ask them to select one of the property cards.

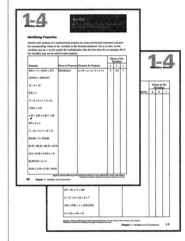

5. Ask one member of that group to identify one instance of that property from the list on the blackline master and to state the formula and the values for the variable(s).

6. Ask another member of that group to identify another instance of that property from the list on the blackline master and to state the formula and the values for the variable(s).

7. Repeat this process until a student indicates that there are no more instances of that property on the blackline master.

8. Repeat steps 4 through 7 with another group.

9. *Note:* Not every student in each group may be called on. This is acceptable because the group is responsible for working all of the problems on the blackline master, and all members should be prepared.

Easy Computation

Directions:

1. Explain to the students that there are properties in mathematics that are used over and over in algebra. It is important for all students to understand these properties and to be able to use them in a variety of ways. The following steps discuss these properties.

2. ***Additive Identity:*** $a + 0 = a$. Ask the students for an example (e.g., $3 + 0 = 3$). Most students will see this as obvious because they have been adding zero since kindergarten. Give the students the problem $8 + 3 - 3 = ?$ Discuss that $3 - 3 = 0$, so $8 + 3 - 3 = 8$. It is an application of $a + 0 = a$. Also discuss a problem such as $x + 1 + 1 + 1 - 1 - 1 - 1 = ?$ Again, $+1 + (-1)$ is the same as zero, so the answer is x.

3. ***Multiplicative Identity:*** $a \times 1 = a$. Ask the students for an example (e.g., $6 \times 1 = 6$). Ask if everyone believes this property is true for all numbers. Ask if anyone can give a counterexample. Students know it is true and have been using the property since third grade. Give students the problem $\frac{2}{3} + \frac{3}{3} = ?$ Most students will give $\frac{6}{9}$, which is a correct response, but the answer could also be $\frac{2}{3}$ because $\frac{3}{3}$ is the same as 1, and $\frac{2}{3} \times 1 = \frac{2}{3}$. Both are names

for the same number. This property will be used in algebra with different names for 1. Ask, "What is the answer to the problem $14 \times \frac{1}{2} \times 2 = ?$" Note that $\frac{1}{2} \times 2 = 1$, so the answer is 14.

4. ***Multiplicative Property of Zero:*** $a \times 0 = 0$. Ask the students for an example (e.g., $8 \times 0 = 0$). Ask whether the students believe this is true for all numbers or if they can find a counterexample. In algebra, we may see a problem such as $9 \times (3 - 3) = ?$ Since $3 - 3 = 0, 9 \times 0 = 0$. Another example to discuss is if $a \times b = 0$, what do we know about a or b?

5. ***Multiplicative Inverse:*** $\frac{a}{b} \times \frac{b}{a} = 1$, (a and b $\neq$ 0). Ask the students for an example (e.g., $\frac{2}{3} \times \frac{3}{2} = 1$). Ask the students why this is true. **(When you multiply, you always get the same number divided by itself.)** Give the example
$$\frac{6 \times 7}{\frac{3}{8}} = \frac{6 \times 7 \times \frac{8}{3}}{\frac{3}{8} \times \frac{8}{3}} = \frac{6 \times 7 \times \frac{8}{3}}{1} = 112.$$
Another example is $\frac{1}{2} \times \frac{5}{6} \times 2 = ?$ Since $\frac{1}{2} \times 2 = 1$, we have $1 \times \frac{5}{6} = \frac{5}{6}$.

6. ***Distributive Property:*** $a \times (b + c) = a \times b + a \times c$. Ask the students for an example [e.g., $4 \times (5 + 9) = 4 \times 5 + 4 \times 9$]. Discuss how to multiply numbers such as 15×24 by using the distributive property: $15 \times 24 = 15 \times (20 + 4) = 15 \times 20 + 15 \times 4 = 300 + 60 = 360$. Another example to discuss is $3(N + 4) = 3N + 3 \times 4 = 3N + 12$. A third example is $6 \times 7 + 6 \times 3 = 6 \times (7 + 3) = 6 \times 10 = 60$.

7. ***Commutative Property of Addition:*** $a + b = b + a$. Ask the students for an example [e.g., $(11 + 15) = (15 + 11)$]. This property indicates that you can add in any order. For example, $6 + 17 + 4 + 11 = (6 + 4) + 17 + 11 = 38$. Explain that problems can be made easier if you look for sums that are easy for you. Discuss that this property works only for problems that are *all* addition. Discuss examples such as $6 \times 8 + 9 + 2 \neq 6 \times 10 + 9$. Ask the students for the answer to $14 + 19 + 6 + 1 = ?$ Ask, "How can you arrange the addends to make it easy?" **[(14 + 6) + (19 + 1) = 20 + 20 = 40]**

8. ***Commutative Property of Multiplication:*** $a \times b = b \times a$. Ask the students for an example (e.g., $6 \times 9 = 9 \times 6$). Discuss that this property indicates that the order of multiplication can be changed. For example, $5 \times 21 \times 4 = 5 \times 4 \times 21$. The students should watch for problems that can be made easier by changing

Teacher's Tip:

Worksheets 1 and 2 for this objective, **pages 1-18 and 1-19**, support this concept with practice exercises.

the order. Discuss that this property works for problems containing all products, but *not* for those with a mixture of operations, such as $8 \times 4 + 2 \times 5 \neq 8 \times 5 \times 4 + 2$.

9. ***Associative Property of Addition:*** $(a + b) + c = a + (b + c)$. Ask the students for an example [e.g., $(5 + 8) + 3 = 5 + (8 + 3)$]. This property shows that we can add different groupings if the problem is all addition. Show that combining this property with the commutative property allows rearrangement of terms to make a sum easier to find. For example, $(8 + 17) + 3 = 8 + (17 + 3) = 8 + 20 = 28$. Another example is $(7 + 19) + 1 + (5 + 3) = (7 + 3) + (19 + 1) + 5 = 10 + 20 + 5 = 35$.

10. ***Associative Property of Multiplication:*** $(a \times b) \times c = a \times (b \times c)$. Ask the students for an example [e.g., $(9 \times 8) \times 12 = 9 \times (8 \times 12)$]. Discuss that this property shows that we can multiply different groupings of numbers if the problem is all multiplication. Show that combining this property with the commutative property of multiplication allows rearrangement of factors to make the product easier to find. For example, $4 \times 18 \times 25 = (4 \times 25) \times 18 = 100 \times 18 = 1,800$. Another example is $(5 \times 17) \times 2 = (2 \times 5) \times 17 = 10 \times 17 = 170$.

11. Ask the students how they would rearrange the following problems to make them easy to solve. Have them name the properties they would use.

   a. $(7 + 29) + 3 = ?$

   b. $(81 + 3) - 3 = ?$

   c. $\frac{2}{3} \times \left(\frac{3}{2} \times \frac{1}{8} \right) = ?$

   d. $(9 \times 8) + (9 \times 2) = ?$

   e. $(47 + 9) + (13 + 11) = ?$

Mathematical Expressions Using the Distributive Property 💡

Directions:

1. Review the distributive property with students. Explain that there may be more than two addends, for example, $3(9 + 5 + 2 + 7) = 3(9) + 3(5) + 3(2) + 3(7)$.

2. Cut one copy of the blackline master **Mathematical Expressions Using the Distributive Property** into horizontal strips, separating each row of the matrix from every other row.

3. Place the separated rows from the matrix into a hat and have each student draw out one row.

4. Ask the students to solve the problem they have drawn.

5. Have each student find the other student in the class who has the same situation but instructions to develop an expression in a different form.

6. Ask the student pairs to check each other's work.

7. Replace the rows from the matrix into the hat and have the students draw again, repeating steps 4 through 6. Most students should get a different problem than they had previously.

8. Repeat the process several times until all members of the class understand the two models for calculation represented by the distributive property.

9. Ask the student pairs from the last pairing to write a word problem of their own that requires both types of modeling using the distributive property.

10. Have the groups exchange problems, solve the problems, and check each other's work.

Materials:

► Blackline master **Mathematical Expressions Using the Distributive Property** is located in the *Teacher's Resource Manual*, **pages 12 through 15.**

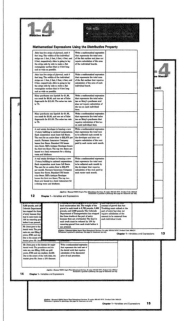

Practice Activities

Compute and Name a Property

Directions:

1. Ask the students to write each of the problems below on the front of a card, one problem per card, and the answer and property for the problem on the back of the card. They can do this in groups of four so that there is one complete set of cards for every four students.

Problem (front of card)	Answer and Property (back of card)
a. $(77 + 7) + 3 =$	a. 87; associative (+)
b. $20 \times (59 \times 5) =$	b. 5,900; commutative ($\times$) or associative ($\times$)
c. $38 \times (14 \times 0) =$	c. 0; multiplicative property of zero, associative ($\times$)
d. $13 + 8 + 7 + 2 =$	d. 30; commutative (+) or associative (+)
e. $19,876 \times 1 =$	e. 19,876; multiplicative identity
f. $\frac{3}{4} \times \left(\frac{4}{3} \times 8\right) =$	f. 8; multiplicative inverse, associative ($\times$)
g. $\frac{3}{5} + \left(\frac{1}{8} + \frac{2}{5}\right) =$	g. $1\frac{1}{8}$; commutative (+), associative (+)
h. $19(8) + 19(2) =$	h. 190; distributive
i. $(18 \times 7) \times 1 \times (14 \times 0) =$	i. 0; multiplicative property of zero, commutative ($\times$), associative ($\times$)
j. $9 + 2 + 8 + 1 =$	j. 20; commutative (+), associative (+)
k. $\left(\frac{1}{9} + \frac{3}{8}\right) + \frac{5}{8} =$	k. $1\frac{1}{9}$; associative (+)
l. $\frac{5}{6} + 0 + \frac{2}{6} =$	l. $1\frac{1}{6}$; additive identity
m. $64 + (75 + 36) =$	m. 175; commutative (+), associative (+)
n. $(29 + 1) + 0 =$	n. 30; additive identity
o. $\frac{4}{5} \times \left(12 \times \frac{5}{4}\right) =$	o. 12; multiplicative inverse
p. $(1.5 + 13.83) + 0.5 =$	p. 15.83; commutative (+), associative (+)
q. $(41 \times 6) + (9 \times 6) =$	q. 300; distributive
r. $(348 + 35) + 65 =$	r. 448; associative (+)

Chapter 1—Variables and Expressions

2. After all the cards have been made, have the students mix them up with all the fronts (problems) facing up.

3. Have the students take turns finding the answers by making the problems as easy as possible by using the properties. Students can use paper and pencil. Along with the answer, they should name *one* property they used to find the answer. For example, for the problem $7 + 4 \times \frac{1}{4} + 6 \times 0 = ?$ the answer is 8, and the properties used are the multiplicative property of zero and multiplicative inverse.

4. Each student should get two points for a correct answer and one point for a correct property. Each group should keep a tally for the students in the group.

5. When the students go through the deck, they can shuffle the deck and continue.

Share It

Directions:

1. Write the nine basic math properties on the board or make an overhead transparency of the blackline master **Properties**. The basic properties are:

   a. $a + 0 = a$

   b. $a \times 1 = a$

   c. $a \times 0 = 0$

   d. $\frac{a}{b} \times \frac{b}{a} = 1, a \neq 0, b \neq 0$

   e. $a \times (b + c) = a \times b + a \times c$

   f. $a + b = b + a$

   g. $a \times b = b \times a$

   h. $(a + b) + c = a + (b + c)$

   i. $(a \times b) \times c = a \times (b \times c)$

2. Have each student write a numerical example of any property he or she chooses. For example, $9 \times 14 = 14 \times 9$.

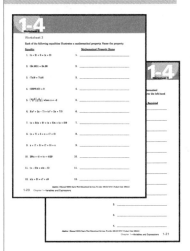

3. Divide the class into groups of four and have the members of each group identify one another's properties.

4. Discuss how a quantity can serve as a variable. For example, we can make a = (3 + 9) and b = (13 + 24), so for the property a + b = b + a, we could write (3 + 9) + (13 + 24) = (13 + 24) + (3 + 9).

5. Have each student write another numerical example of any property using quantities for the variables.

6. Have the members of each group identify one another's properties. Then, have them exchange their four examples with other groups for identification.

7. Have each group make a problem as difficult as possible using one of the properties of their choice.

8. Have each group exchange their problem with another group for identification. All members of a group should be able to explain the property their problem models.

Problem-Solving Activity

Mathematical Properties Game ☀

Directions:

1. Divide the class into groups of two to six students. Have the students make decks of cards as described below, one deck per group:

Deck of 81 playing cards with the following symbols:

16 cards with the symbol	a
10 cards with the symbol	b
6 cards with the symbol	c
6 cards with the symbol	(
6 cards with the symbol	)
12 cards with the symbol	×
9 cards with the symbol	+
9 cards with the symbol	=
3 cards with the symbol	0
2 cards with the symbol	1
1 card with the symbol	$\frac{a}{b}$
1 card with the symbol	$\frac{b}{a}$

Materials:

▶ Blackline master **Properties** is located in the *Teacher's Resource Manual,* **page 16.**

▶ Blank cards or 💿

2. Give each student a copy of the blackline master **Properties**.

3. The object of this game is for each player to use the cards to compose as many real number property statements as possible in front of himself or herself and to use all of his or her cards.

4. Each group selects one player to be the first dealer. The dealer shuffles the cards and deals eight cards to each player. The remaining cards are placed face down in the middle of the table.

5. Play begins to the left of the dealer and moves clockwise. At each player's turn, the player draws a card from the deck on the table.

6. The player can then do any one of the following:

   a. Place at least three cards from his or her own hand face up on the table to begin one mathematical property statement reading from left to right. The statement must be one of those listed on the blackline master, and each property statement may be used no more than once by a player in each game.

   b. Use as many cards from his or her hand as possible to continue the statements made by any player. However, the player must have started a statement himself or herself in a previous turn before playing on any other player's statement.

   c. Pass without playing any cards.

7. The play continues until one player has used all of his or her cards and has at least one complete property statement on the table in front of himself or herself. If the player has started more than one property statement, all of his or her property statements must be complete.

8. Rules:

   a. Each player starts mathematical property statements in front of himself or herself, playing at least three cards (reading left to right).

   b. Each player may play any number of cards on any partially completed property statement in front of himself or herself or in front of any other player after he or she has started a statement in front of himself or herself.

   c. During each turn, a player can play on more than one other player's statements.

d. Each mathematical property statement from the blackline master can appear only once during the game for any one player.

e. All property statements must be complete in front of the player going out. Otherwise, the player must continue to draw cards and play.

9. Scoring is as follows for each individual:

a. 20 points awarded for all cards played and all statements complete.

b. 10 points awarded for each completed statement.

c. 5 points subtracted for each statement started but not completed.

d. 1 point subtracted for each card held when another player goes out.

10. Winner is the first player to obtain a score of 100 or more.

Exploring Rational Numbers

2-1 Graph rational numbers on the number line.

2-2 Add and subtract rational numbers.

2-3 Compare and order rational numbers.

2-4 Multiply and divide rational numbers.

2-5 Find the principal square root of a number.

2-1 *Objective:* **Graph rational numbers on the number line.**

Sample Test: Graph each set on the given number line.

1. {−1, 1, 2} **Solution:**

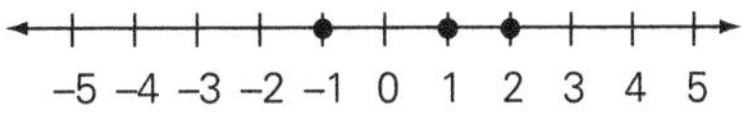

2. $\left\{-1\frac{1}{2},\ 0.5,\ 2\right\}$ **Solution:**

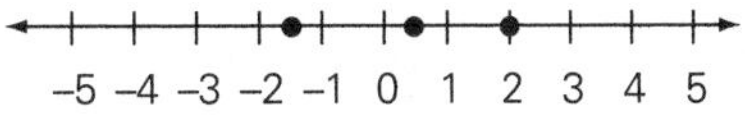

3. {Integers between 2 and −2} **Solution:**

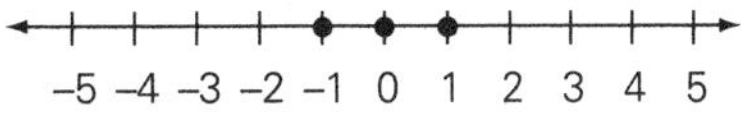

Concept Development

Concept Development Activities

Number Line Development

Directions:

1. Distribute one copy of a number line page to each student.

2. Draw a horizontal line on the board or overhead transparency. Ask the class, "What is this?" Discuss the properties of a line. For example, it is unending, it is a set of points, it goes on forever, it is named by two points.

3. Ask students to describe a number line. What is it? What is it used for? How do we make one? The following concepts are among those to be reviewed:

   a. A number line is a tool used to represent all the numbers in graphic form.

   b. Every number can be represented on the number line.

   c. The integers are evenly spaced.

   d. Both positive and negative numbers can be shown on the number line. Zero is between the positives and the negatives and is a member of neither set.

   e. We can use segments of the number line to represent or graph a given set.

   f. The arrows on the number line show that it continues in those directions indefinitely. (Positive and negative integers are infinite.)

4. Mark zero on the number line on the board or transparency and mark off spaces for positive and negative numbers. Then ask the class if anyone can come to the front and find +3 on the number line.

5. Continue this process, having other students find numbers such as 6, 1, –3, –5, –10, +9, etc., on the number line. Ask for a large number, such as 1,000, and discuss what changes need to be made in the scale of the number line. For example,

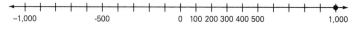

Materials:

▶ Blackline masters for **number lines** are in the Appendix.

Teacher's Tip:

Worksheet 1 for this objective, **page 2-2**, supports this activity with practice exercises.

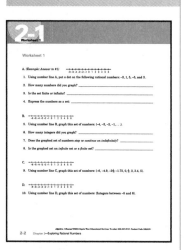

6. Make another number line on the board or overhead transparency. Mark integers –5 to +5. Also have the students make their own number lines at their seats using the number line page you distributed. Have the students mark integers –5 to +5.

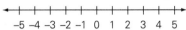

7. Discuss how to locate numbers such as $+1\frac{1}{2}$ and $-3\frac{3}{4}$ between the integers. Have the students mark or graph the numbers +2, –4, 0, $+1\frac{1}{2}$, and $-3\frac{3}{4}$ on the number line page.

8. Have the students make a number line from –5 to +5. Ask them to mark all integers greater than +1. See what alternatives the students might use to graph this set. Discuss using an arrowhead to show that the pattern continues. The arrowhead symbol "▶" means it continues forever. For example,

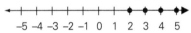

9. Discuss graphing the infinite set, as was done in #8 above. Have the students try some other sets. For example, {integers less than 4}, {integers between 3 and –4}, {integers greater than –3}.

Graphing on the Number Line

Directions:

1. Give each student a copy of a number line page.

2. Ask the students to label a number line and graph each of these sets: {integers}, {negative integers}, {positive integers}, {positive integers between 9 and 25}, {negative integers between –9 and –1}. Include any other sets you want.

3. Give the students some fractions to graph, such as $\frac{1}{8}$, $\frac{1}{4}$, 0.6, $\frac{3}{4}$, 0.9. For example,

Discuss how these numbers are located between 0 and 1, and that we may choose to use just that part of the number line if we wish.

Materials:

▶ Blackline masters for **number lines** are in the Appendix.

Teacher's Tip:

Worksheets 2 and 3 for this objective, **pages 2-3 and 2-4,** support this activity with practice exercises.

4. Also discuss how not all numbers can be labeled or graphed at the same time because there are too many too close together (density property). However, by selecting the appropriate scale, it is possible to picture numbers that are very close together.

5. Ask the students to make a number line from −1 to +1 and to graph the following set of numbers: $\{-0.8, -\frac{1}{4}, -0.5, -\frac{1}{8}, +\frac{1}{8}, +0.5, +\frac{3}{4}, +0.8\}$.

Practice Activity

Graph It

Directions:

1. Have the students work in groups of two. Give each student a die and a copy of the number line page, and ask the students to label the number line from 1 to 6.

2. The students should take turns rolling their die and graphing the numbers that come up. Each student graphs only the numbers he or she rolls. Some rolls will be repeats.

3. Students continue to roll until they have graphed all the numbers 1 through 6. The student who graphs all the numbers with the fewest number of die rolls wins.

4. The students should keep track of the number of rolls it takes to complete the line. Then, the class should find the average number of rolls taken to complete the lines.

5. Repeat the activity with each student using two dice and a number line marked from 2 to 12. Have each student guess how many rolls it will take to get all 12 numbers graphed.

Problem-Solving Activities

Data Plotting—I

Directions:

1. Divide the class into groups of two to four. Have one member of each group go to all the other groups and collect numbers representing the day of the month of the group members' birthdays (1 through 31).

Materials:

▶ Blackline masters for **number lines** are in the Appendix.

▶ Pair of dice with two different colors for each pair of students

2. When the students bring the data back to their groups, one student should be chosen as the recorder to graph the numbers collected on a number line page. The group will have to decide how their number line should be labeled. For example,

3. The groups should label any repeats, writing the number of repeats above the date.

4. Direct a discussion about the process of selecting the labeling for the number line, and compare the number line graphs of the different groups.

5. Discuss the graphed data, covering the topics of same birthday, average, mode, median, and how these are related.

Data Plotting—II

Directions:

1. Divide the class into groups of two to four. One member of each group should go to all the other groups and collect numbers representing the students' heights.

2. When the data are brought back to the group, the heights should be converted into inches. For example, 5 feet 3 inches = 63 inches. One student from each group, the recorder, should graph the numbers collected on a number line page. Each group must decide how their number line will be labeled. For example,

3. Have each group determine the average height from the number line graph and then write an explanation of how they reached this answer.

4. Have the groups use calculators to find the average height and then compare the value to the answer they got using the graph.

5. Direct a discussion about the process of determining the average height with a number line, and compare the methods of the different groups.

> **Materials:**
>
> ► Blackline masters for **number lines** are in the Appendix.
>
> ► Data collected by students

2-2 *Objective*: Add and subtract rational numbers.

Sample Test: Simplify:

1. $4 + (-7) =$ _____

    Solution: –3

2. $4 - (-7) =$ _____

    Solution: 11

3. $-2.3 - 5.1 =$ _____

    Solution: –7.4

4. $-1\frac{1}{2} + 5\frac{1}{2} =$ _____

    Solution: 4

Concept Development Activities

Applying Adding Positives and Negatives

Directions:

1. Initiate discussion about a running back's function on the offense of a football team (i.e., running with the ball to gain yardage and first downs for the team).

2. Discuss how many yards (10) are needed to get another down, or chance, and how many yards can be lost if the running back doesn't make it past the line of scrimmage, or starting point.

3. Yards gained by the running back are positive (+) yards, and yards lost are negative (−) yards. Thus, combinations of runs by a running back provide a good example of adding positives and negatives. For example, suppose that in four tries, or downs, a running back has the following yardage: (a) gained 5 (+5); (b) gained 3 (+3); (c) lost 2 (−2); and (d) gained $4\frac{1}{2}$ (+$4\frac{1}{2}$). Did the running back gain enough for a first down (10 yards)? Calculate: $(+5) + (+3) + (-2) + (+4\frac{1}{2}) = +10\frac{1}{2}$. Yes, the running back did gain enough yards.

4. Do a few more similar examples. Then give the students a copy of the blackline master **Football Running Back** to practice the idea of adding negatives and positives. For this exercise, explain that only running plays are used.

Materials:

► Blackline master **Football Running Back** is located in the *Teacher's Resource Manual,* **page 17.**

Chapter 2—Exploring Rational Numbers

Tile Addition

Directions:

Materials:

► Objects of two colors, such as red and white tiles cut from construction paper, sprayed beans, or the "ones" from the algebra tiles

1. Have the students form small groups and give each student 20 objects, 10 of one color and 10 of another. Let one color represent negative and the other represent positive. (Red and white are used in the following instructions to represent negative and positive, respectively.)

2. Establish the idea that a gain of one (+1) and a loss of one (−1) makes no gain at all, or zero gain. Write on the board:

$$+1 + (-1) = 0$$

3. With the concept understood, present the following examples to the class: +3 + −2 = ?   −3 + (+5) = ?

   1 white left, so value is +1   2 whites left, so value is +2

Teacher's Tip:

Worksheet 1 for this objective, **page 2-7**, supports this activity with practice exercises.

4. Ask the students to model these addition problems using the colored objects:

   −3 + (+2) = _____   −4 + (+6) = _____   +10 + (−3) = _____

   −4 + (−4) = _____   +4 + (+3) = _____   −7 + (+4) = _____

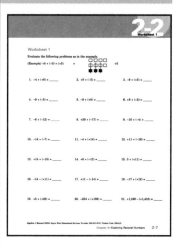

5. Let the students in each group try to come up with a general rule: "If the two numbers have like signs, find the sum; if they have unlike signs, find the difference and use the sign of the number with the larger absolute value." Each group should write down their rule (generalization). If they have trouble coming up with the generalization, have them use the tiles until they come up with it on their own.

Materials:

▶ Objects of two colors, such as red and white tiles cut from construction paper, sprayed beans, or the "ones" from the algebra tiles

Materials:

▶ Objects of two colors, such as red and white tiles cut from construction paper, sprayed beans, or the "ones" from the algebra tiles

Teacher's Tip:

Worksheet 2 for this objective, **page 2-8**, supports this activity with practice exercises.

[Worksheet 2-2 thumbnail image]

Tile Subtraction

Directions:

1. Have the students form small groups and give each student 20 objects, 10 of one color and 10 of another. Let one color represent negative and the other represent positive. (Red and white are used in the following instructions to represent negative and positive, respectively.)

2. Establish the idea that a gain of one (+1) and a loss of one (−1) makes no gain at all, or zero gain. Write on the board:

   +1 + (−1) = 0, Additive Identity Property

3. Do several problems of subtraction of two positives on the board to show that subtraction is "taking away." For example, +8 − (+3), or 8 − 3, equals 5, or +5.  leaves 5, or +5

4. Do several problems of subtraction of two negatives by taking away. For example:

   −6 − (−2) = −4   −6 − (−4) = −2

   Take away 2 reds from 6   Take away 4 reds from 6
   reds; leaves 4 reds, or −4   reds; leaves 2 reds, or −2

5. Now do an example in which "zero pairs" (one object of each color) must be introduced. For example, +4 − (−3) = ? You start with four whites (positives), but no reds (negatives). You cannot take away three reds (negatives) without introducing enough zero pairs so you will have three reds to take away.

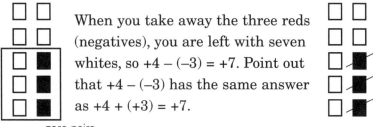

When you take away the three reds (negatives), you are left with seven whites, so +4 − (−3) = +7. Point out that +4 − (−3) has the same answer as +4 + (+3) = +7.

zero pairs

6. As another example, consider +3 − (−1) = ? You have to introduce one zero pair so you have a red to take away, and then you are left with four whites, or +4.

☐ ☐
☐
☐ ◼   leaves four whites, or +4.

7. Do more examples until the students catch on to what is happening. The goal is to see the rule that subtracting is like "adding the opposite." Write these examples on the board so all students can see them:

−6 − (−2) = −6 + (+2) = −4   −6 − (−4) = −6 + (+4) = −2

+4 − (−3) = +4 + (+3) = +7   +3 − (−1) = +3 + (+1) = +4

8. Let the students try to come up with the general rule: **To subtract an integer, add its opposite.** The students might come up with variations of this, which is okay as long as they understand the concept and can model why it is true.

Adding and Subtracting on the Number Line

Directions:

Materials:

► Blackline masters for **number lines** are in the Appendix.

1. Distribute copies of a number line page to the students and have them label the center as "0" and go to at least +10 and −10.

2. Explain that when adding integers, positives go toward the right of 0 and negatives go toward the left of 0. Where you end up is what the answer is. For example:

+3 + (−1) = +2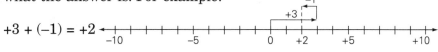

−5 +(+7) = +2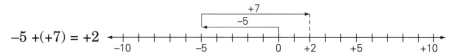

3. Ask the students how subtraction can be shown. Explain that you must *change direction* for the number being subtracted, so when subtracting a positive number, you go to the *left,* and when subtracting a negative number, you go to the *right.*

Teacher's Tip:

Worksheet 3 for this objective, **page 2-9**, supports this activity with practice exercises.

Materials:

- ▶ Blackline master **Contig Game Board** is located in the *Teacher's Resource Manual*, **page 18.**

- ▶ Six dice (three pair) per group, three red and three white

- ▶ Game markers to cover squares

Answer Key for #5:
a. –10   b. –8   c. +9
d. +1   e. –3   f. +5
g. +7

Examples:

$$+3 - (-1) = +4$$

$$-3 - (-2) = -1$$

4. If the students have trouble seeing why there is a change of direction, use a problem with two positives, such as $+3 - (+1)$, or $3 - 1$. Show this on the number line. Starting at zero, move to the right to +3, then move one to the left because you are taking it away. This sets up the pattern for subtraction to change direction on the number line.

5. Ask the students to practice on the number lines with the following problems, and/or make up some of your own. At this point, you may want to mix up addition and subtraction.

   a. $-5 - (+5) =$ _____   b. $-5 + (-3) =$ _____   c. $+5 - (-4) =$ _____

   d. $+5 + (-4) =$ _____   e. $-6 - (-3) =$ _____   f. $-8 + (+13) =$ _____

   g. $-8 - (-15) =$ _____

Practice Activities

Contig Addition and Subtraction

Directions:

1. Have the students form groups of three or four. Distribute six dice (three red and three white), one copy of the blackline master **Contig Game Board**, and markers to each group. Students will take turns rolling three dice, any combination of red and white. Red represents negative numbers and white represents positive numbers.

2. The object is to take the three rolled numbers and form a problem in addition and/or subtraction to equal one of the game board numbers that is not covered.

3. Each student should take a turn rolling the dice. One point is awarded if the student is able to cover an answer on the board. Answers must be verified by the other students in the group.

4. Once an answer on the board is covered, it cannot be used again in rolls of other students in the group.

5. Additional points can be scored by covering a square that touches (is contiguous to) other covered answers, either at a corner or on a side. A student can earn up to eight additional points in this manner.

last chip played

For example, in this case, the player gets three total points: two points because the marker is contiguous to two other markers and one point for covering an empty square.

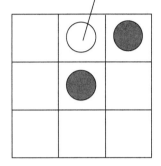

6. Students can work individually or as a group to find the answer that will score the maximum points.

Winter Temperature Changes

Directions:

1. Give each student a copy of the blackline master **Winter Temperature Changes**, which shows high and low temperatures for eight days.

2. The object of the activity is to show how subtraction is used to find the changes in temperature from one day to the next, or from the high temperature to the low temperature in a day.

3. Changes in temperature can be negative, as in a decrease, or positive, as in an increase. Do some examples with the class in finding changes in temperature.

   a. For example, find the change in temperature from the high on day 1 to the low on day 1:

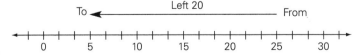

   From the number line, left 20 degrees shows a decrease of 20 degrees or –20° (negative 20°). Stress that mathematically, we *subtract the first number from the second:*

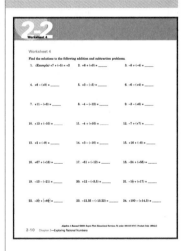

Teacher's Tip:

Worksheet 4 for this objective, **page 2-10**, supports this activity with practice exercises.

Materials:

▶ Blackline master
**Winter
Temperature
Changes** is located
in the *Teacher's
Resource Manual,*
page 19.

2-2
Blackline Master

Winter Temperature Changes

Winter Temperature Changes		
Day	High Temp.	Low Temp.
1	25°F	5°F
2	20°F	−3°F
3	10°F	−11°F
4	−4°F	−15°F
5	33°F	16°F
6	50°F	22°F
7	20°F	4°F
8	12°F	−12°F

Chapter 2—Exploring Rational Numbers   **19**

Answer Key for #4:
a. –23°   b. –21°
c. –40°   d. –45°
e. –24°   f. +48°

Low of day 1 – High of day 1 = 5 – (+25) = 5 + (−25) = −20°
(decrease of 20 degrees)

b. As another example, find the change in temperature from the
high of day 1 to the low of day 2:

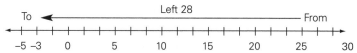

The number line shows a decrease of 28 degrees, or −28°
change from the high of day 1 to the low of day 2.
Mathematically, subtract the first number from the second:

Low of day 2 – High of day 1 = −3 – (+25) = −3 + (−25) = −28°
(decrease of 28 degrees)

4. Have the students form groups of two or three to find the
following changes in temperature. Write these problems on the
board, and ask the students to express the changes as positive or
negative numbers and to show their work. You can add more
problems of your own.

a. Find the change in temperature from the high of day 2 to the
low of day 2.

b. Find the change in temperature from the high of day 3 to the
low of day 3.

c. Find the change in temperature from the high of day 1 to the
low of day 4.

d. Find the change in temperature from the high of day 5 to the
low of day 8.

e. Find the change in temperature from the high of day 8 to the
low of day 8.

f. Find the change in temperature from the low of day 4 to the
high of day 5.

Graph It Two

Directions:

1. Have the students work in groups of two. Give each pair of students four dice (two red and two white) and give each student a copy of a number line page. Ask the students to label the number line from −8 to +8.

2. The students should take turns rolling the four dice. The white dice denote positive integers and the red dice denote negative integers. The roller can select any two of the four dice and use the sum as a point to be graphed. For example, if the roll comes up +3, +4, −1, −4, the students can select +3 and +4 to graph +7, or +3 and −1 to graph +2, etc.

3. Students should continue to roll until all the numbers −8 through 8 have been graphed. The student who graphs all the numbers first wins.

4. Have the students repeat the activity a few times and then discuss any strategies the students used. For example, they may be covering −8, −7, −6, +6, +7, and +8 first.

5. Repeat the game but let the students add the numbers on 2, 3, or all 4 of the dice to get the numbers to graph on the number line.

Materials:

▶ Blackline masters for **number lines** are in the Appendix.

▶ Four dice of two different colors (two red and two white) for each pair of students

Materials:

▶ Three dice, two of one color and one of another color, for example, two red and one white

Problem-Solving Activity

How Many Answers? :ŷ:

Directions:

1. Have the students form groups of two or three. The students in each group should take turns rolling the dice. In these instructions, two red dice represent negative numbers and one white die represents positive numbers.

2. Using as many combinations of addition and subtraction, order, and grouping as they can, the students should, as a group, see how many answers they can form. For example, if the numbers +4, −3, and −2 are rolled, the following are some of the possibilities:

   $+4 + (−3) + (−2) = −1$

   $+4 + (−3) − (−2) = +4 + (−3) + (+2) = +3$

   $+4 − (−3) − (−2) = +4 + (+3) + (+2) = +9$

   $+4 − [−3 + (−2)] = +4 − (−5) = +4 + (+5) = +9$
   (same answer as above)

3. Because many answers are possible, a time limit is in order— perhaps 3 to 5 minutes.

4. Discuss with the students strategies for finding different answers.

5. Repeat the process as time permits.

6. **Variation:** Give all of the students the same three numbers and see which group can come up with the most different problems and answers.
   Variation: Give this activity to the students individually as a homework assignment.

2-3 *Objective:* Compare and order rational numbers.

Sample Test: Place the symbol <, >, or = between each pair of numbers to make the sentence true.

1. $+\frac{1}{4}$ ___ $+\frac{1}{3}$
2. -2.8 ___ -3
3. -10 ___ 25

Solution: <   **Solution: >**   **Solution: <**

4. Arrange the following numbers in order from the smallest to the largest: 3, −2.4, −3, 2.4, 0

Solution: −3, −2.4, 0, 2.4, 3

Concept Development Activities

Number Line Modeling

Directions:

1. Distribute a number line page to each student.

2. Ask the students to label the numbers −8 to +8 on the number line and to plot the following pairs of numbers:

   a. +2 and +6. Stress that the number to the right on the number line is always greater, so +6 > +2.

   b. −3 and +2. Again discuss the order, so +2 > −3, or −3 < +2.

   c. −3 and −6. Again, since −3 is farther to the right on the number line, −3 is larger, so −3 > −6, or −6 < −3.

3. The students should see on each example plotted that ">" is equivalent to "is to the right of," and "<" is equivalent to "is to the left of."

4. Do other examples on number lines and discuss the positions on the number line and how position affects order and comparative values.

5. Present some examples in which three to six rational numbers must be placed in order from smallest to largest. For example, place +3, −1, −2, $1\frac{1}{2}$, −1.4, and 2.1 in order.

Materials:

▶ Blackline masters for **number lines** are in the Appendix.

Teacher's Tip:

Worksheet 1 for this objective, **page 2-13**, supports this activity with practice exercises.

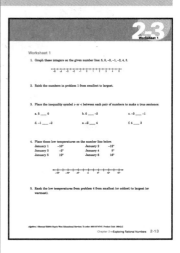

6. One standby method of remembering the order of rational numbers is to think of an alligator. The alligator's mouth represents the inequality sign, and the alligator always eats the larger number. So, if the numbers are 5 and 6, the inequality would be 5 < 6. The alligator is eating the larger number, 6.

$$5 < 6$$

Ranking Temperatures

Directions:

1. Divide the class into groups of two. Distribute one copy of the blackline master **Winter Temperature Changes** to each pair.

2. Ask each group to write at least 14 number sentences using < or > that compare two low or two high temperatures. For example:

   Day 1 high to day 2 high: 25° > 20°

   Day 2 high to day 3 high: 20° > 10°

   Day 3 high to day 4 high: 10° > −4°

   Day 4 high to day 5 high: −4° < 33°

3. Ask the students to write as many comparisons as they can for the high winter temperatures (for example, day 1 high to day 3 high). Have them write number sentences for their comparisons.

4. When they are done comparing the highs, ask them to do the same for the low temperatures. For example:

   Day 1 low to day 2 low: 5° > −3°

   Day 2 low to day 3 low: −3° > −11°

5. As a bonus question, ask the groups to rank the high temperatures in order from smallest (coldest) to largest (warmest). When this is complete, ask them to do the same with the low temperatures.

Materials:

▶ Blackline master **Winter Temperature Changes** is located in the *Teacher's Resource Manual,* **page 19.**

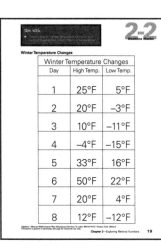

Winter Temperature Changes

Day	High Temp.	Low Temp.
1	25°F	5°F
2	20°F	−3°F
3	10°F	−11°F
4	−4°F	−15°F
5	33°F	16°F
6	50°F	22°F
7	20°F	4°F
8	12°F	−12°F

6. Ask the students, "Can you write any sentence in which the low temperature for a day is greater than the high temperature for another day?" Have the students write an example if they respond positively.

Practice Activities

Roll a Fraction

Directions:

1. Divide the class into groups of two. Give each group a pair of dice of different colors and a number line page.

2. Ask the students to label the number line from –6 to +6.

3. In each group, one student will roll the dice twice. For each roll, one color die (red) will represent the numerator of a fraction and the other color die (white) will represent the denominator. For the first roll, the numbers on the dice are positive numbers; the fractions when the students take their second roll are negative.

4. The other student in the pair will find, label, and plot the fractions on the number line and then write on a sheet of paper a comparative sentence using the two fractions from the two rolls of the dice.

5. The following table shows some possible results of **Roll a Fraction**:

Student and Roll	Sign of Fractions	Red Die Numerator	White Die Denominator	Sentence
FIRST TURNS				
Student 1, Roll 1	+	3	4	
Student 1, Roll 2	+	1	6	$\frac{3}{4} > \frac{1}{6}$
Student 2, Roll 1	+	6	5	
Student 2, Roll 2	+	5	2	$\frac{6}{5} < \frac{5}{2}$

Teacher's Tip:

Worksheet 2 for this objective, **page 2-14**, supports this activity with practice exercises.

2-3
Worksheet 2

Worksheet 2
Rearrange the following numbers from smallest to largest:

1. –8, 5, 10, –10, 8, –2   _____

2. 3, 2, 0, –2, 4, 1   _____

3. 1, –8, 5, –8, 3, –1   _____

4. –100, –101, –99, +99, 100, –98   _____

5. –1½, 1½, 2, 1, –3, –1, 0   _____

Place the symbol <, >, or = between the numbers to make a true statement.

6. –1 ___ 1   7. –1 ___ 0   8. –1 ___ –2

9. –1 ___ –1½   10. –1 ___ –½   11. –1 ___ –1.1

12. –13 ___ –12   13. –13 ___ –14   14. .13 ___ .13.1

15. –.13 ___ –13.1 16. –4 ___ –3   17. 4 ___ 3

18. 14 ___ 13   19. –14 ___ –13   20. –1 ___ 100

2-14 Chapter 2—Exploring Rational Numbers

Materials:

▶ Blackline masters for **number lines** are in the Appendix.

▶ Two dice, one red and one white, for each group

▶ Paper to keep track of sentences produced

Student and Roll	Sign of Fractions	Red Die Numerator	White Die Denominator	Sentence
SECOND TURNS				
Student 1, Roll 1	–	3	3	$-\frac{3}{3} < -\frac{1}{6}$
Student 1, Roll 2	–	1	6	
Student 2, Roll 1	–	2	3	$-\frac{2}{3} > -\frac{5}{1}$
Student 2, Roll 2	–	5	1	

Profits and Losses

Directions:

Materials:

► Blackline master **Profits and Losses** is located in the *Teacher's Resource Manual,* **page 20.**

1. Divide the class into groups of two. Give each group a copy of the blackline master **Profits and Losses**.

2. Discuss how running a school store can result in a profit or a loss. A profit is represented by a positive rational number, and a loss is represented by a negative rational number.

3. Discuss how negative earnings are the same as losses. For example, earnings of –$3.50 would actually be a loss of $3.50.

4. Ask the student pairs to fill in the blanks on the blackline master and to also compute tasks 2 and 3.

5. Discuss the graphing of each number and the sequence of the numbers.

Comparing Numbers

Directions:

1. The students will work individually on this activity.

2. Write these numbers on the board or overhead: $3, \frac{11}{4}, -2.7, 2.3,$
   $2.7, -\frac{11}{4}, -3, -2.3$.

3. Ask the students to draw a number line on their papers like the
   one shown here:

   $-3\ -2.5\ -2\ -1.5\ -1\ -.5\ 0\ .5\ 1\ 1.5\ 2\ 2.5\ 3$

   Have the students graph each of the numbers given in step 2.
   (*Note:* For the fractions, students may use calculators to change
   them to a decimal equivalent.)

4. Discuss the plotting of the numbers on the number line and
   check for the correct sequence.

5. Ask the students to write comparative sentences with pairs of
   the given numbers, starting at the left. For example, $3 > \frac{11}{4}, \frac{11}{4} >$
   $-2.7, -2.7 < 2.3,\ldots$

6. Ask the students to write 5 to 10 more sentences using any of the
   numbers and the < or > signs.

7. Ask the students to rank the numbers from smallest to largest.
   This is, of course, already done on the number line, but this is a
   check to show the students how they can do a sequence from the
   number line.

Teacher's Tip:

Worksheet 3 for this
objective, **page 2-15**,
supports this activity
with practice exercises.

Problem-Solving Activities

Temperatures

Directions:

1. Find the average monthly temperatures for many different cities
   and make a chart that shows average high and low temperatures.
   This could also be a project taken on by students,
   individually or in groups. Be sure to include cities that have
   negative temperatures.

2. When the chart is completed, ask the students to graph, rank,
   and compare the average temperatures.

Materials:

▶ An almanac or a
book on climate
from the school
library

Materials:

Materials:

▶ Calculators

Closer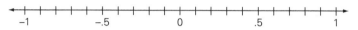

Directions:

1. Draw a number line on the board like the one shown below, with tenths marked on it.

$$-1 \qquad -.5 \qquad 0 \qquad .5 \qquad 1$$

2. Write the fraction $\frac{2}{5}$ on the board and ask the students if they can locate it on the number line. Students may use calculators to change it to a decimal and then plot it.

3. Ask the students to name a fraction that is closer to 0 than $\frac{2}{5}$. Then ask them to name a fraction that is closer to 1 than $\frac{2}{5}$. Answers can be common fractions or decimal fractions.

4. Discuss the students' responses and why the fractions they named are closer to 0 or 1.

5. Ask the students to finish the following table (write it on the board; answers will vary):

	Fraction	Find a Fraction Closer to:	Answer
a.	0.85	1	_____
b.	$\frac{1}{9}$	0	_____
c.	$-\frac{4}{5}$	0	_____
d.	$-\frac{4}{5}$	-1	_____
e.	$\frac{7}{8}$	1	_____
f.	$-\frac{2}{3}$	-1	_____
g.	0.99	1	_____
h.	0.01	0	_____
i.	-0.1	0	_____

2-4 *Objective:* **Multiply and divide rational numbers.**

Sample Test: Simplify:

1. $-3 \times 4 = $ _____

   Solution: –12

2. $\left(\frac{2}{3}\right) \times \left(-\frac{4}{5}\right) = $ _____

   Solution: $-\frac{8}{15}$

3. $-10 \div (-5) = $ _____

   Solution: 2

4. $\left(\frac{2}{3}\right) \div \left(-\frac{4}{5}\right) = $ _____

   Solution: $-\frac{10}{12}$, or $-\frac{5}{6}$

Concept Development Activities

Multiplying Integers

Directions:

1. Have students work individually. Ask the students to write $4 \times (-3)$ on their papers.

2. Ask the students, "What does this mean?" Lead them to the conclusion that multiplying is consecutive additions. In this example, $4 \times (-3)$ means adding four negative threes. That is, $(-3) + (-3) + (-3) + (-3) = -12$, so $4 \times (-3) = -12$.

3. Ask the students to write -2×3 on their papers. By the commutative property of multiplication, this is the same as $3 \times (-2)$. This can be thought of as $(-2) + (-2) + (-2)$, or -6. So $-2 \times 3 = 3 \times (-2) =$ three negative twos $= (-2) + (-2) + (-2)$, or -6.

4. These arguments work well for multiplying unlike signs or two positive numbers, but they do not work for multiplying two negatives. To show multiplication of two negatives, ask the students to complete this pattern: $-3 \times 4 = -12$; $-3 \times 3 = -9$; $-3 \times 2 = -6$; $-3 \times 1 = -3$; $-3 \times 0 = 0$; $-3 \times (-1) = $ _____. Ask, "What is the next number in the sequence of answers, $-12, -9, -6, -3, 0,$ _____?" Most students should see that $-3 \times (-1) = $ must be $+3$, and likewise, $-3 \times (-2) = +6$, etc. Lead the students to the conclusion that multiplying two negatives *MUST* yield a positive.

5. Ask the students to make up their own pattern to show that the product of two negatives must be a positive.

Materials:

► Blackline master **Pump, Tank, and Movie** is located in the *Teacher's Resource Manual,* **page 21.**

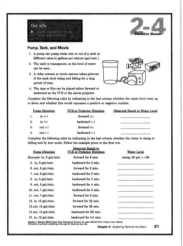

Teacher's Tip:

Worksheet 1 for this objective, **page 2-18,** supports this activity with practice exercises.

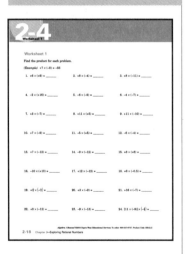

Pump, Tank, and Movie

Directions:

1. Develop the idea of a pump that can pump water into (+) or out of (−) a transparent tank, making the water level rise or fall.

2. A crude drawing on the board of the pump and tank will help. Now add to the drawing a movie camera or video camera to record the pumping activity for an extended period of time. Students' imaginations will thrive on this pretend situation.

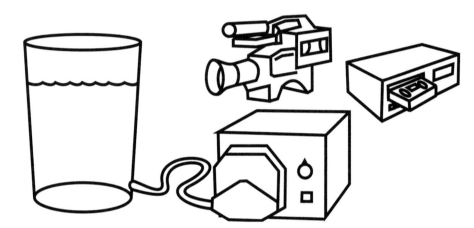

3. Give each student a copy of the blackline master **Pump, Tank, and Movie**. The students should work on the sheet as you present the following explanation to the class.

4. Introduce the concept of a VCR or movie projector that can run backward or forward. Ask the class: "What happens to the water level when the tape of the tank filling (+) is played backward (−)?" They will answer that it will look like the level is going down (−). Thus, a positive times a negative is a negative.

5. Go through the other possibilities, such as:

    a. The tank is filling (+) and the tape is running forward (+).

    b. The tank level is falling (−) and the tape is running forward (+).

    c. The tank level is falling (−) and the tape is running backward (−).

6. As soon as the students see the observed results as positive or negative, you can introduce numbers. Discuss the following examples:

Pumping in 3 gallons per minute +3	Tape played forward for 4 minutes +4	Observed change in level: up 12 gallons +12
Pumping in 3 gallons per minute +3	Tape played backward for 4 minutes −4	Observed change in level: down 12 gallons −12
Pumping out 3 gallons per minute −3	Tape played backward for 4 minutes −4	Observed change in level: up 12 gallons +12

7. Write the mathematical sentences on the board. For example,
$+3 \times (+4) = +12$, $+3 \times (−4) = −12$, $−3 \times (−4) = +12$.

8. Have the students complete the blackline master.

Inverse Operations

Directions:

1. Review with the students the concept that multiplication and division are inverse operations. One "undoes" the other. For example, if $2 \times 6 = 12$, then $12 \div 6 = 2$ or $12 \div 2 = 6$.

2. Present the problem $9 \times 4 = 36$ to the students. Ask them to give the inverse operation ($\div$) problems related to it.

3. Discuss that these are related problems and that all three equations result in a true sentence.

4. Now have the students write related sentences for inverse operations using integers. Give the following problems to the students and ask them to write the related division sentences (answers given).

Problems	Related Sentences	
$+6 \times (+7) = +42$	$+42 \div (+6) = +7$	$+42 \div (+7) = +6$
$−5 \times (+8) = −40$	$−40 \div (+8) = −5$	$−40 \div (−5) = +8$
$+7 \times (−4) = −28$	$−28 \div (−4) = +7$	$−28 \div (+7) = −4$
$−4 \times (−9) = +36$	$+36 \div (−4) = −9$	$+36 \div (−9) = −4$

Answer Key for #2:
$36 \div 4 = 9$ and $36 \div 9 = 4$

Teacher's Tip:

Worksheet 2 for this objective, **page 2-19**, supports this activity with practice exercises.

Answer Key for #5:
a. Positive b. Negative
c. Positive d. Negative

Teacher's Tip:

Worksheets 3 and 4 for this objective, **pages 2-20 and 2-21**, support this activity with practice exercises.

5. Ask the students to think of number sentences that model the following and then to answer the questions:

   a. A positive number divided by a positive number. What kind of number is the answer?

   b. A negative number divided by a positive number. What kind of number is the answer?

   c. A negative number divided by a negative number. What kind of number is the answer?

   d. A positive number divided by a negative number. What kind of number is the answer?

6. Ask the students to generalize about the value when doing division. (It is the same generalization as for multiplication: Like signs yield a positive answer and unlike signs yield a negative answer.)

Division of Rational Numbers Using Reciprocals

Directions:

1. Review with the students that multiplying like signs results in a positive answer and multiplying unlike signs results in a negative answer.

2. Convince the class that division is nothing more than multiplying by the reciprocal. For example, $10 \div 2 = 10 \times \frac{1}{2} = 5$ (dividing by 2 is the same as multiplying by $\frac{1}{2}$). Other examples are $-10 \div 2 = -10 \times \frac{1}{2} = -5$ and $-10 \div (-2) = -10 \times \left(-\frac{1}{2}\right) = 5$. *Note:* A short definition of "reciprocals" may be necessary.

3. Since division is the same as multiplying by a different number, you should be able to convince the class that the rules for the signs are the same.

4. Ask the students to write each of the following examples of division as a multiplication problem and then to solve the problems (answers given):

   a. $12 \div (-3)$ b. $-12 \div (+3)$

   c. $-12 \div (-3)$ d. $15 \div \left(-\frac{5}{6}\right)$

   e. $-15 \div \left(-\frac{5}{6}\right)$

5. Ask the students to give a generalization about dividing rational numbers.

Answer Key for #4:
a. $12 \times \left(-\frac{1}{3}\right) = -4$
b. $-12 \times \left(+\frac{1}{3}\right) = -4$
c. $-12 \times \left(-\frac{1}{3}\right) = +4$
d. $15 \times \left(-\frac{6}{5}\right) = -18$
e. $-15 \times \left(-\frac{6}{5}\right) = +18$

Practice Activities

Contig Multiplication 💡

Directions:

1. Have the students form groups of two to four. Give each group four dice (two red and two white), one copy of the blackline master **Contig Game Board**, and enough markers to cover each square.

2. Each student in the group should roll a die. The student with the highest number will go first. That student selects three dice to roll. Red denotes negative numbers and white denotes positive numbers. The student's choice should depend on what kind of answer is desired (positive or negative).

3. The object of the game is to create a problem with the numbers rolled that has an answer corresponding to one of the unoccupied squares on the Contig Game Board. The student may use any of the four operations ($+, -, \times, \div$) and may use the numbers rolled in any order. For example, if the student rolled +3, –2, and –4, some possible combinations would include:

$$+3 + (-2) - (-4) = +5 \qquad +3 \times (-2) \times (-4) = +24$$

$$+3 \times (-4 \div -2) = +6 \qquad -4 \times [-2 - (+3)] = +20$$

4. Once a player creates a problem, that player writes the problem on paper and the other players check to see if the answer is correct. If the answer is correct, the player puts a marker on that square. The square can be used only once.

5. *Scoring:* One point is awarded for placing a marker on an unoccupied square, plus one additional point is awarded for each touching (contiguous) square that has a marker on it.

6. A tally is kept for each student. At each turn, a student is allowed to use only *one* problem to determine where his or her marker will go on the game board. The student selects one problem from all the possibilities.

7. A time limit may be imposed for each player's turn and to end the game. For example, a player may have 1 minute to find a problem to use, and the game will last for 25 minutes.

Materials:

▶ Blackline master **Contig Game Board** is located in the *Teacher's Resource Manual,* **page 22.**

▶ Game markers to cover squares

▶ Dice of two different colors (red and white)

2-4
Blackline Master

Contig Game Board

+1	–2	+3	–4	+5	–6	+7	–8
+9	–10	+11	–12	+13	–14	+15	–16
+17	–18	+19	–20	+21	–22	+23	–24
+25	–26	+27	–28	+29	–30	+31	–32
+33	–34	+35	–36	+37	–38	+39	–40
+41	–42	+44	–45	+48	–50	+54	–55
+60	–64	+66	–72	+75	–80	+90	–96
+100	–108	+120	–125	+144	–150	+180	–216

Each player writes
R-4 W+3 R+6
+then writes multiple exp.
while next player rolls

or require 4-5 expressions per set of dice

Multiplication Millionaire

Directions:

1. The goal of this activity is for students to try to become multiplication/division millionaires by answering the questions correctly, starting at the 100-point level. With each correct answer, students continue to the next level. Each student can write answers on his or her paper, seeing how high he or she can go without a mistake.

2. If you allow the students to use calculators, it is preferable for them to use four-function calculators rather than scientific or graphic calculators.

3. A sample set of questions is listed below (answers are in parentheses). Other sets can be generated by following the examples given and changing the digits but preserving the question value.

Value	Sample Question 1	Sample Question 2
100	$-3 \times (+6) =$ **(−18)**	$-5 \times (+8) =$ **(−40)**
200	$-11 \times (-6) =$ **(+66)**	$-14 \times (-6) =$ **(+84)**
300	$-46 \times (+19) =$ **(−874)**	$+47 \times (-24) =$ **(−1,128)**
500	$-2,020 \div (-5) =$ **(+404)**	$-6,325 \div (-5) =$ **(+1,265)**
1,000	$-1,403 \div (+61) =$ **(−23)**	$+703 \div (-37) =$ **(−19)**
2,000	$+1.5 \times (-2.7) =$ **(−4.05)**	$+1.6 \times (-3.7) =$ **(−5.92)**
4,000	$-63.6 \div (-1.2) =$ **(+53)**	$-64.8 \div (-1.8) =$ **(+36)**
8,000	$138 \div (-0.0005) =$ **(−276,000)**	$164 \div (-0.0004) =$ **(−410,000)**
16,000	$-24 \times (-6) \div (+8) =$ **(+18)**	$-32 \times (+9) \div (-12) =$ **(+24)**
32,000	$-\frac{1}{4} \times \left(+\frac{2}{5}\right) =$ **($-\frac{1}{10}$)**	$-\frac{1}{6} \times \left(+\frac{3}{4}\right) =$ **($-\frac{1}{8}$)**
64,000	$+2\frac{4}{5} \div \left(+1\frac{1}{2}\right) =$ **($+1\frac{13}{15}$)**	$+4\frac{3}{4} \div \left(+1\frac{1}{8}\right) =$ **($+4\frac{2}{9}$)**
125,000	$-12 \div (+0.75) \div \left(-\frac{2}{5}\right) =$ **(+40)**	$-16 \div (+0.25) \div \left(-\frac{1}{5}\right) =$ **(+320)**
250,000	$-8 \times \left(-1\frac{4}{5}\right) \div (-10) =$ **(−1.44)**	$-12 \times \left(-1\frac{1}{4}\right) \div 8 =$ **(+1.875)**
500,000	$-0.67 \times \left(+2\frac{1}{4}\right) \div (+0.15)$ $=$ **(−10.05)**	$-0.38 \times \left(+4\frac{1}{5}\right) \div (+0.12)$ $=$ **(−13.3)**
1,000,000	$-\frac{1}{3} \times (+0.825) \div (+1.1)$ $=$ **(−0.25)**	$+\frac{2}{3} \times (-0.942) \div \left(-\frac{2}{5}\right) =$ **(1.57)**

Chapter 2—Exploring Rational Numbers

Problem-Solving Activity

Fill in the Blanks

Directions:

1. Discuss with the class the rules for multiplication and division of integers, including both positive and negative integers.

2. Put on the board the following **Fill in the Blanks** activity. Include only the blocks, operation signs, first integer (5), and the answer blocks. Do not show the solution (presented below the activity) to the students.

5	×		÷		**−20**
×	■	×	■	×	
	×		×		**−42**
÷	■	÷	■	×	
	×		×		**108**

−10	**−14**	**18**

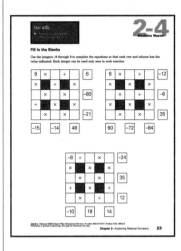

Materials:

► Blackline master **Fill in the Blanks** is located in the *Teacher's Resource Manual*, **page 23.**

Solution:

5	×	**−8**	÷	2	**−20**
×	■	×	■	×	
−6	×	7	×	1	**−42**
÷	■	÷	■	×	
3	×	4	×	9	**108**

−10	**−14**	**18**

3. Instruct the students to use any integers –9 through 9 to complete the equations so that each row and column has the value indicated. Tell them that each integer can be used only once, however.

4. Explain that to get the first row, you have to solve $5 \times \_\_ \div \_\_ = -20$, and to get the first column, you have to solve $5 \times \_\_ \div \_\_ = -10$.

5. Remind the students that for an equation to have a negative answer, an odd number of factors would have to be negative. In each case described in #4, one of the missing integers must be negative.

6. Discuss the strategy of working backwards (inverse relationships with multiplication and division).

7. Allow the students to experiment with a variety of numbers until they find combinations that will work. Caution them that their solutions must furthermore solve the equations of the other rows and columns. For example, even though $5 \times 4 \div (-1) = -20$ is a solution for the first row, it does not work with the other rows and columns. However, once the students find the correct two equations (for the first row and first column), the remainder of the squares should be completed fairly quickly.

8. Give each student a copy of the blackline master **Fill in the Blanks**.

9. Review the directions as a class: "Complete each of the equations using the integers –9 through 9. Each number may be used only once." Students may work individually or as teams.

2-5 *Objective:* Find the principal square root of a number.

Sample Test: Find the following square roots:

1. $\sqrt{4}$ 2. $\sqrt{1}$ 3. $\pm\sqrt{16}$ 4. $-\sqrt{100}$

Solution: 2 Solution: 1 Solution: ±4 Solution: –10

Concept Development Activities

The Computing Machine

Directions:

1. Draw an imaginary computing machine, such as the one shown here, on the board:

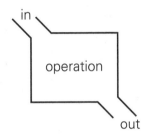

2. Discuss the machine's capabilities with the class as follows. You put in a number, an operation is performed, and another number (the answer) comes out. The operation can be changed.

3. Show the class some examples of numbers for "ins" and "outs" and ask them to determine the operation. For example,

   a. Show: $2 \rightarrow 6$ (read as "2 gives 6"), $4 \rightarrow 12$, $7 \rightarrow 21$.

      Ask the students to consider $3 \rightarrow 9$, $5 \rightarrow 15$, $15 \rightarrow 45$.

      What is the operation?

   b. Show: $7 \rightarrow 14$, $9 \rightarrow 16$, $12 \rightarrow 19$.

      Ask the students to consider $3 \rightarrow 10$, $14 \rightarrow 21$, $100 \rightarrow 107$.

      What is the operation?

   c. Show: $4 \rightarrow 9$, $7 \rightarrow 15$, $8 \rightarrow 17$.

      Ask the students to consider $2 \rightarrow 5$, $5 \rightarrow 11$, $15 \rightarrow 31$.

      What is the operation?

Answer Key for #3:
a. Multiply by 3
b. Add 7
c. Double and add 1

Concept Development

Answer Key:
4. Squaring (x²), or multiplying by the same number
5. Unsquaring (square root)
7. 2, 3, 11, 20

Teacher's Tip:

Worksheet 1 for this objective, **page 2-24**, supports this activity with practice exercises.

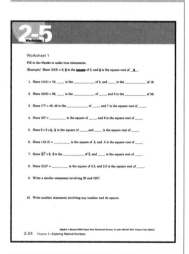

Materials:

► Objects such as beans or chips

4. After reviewing a few more examples of your own, introduce the students to squaring and unsquaring (finding the square root).

   a. Show: $2 \to 4$, $3 \to 9$, $4 \to 16$.

   Ask the students to consider $5 \to 25$, $6 \to 36$, $7 \to 49$.

   What is the operation?

5. Pretend with your students that the machine was dropped and damaged while it was set on squaring, and the following results were then observed:

   a. Show: $9 \to 3$, $25 \to 5$, $81 \to 9$.

   Ask the students to consider $16 \to 4$, $36 \to 6$, $64 \to 8$.

   What is the operation?

6. A way to help the students remember the radical sign ($\sqrt{}$) is to tell them the following:

   In the late 15th century, mathematicians worked with the concept of roots of numbers. The Latin word for root is *radix* (hence, the word radical). At that time, mathematicians used the letter r to indicate the root, or *radix,* of a number; for example r4 = 2. The letter r was written more loosely then, and looked more like $\sqrt{}$. Eventually, this became the symbol for "root."

7. Ask the students to identify the square root for these numbers: 4, 9, 121, 400.

Building Squares

Directions:

1. Divide the students into pairs and provide each pair with a pile of objects, such as beans or chips.

2. Ask the students to build a square by placing the objects in an array such as:

• • •

• • •

• • •

Chapter 2—Exploring Rational Numbers

3. Discuss how this particular square is "the square of three." (It is three on a side.) The square of three requires nine beans. Thus, the square of three is nine, or $3^2 = 9$. Also, the array shows that the root of the square is three, or $\sqrt{9} = 3$. The positive square root is often called the *principal* square root.

4. Try other squares:

$2^2 = 4$ (4 is the square of 2)

               (2 is the square root of 4)

$4^2 = 16$ (16 is the square of 4)

               (4 is the square root of 16)

5. Try more examples with the students until they are comfortable with the terms "square" and "square root."

Estimating Square Roots

Directions:

1. Write $\sqrt{16}$ on the board. Ask the students for the solution. Discuss that 4 is the principal square root and that $-\sqrt{16} = -4$ is the negative square root. Solving equations of the form $x^2 = 16$ will be done in Chapter 9.

2. Write $\sqrt{19}$ on the board. Ask the students for the solution. Discuss different answers from the class. Point out that the answer is *not* an integer because $4^2 = 16$ and $5^2 = 25$. Therefore, the answer is between 4 and 5.

3. Draw a number line on the board. Ask the class to graph $\sqrt{19}$ on the number line. Discuss where it is located on the number line. Ask, "Is $\sqrt{19}$ closer to 4 or 5?" Note that 19 is closer to 16 than it is to 25.

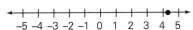

Teacher's Tip:

Worksheet 2 for this objective, **page 2-25**, supports this activity with practice exercises.

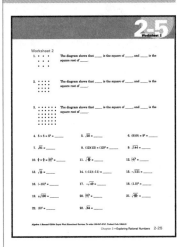

Materials:

► Calculators with square root keys

Concept/Practice

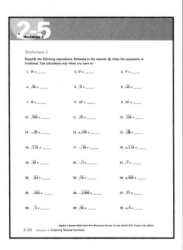

Teacher's Tip:

Worksheet 3 for this objective, **page 2-26**, supports this activity with practice exercises.

Materials:

▶ Blackline master **Estimate, Then Calculate** is located in the *Teacher's Resource Manual*, **page 24**.

4. Ask some students to guess at a decimal value to the nearest $\frac{1}{10}$ for $\sqrt{19}$. Suppose they guess 4.2. Have them multiply $4.2 \times 4.2 = 17.64$. Ask if another guess would come closer to 19. Try other values ($4.3 \times 4.3 = 18.49$, $4.4 \times 4.4 = 19.36$, $4.5 \times 4.5 = 20.25$).

5. Ask the class which value is the closest to 19. It is 4.4.

6. Now show the students how to use the $\sqrt{}$ key on the calculator. Have the students enter 19 and then press the $\sqrt{}$ key. The display should show 4.35889. To the nearest $\frac{1}{10}$ it is 4.4.

7. Try some other examples. Have the students estimate the answer and multiply it times itself on the calculator to find the approximate answer to the nearest $\frac{1}{100}$. Then use the $\sqrt{}$ key to check the estimate. Suggested problems are $\sqrt{10}$, $\sqrt{33}$, $\sqrt{68}$, and $\sqrt{95}$. Have the students plot the examples on the number line.

8. Have students practice writing the square roots of numbers to the nearest $\frac{1}{100}$ using the $\sqrt{}$ key on the calculator. For example, $\sqrt{15} \approx 3.87$, $\sqrt{30} \approx 5.48$, $\sqrt{50} \approx 7.07$, $\sqrt{44} \approx 6.63$, $\sqrt{77} \approx 8.77$, $\sqrt{23} \approx 4.80$.

9. Explain that it is important to have some approximate idea of an answer before using the calculator, as a self-check, because sometimes we push the wrong buttons on the calculator!

Practice Activities

Estimate, Then Calculate

Directions:

1. Divide the students into groups of two to four. Give each student a copy of the blackline master **Estimate, Then Calculate**.

2. One student in each group should be designated the checker. He or she will check to see if the others in the group got the square root correct to the nearest tenth. The checker should use the $\sqrt{}$ button on calculator to check.

3. The other students in the group should be given a limited amount of time to figure the square root of each number with paper and pencil only. The checker will determine who is correct.

4. One way for the students to estimate the square roots is to graph the number on the number line and compare it to the perfect squares on each side. For example, for $\sqrt{40}$,

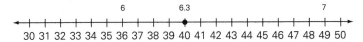

5. Points can be scored by students who are correct. A winner can be determined in each group after the worksheet is completed. The winners from each group can then compete against each other, tournament-style, doing additional problems.

6. You should help the students to develop a feeling for irrational square roots and their location between rational numbers.

7. **Variation:** Allow all the students to use calculators to do the computations for the multiplication of their "best guess" for each problem (e.g., 4.2×4.2). However, only the checker can use the $\sqrt{}$ key.

$\sqrt{\text{Roll It Bingo}}$

Directions:

1. Distribute one copy of the blackline master **Roll It Card** to each student.

2. Ask the students to choose from the following numbers to fill in the blanks on the cards in a random fashion:

   1, 1.4, 1.7, 2, 2.2, 2.4, 2.8, 3, 3.2, 3.5, 3.9, 4, 4.2, 4.5, 4.9, 5, 5.5, 6

   (*Note:* These numbers are the square roots of 1, 2, 3, 4, 5, 6, 8, 9, 10, 12, 15, 16, 18, 20, 24, 25, 30, and 36 to the nearest tenth, respectively.)

3. One student, or the teacher, should be designated the caller. He or she will roll the two dice. The product of the two numbers rolled is the number for which the students have to find the square root. For example, if 4 and 6 are rolled, the caller calls out the number 24, and that is the number for which the students must find the square root using a calculator. The caller should record the number and its square root on a sheet of paper, and if

Materials:

► Blackline master **Roll It Card** is located in the *Teacher's Resource Manual,* **page 25.**

► Pair of dice for caller

► One calculator for each student

► Game markers to cover squares

Teacher's Tip:

Several games can be going on at the same time, but each caller must have a calculator to determine the correct answers.

Materials:

▶ Three dice

▶ Paper and pencil (no calculators) for each student

▶ One calculator for the caller

a repeat of that number is rolled, the caller should roll again. A time limit between rolls should be established.

4. Play proceeds until someone covers all the numbers in a row, across, down, or diagonally, and calls "Bingo!" The caller then confirms the bingo.

5. A more difficult version of this game could be produced by rolling three dice and using products of all three dice.

$\sqrt{\text{Roll It}}$

Directions:

1. Students can work individually or in groups.

2. The teacher or a designated student should act as the caller and roll the dice (two or three). The product of the two or three numbers rolled is the number for which the students must find the square root to the nearest tenth.

3. Establish a time limit between rolls, but be flexible for more difficult numbers. After the time is up, the caller should read the correct answer to the nearest tenth.

4. Correct answers earn one point. The first student to reach a certain predetermined point total wins the game.

5. A different set of numbers can be generated by taking the sum of the two, three, or more dice rolled.

Problem-Solving Activity

Areas of Squares 🔆

Directions:

1. Draw a square with side s on the board or overhead. Review that the area of the square is $A = s^2$. Give an example, such as, "If the area of a square is 25 square inches, the side s is 5 inches."

$$A = s^2 \quad \Big| \quad s$$

2. Ask the students to fill in the blanks for the following problems:

    a. s = _____ ft. if A = 4 sq. ft.

    b. s = _____ ft. if A = 64 sq. ft.

    c. s = _____ yd. if A = 100 sq. yd.

    d. s = _____ in. if A = 144 sq. in.

    e. Give the answer to question d in feet: s = _____ ft.

3. Give the problem: s = _____ ft. if A = 10 sq. ft. Ask, "Are you puzzled about how to find the answer to this problem? Do you think the answer is *more* or *less* than 3?"

    Ask, "Do you think the answer is *more* or *less* than 3.1?" Give the hint that the students should try $(3.1)^2$.

    Then ask, "Is the answer closer to 3.1 or 3.2?"

    Finally, note that the students can now say that to the nearest tenth, $\sqrt{10} = 3.2$.

4. Have the students find $\sqrt{60}$ in the same way, to the nearest tenth. Give the hint that the answer is close to 8.

5. Then have them find $\sqrt{150}$ to the nearest tenth and $\sqrt{2,000}$ to the nearest tenth.

6. Ask the students, "Do you believe problems 3–5 have exact answers?" (Yes or No)

Solving Linear Equations

3-1 Solve linear equations with addition and subtraction.

3-2 Solve linear equations with multiplication and division.

3-3 Solve linear equations using one or more operations.

3-4 Solve problems that can be represented as equations.

3-5 Solve a proportion with a missing part.

3-6 Use proportions to solve percent problems.

3-1 *Objective:* Solve linear equations with addition and subtraction.

Sample Test: Solve the following equations for the variables.

1. $19 - x = 21$

   Solution: $x = -2$

2. $2d - (-3.7) = 4.2 + d$

   Solution: $d = 0.5$

3-1

Concept Development

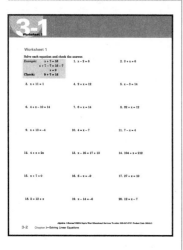

Concept Development Activities

Addition Property of Equality With Arithmetic

Directions:

1. Write on the board the following three math sentences.

   $x + 4 = 9$ $7 = 7$ $6 = 5$

2. Ask the class which sentence is true. **(7 = 7)**
   Ask which sentence is open. **(x + 4 = 9)**
   Ask which sentence is false. **(6 = 5)**

3. Erase the three sentences and write the following three sentences on the board.

   $7 = 7$ $7 + 2 = 7 + 3$ $7 + 3 = 7 + 3$

4. Ask the class which sentences are true and why. **(7 = 7);**
   (7 + 3 = 7 + 3)

   Discuss that $7 + 3 = 7 + 3$ or $10 = 10$ is true and that $7 + 2 \neq 7 + 3$. Ask why this sentence is false. **(Different amounts are added to each side.)**

5. Write the sentence $12 = 12$ on the board or overhead. Be sure the class understands that it is a true sentence. Then have the class tell you whether each of the following sentences is true or false. Write one sentence at a time on the board or overhead. When the class says true or false, ask a student why. The class needs to see that if the same amount is added to or subtracted from each side of an equation (=), the sentence will be true. If a different amount is added to or subtracted from each side, the sentence will be false.

$12 - 3 = 12 - 3$ **(true)**	$12 + 6 = 12 - 6$ **(false)**
$12 + 12 = 12 + 12$ **(true)**	$12 - 0 = 12 - 0$ **(true)**
$12 + 7 = 12 + 7$ **(true)**	$12 + 1 = 12 + 6$ **(false)**
$12 + (3 + 4) = 12 + (3 + 4)$ **(true)**	$12 - 8 = 12 - 8$ **(true)**
$12 - 4 = 12 + 4$ **(false)**	$12 - 7 = 12 + 7$ **(false)**

6. Now write $x + 4 = 18$ on the board. Ask the class what type of sentence it is—true, false, or open. This is an open sentence. We don't know if it is true or false until we give "x" a value. Ask the class what value for x will make the sentence true. **(14)**

7. Ask if the value for x [14] will change if 4 is subtracted from each side.

$$x + 4 - 4 = 18 - 4$$
$$x + 0 = 14$$
$$\mathbf{x = 14}$$

8. Ask if the value for x will change if 2 is added to one side and 3 to the other.

$$x + 4 + 2 = 18 + 3$$
$$x + 6 = 21$$

To make this sentence true, x would have to be 15.

9. Ask, "Why did the value for x change?" **(Because the same amount was not added to or subtracted from each side.)** Remember from above, if 7 = 7 then $7 + 2 \neq 7 + 3$. For the sentence to be true, the *same* amount must be added or subtracted.

10. Do another example with the class, such as x − 2 = 15. Add 2 to each side and then add a different amount to each side.

11. Discuss the addition property of equality.

$$\text{If } x = y \text{ then } x + z = y + z$$

Algebra Tiles (Addition and Subtraction)

Directions:

Materials:

▶ Algebra tiles

1. Group the students into pairs. Provide a set of algebra tiles for every two students.

2. Discuss what each piece in the set of algebra tiles represents:

   □ = units

   = a square with dimensions of x, or x^2.

   x

   x

   ⬜ = variable x

   The x^2 pieces will not be used in this activity, so have the students put them back in the container.

3. The is usually referred to as a variable or as x. It is the unknown, and the object is to find out what number it represents.

3.1 Concept Development

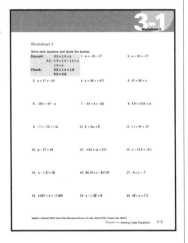

Teacher's Tip:

Worksheet 2 for this objective, **page 3-3**, supports this activity with practice exercises.

Teacher's Tip:

The **Equation Mat** could be used here.

4. Discuss that the variables piece has a different color on each side. One side is black [black bar] (which represents x, a positive or negative number), and the other is red [red bar] (which represents –x, the opposite of x). The units piece also has a different color on each side. One side is black ■ (which will represent +1), and the other is yellow □ (which will represent –1).

5. Ask the students what the result is when you combine (add) +1 and –1. **(Zero)** Model that a black unit and a yellow unit (+1 and –1) make 0. Show two black and two yellow units, and ask, "What is the result of adding +2 and –2?" **(Zero)**. This is a very important concept when using algebra tiles. A black unit (+1) and a yellow unit (–1) are a "zero pair." That is, when +1 and –1 are combined, the result is zero.

6. Write the equation x + 1 = 8 on the board. Discuss that you want the students to find the value of a number (x) such that when 1 is added to it, the result is 8. Ask what the value of the number is. **(7)**

7. Most students will know that the answer is 7: If you add +1 to 7, you get 8. However, this is a good problem for modeling the use of algebra tiles. Ask the students to model the problem by using the tiles.

   [algebra tiles model] ■ = ■ ■ ■ ■ ■ ■ ■ ■

8. Explain that two approaches can be used to determine what the [black bar] represents.

   a. One choice is to use the addition property of equality, adding a negative one (□) to both sides:

      [algebra tiles model] ■ □ = ■ ■ ■ ■ ■ ■ ■ ■ □

      Since ■ □ is a zero pair, the model becomes:

      [algebra tiles model] = ■ ■ ■ ■ ■ ■ ■

      Therefore, the model represents x = 7.

   b. The other choice is to take away the same thing from both sides of the equation. For example,

      [algebra tiles model] ✗ = ■ ■ ■ ■ ■ ■ ■ ✗

      By removing a ■ from each side, x = 7.

9. Model other equations by using the tiles. For example, x – 3 = 4.

   [algebra tiles model] □ □ □ = ■ ■ ■ ■

Adding +3 to both sides yields

Again, three yellow tiles and three black tiles represent three zero pairs, or 0.

■■■■ = ■ ■ ■ ■ ■ ■ ■ , so x = 7.

10. Show the above model in algebraic terms:

$$x - 3 = 4$$
$$x - 3 + 3 = 4 + 3$$
$$x + 0 = 7$$
$$x = 7$$

11. Model other equations, such as:

x + 2 = 1	x − 4 = 2	−x − 3 = 2
4 − x = 0	x + 3 = 2	6 − x = −2

As you model the problems, show the algebraic work.

Equation Mat (Addition and Subtraction)

Directions:

1. Have the class form groups of three to five students. Distribute a copy of the blackline master **Equation Mat (Addition and Subtraction)** and blank cards to each group.

2. Explain that the equation mat can help the students understand the solution of equations. Like a balance scale, an operation on one side of the equal sign must also be performed on the other side of the equal sign for the equation to "balance."

3. Give the students the equation x + 4 = −2. Write each element in the equation, x, +4, and −2, on separate cards. Ask the student groups to do the same using three blank cards. (The equations in this activity are selected so that many of the same cards may be used with the solution of the various equations.)

4. Explain the rules for solving equations on the equation mat with expression cards as listed on the blackline master **Equation Mat (Addition and Subtraction)**. Demonstrate each rule as you make expression cards and proceed with the solution. Before applying a rule, state the rule you are applying and why. Tell the students that they will be expected to do the same.

Teacher's Tip:

The students may use the tiles if they wish on **Worksheets 1 and 2**, pages 3-2 and 3-3.

Materials:

▶ Blackline master **Equation Mat (Addition and Subtraction)** is located in the *Teacher's Resource Manual*, **page 26**.

▶ Blank cards

▶ Marking pens

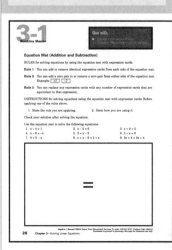

5. Proceed with the example by writing –4 on each of two additional cards. Place a –4 card on each side of the equal sign of the equation (Rule 1 on the equation mat). Explain that –4 and +4 are a zero pair, which, when removed from one side of the equation (Rule 2), will isolate the variable on that side of the equation, with the equivalent expression for –2 –4 (= –6) on the other side (Rule 3). Thus, x + 4 –4 = –2 –4, which yields x = –6.

6. Check the solution by substituting the value –6 for x in the original equation, x + 4 = –2. The new equation –6 + 4 = –2 yields –2 = –2, so the answer is correct.

7. Repeat the procedure with the equation x – 4 = 1. Make a card for +1.

8. Place cards for +4 on each side of the equal sign (Rule 1). By applying Rule 2, you can remove the zero pair, +4 and –4, from the left side of the equation to get x = 1 + 4. By Rule 3, x = 5.

9. Check the solution by substituting the value 5 for x in the original equation. Write 5 – 4 = 1, and indeed 1 = 1, so the equation checks.

10. Have the student groups continue solving equations from the blackline master using the equation mat, making new cards as necessary, and following the rules and instructions. (As noted earlier, the equations in this activity were selected so that many of the same cards may be used with the solutions of the various equations.)

Practice Activities

Bank the Money

Directions:

1. Have the students work in groups of four. Give each group a copy of the blackline master **Bank the Money**.

2. Explain that a student from each group is to select an equation from the **Bank the Money** master. The more complex the equation, the more money it is worth. If an equation is solved correctly, the student can bank that amount of money on his or her register (paper).

Materials:

▶ Blackline master **Bank the Money** is located in the *Teacher's Resource Manual,* **page 27.**

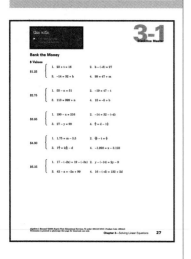

3. Each student in the group solves the equation chosen by "the player." If a group member thinks the equation was solved incorrectly by the player, that student can challenge the player. If the challenge is correct, the challenger gets double the money.

4. No equation can be used more than once in a game.

5. Competitions may be created between students or groups of students.

Find the Solution Path

Directions:

1. Divide the class into groups of four.

2. Distribute one copy of the blackline master **Solve Game Board** to each group. Give each group one die. If possible, use dice that are numbered 1, 2, 3, 1, 2, 3. This will provide more practice.

3. Everyone in a group should put a marker on the start space. The students should take turns rolling the die to determine who will go first. The largest number goes first. The group will continue taking turns clockwise.

4. The first student rolls the die and moves his or her marker the number of spaces shown on the die. The student writes the problem from that space on a piece of paper, then works the problem, which is checked by the group. If the student's answer is correct, the next person takes a turn. If the student's answer is incorrect, the student returns his or her marker to its previous spot.

5. Play continues until a player gets to the finish space.

6. Students may need to work a problem already worked by another student. If this happens, have them do their own work without looking back at the other player's work.

7. This activity can be repeated several times.

Materials:

► Blackline Master **Solve Game Board** is located in the *Teacher's Resource Manual*, **page 28.**

► Dice

► Game marker pieces

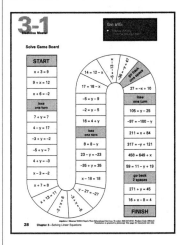

Materials:

▶ Blackline master **Equations** is located in the *Teacher's Resource Manual*, **page 29.**

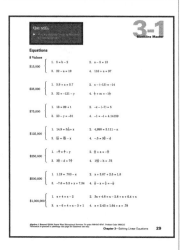

How to Become a Math Millionaire

Directions:

1. Give one copy of the blackline master **Equations** to each group of students.

2. The goal of this activity is for students to try to become math millionaires by answering the questions correctly, starting at the $15,000 level. With each correct answer, students continue to the next level. Each student can write answers on his or her paper, seeing how high he or she can go without a mistake.

3. This activity may be done with small groups of students. A group of five students would be appropriate because each level has four equations, one each for four students in the group, and the fifth student could act as the master of ceremonies and direct the activity. This activity may also be done as a whole class activity by asking each student to solve the equations for the correct answer.

Materials:

▶ Blackline master **Real Life Problems—I** is located in the *Teacher's Resource Manual*, **page 30.**

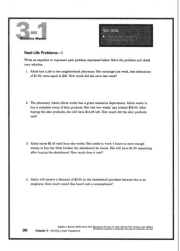

Problem-Solving Activities

Real-Life Problems—I

Directions:

Give each student a copy of the blackline master **Real-Life Problems—I**. Have the students, working individually, write an equation to represent each problem, solve the problems, and check their solutions. The problems are reprinted below.

1. Alicia has a job in her neighborhood pharmacy. Her earnings last week, less deductions of $1.50, were equal to $30. How much did she earn last week?

2. The pharmacy where Alicia works has a great cosmetics department. Alicia wants to buy a complete array of skin products. Her last two weeks' pay totaled $58.00. After buying the skin products, she will have $14.85 left. How much did the skin products cost?

3. Alicia earns $6.45 each hour she works. She needs to work 4 hours to earn enough money to buy her little brother the

skateboard he wants. She will have $1.80 remaining after buying the skateboard. How much does it cost?

4. Alicia will receive a discount of $2.50 on the skateboard purchase because she is an employee. How much would this board cost a nonemployee?

Real-Life Problems—II

Directions:

Give each student a copy of the blackline master **Real-Life Problems—II**. Have the students, working individually, write an equation to represent each problem, solve the problems, and check their solutions. The problems are reprinted below.

1. Carlos works in a sporting goods store on weekends. His earnings last Saturday, less $2.00 for deductions, were $35.00. How much did he earn on Saturday?

2. This sporting goods store has an excellent skateboard department. Carlos wants to buy new wheels for his board. His last paycheck was for $38.00. He has $12 remaining after buying one set of wheels. How much did one set of wheels cost him?

3. The owner of the sporting goods store pays Carlos $6.40 for each hour he works. He needs to work 5 hours to earn enough money to buy his sister the in-line skates she wants for her birthday. Carlos will have $3.20 remaining after he buys the skates. How much will the skates cost Carlos?

4. Carlos received an employee discount of $3.15 when he bought the skates. How much would the skates have cost someone who did not receive an employee discount?

Materials:

▶ Blackline master **Real Life Problems—II** is located in the *Teacher's Resource Manual*, **page 31.**

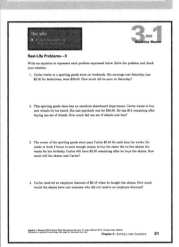

3-2 *Objective:* **Solve linear equations with multiplication and division.**

Sample Test: Solve the following equations for the variables.

1. $3x = 18$

2. $\frac{x}{3} = 9$

   Solution: $x = 6$

   Solution: $x = 27$

Concept Development Activities

Multiplicative Inverse Review

Directions:

1. Students will work individually on this activity. This is a short activity, and you may follow it with either the **Equation Mat** actvity or the **Algebra Tiles** activity, both of which appear later in this section and are done in small groups.

2. Give a copy of the blackline master **Multiplicative Inverse** to each student.

3. Discuss the number 3 and its reciprocal $\left(\frac{1}{3}\right)$. Explain that two numbers that yield 1 when multiplied together are called reciprocals, or multiplicative inverses. $(3 \times \frac{1}{3} = 1)$

4. Ask the students to write the reciprocal or multiplicative inverse for each of the expressions in #1 through #10 on the blackline master.

5. Ask the students if they remember the relation between the numerical factors in these expressions. The relation between 2 and $\frac{1}{2}$ in the expression $\frac{1}{2}(2x)$ is that they are reciprocals, or multiplicative inverses, of one another. Their product is always 1.

6. Before instructing the students to complete the remainder of the problems in this activity, direct their attention to #19 and #20. Ask how they would answer these questions and discuss their answers.

7. Have students complete #11–#18 and #19–#30.

Materials:

▶ Blackline master **Multiplicative Inverse** is located in the *Teacher's Resource Manual,* **page 32.**

Algebra Tiles (Multiplication and Division)

Directions:

Materials:

► Algebra tiles

1. Group the students into pairs. Give a set of algebra tiles to every two students.

2. Discuss what each piece in the set of algebra tiles represents:

   ☐ = units

   ▭ = variable x

   a square with dimensions of x, or x^2.

   The x^2 pieces will not be used in this activity, so have the students put them back in the container.

3. The ▭ is usually referred to as a variable or as x. It is the unknown, and the object is to find out what number it represents.

4. Discuss that the variables piece has a different color on each side. One side is black ▬ (which represents x, a positive or negative number), and the other is red ▬ (which represents –x, the opposite of x). The units piece also has a different color on each side. One side is black ■ (which will represent +1), and the other is yellow ☐ (which will represent –1).

5. Review the concept of "zero pairs" by demonstrating that 3 + (–3) is represented by three black and three yellow tiles. Each black and yellow pair represents a zero pair because +1 + (–1) = 0. Therefore, ☐ ☐ ☐ ■ ■ ■ represents three zero pairs, or 0.

6. Ask the students how they would model 3x with algebra tiles. 3x would be modeled as ▬ ▬ ▬, and black tiles would be used. Now ask the students to model –3x. –3x would be modeled as ▭ ▭ ▭, and red tiles would be used.

7. Write the equation 3x = 6 on the board or overhead. Show how to solve for the value of x by using algebra tiles. Represent 3x and 6 as follows:

Use black variable tiles (positive) and black unit tiles (positive). If you arrange the tiles as shown, the students will be able to see that  = ▋ ▋, or x = 2.

8. Have the students check the answer: 3(2) = 6, or 6 = 6.

9. Model other equations by using the tiles. For example, ask the students how to represent 2x = 6.

$$\text{or } x = 3$$

A check of the solution shows

$$2x = 6$$
$$2(3) = 6$$
$$6 = 6$$

10. Other equations that can be modeled and solved by using tiles are:

5x = 15	3x = −9	−3x = 12
3x = 12	−2x = 8	−3x = 3

Multiplication Property of Equality Using Arithmetic

Directions:

1. Review true (9 = 9), false (6 = 5), and open (x + 3 = 10) sentences.

2. Ask the class for an example of a true sentence (for example, 6 = 6). Write this sentence on the board or overhead. Ask a student to multiply both sides by 3.

$$6 \cdot 3 = 6 \cdot 3$$
$$18 = 18$$

Ask the class if this sentence is true.

3. Write the following sentences on the board or overhead without the "true" and "false" designations.

If 6 = 6, then 6 · 5 = 6 · 5 **(true)**
If 6 = 6, then 6 · (−2) = 6 · (−2) **(true)**
If 6 = 6, then 6 · 4 = 6 · 5 **(false)**
If 6 = 6, then 6 · 3 = 6 · (−2) **(false)**
If 5 = 5, then 5 · 4 = 5 · 5 **(false)**
If 7 = 7, then 3 · 7 = 7 · 3 **(true)**

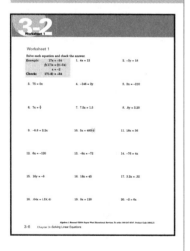

If $14 = 14$, then $14 \cdot (-8) = 14 \cdot (-8)$ **(true)**

If $2 + 3 = 5$, then $6(2 + 3) = 6 \cdot 5$ **(true)**

If $8 - 3 = 10 - 5$, then $2(8 - 3) = 2(10 - 5)$ **(true)**

If $8 - 3 = 5$, then $7(8 - 3) = 5 - 7$ **(false)**

If $8 = 8$, then $\frac{1}{4}(8) = \frac{1}{4}(8)$ **(true)**

4. Discuss which sentences are true. Discuss that a sentence remains true if each side of the equation is multiplied by the same number, i.e., if $x = y$ then $x \cdot z = y \cdot z$. Discuss that sentences also remain true if each side is divided by the same number, since division is the same as multiplying by the reciprocal.

   If $x = y$ then $\frac{x}{z} = \frac{y}{z}$ $(z \neq 0)$.

5. Discuss with the class how to solve an open sentence like $2x = 14$. To keep the sentence true, we need to multiply or divide each side by the same amount $\left(\frac{1}{2}\right)$. $\left(\frac{1}{2}\right)2x = \left(\frac{1}{2}\right)14$, so $x = 7$ if we want the sentence to be true. Have the students try the following:

   $3x = 18$ $\qquad\qquad -4x = 28$ $\qquad\qquad \frac{1}{2}x = 18$

Equation Mat (Multiplication)

Directions:

1. Have the class form groups of three to five students. Distribute a copy of the blackline master **Equation Mat (Multiplication)** and blank cards to each group.

2. Explain that the equation mat can help the students understand the solution of equations. Like a balance scale, an operation on one side of the equal sign must also be performed on the other side of the equal sign for the equation to "balance."

3. Give the students the equation $3x = 12$. Write each element in the equation, 3, x, and 12, on separate cards. Ask the student groups to do the same using three blank cards. (Like the previous equation mat activity, the equations in this activity are selected so that many of the same cards may be used with the solution of the various equations.)

4. Explain the rules for solving equations on the equation mat with expression cards as listed on the blackline master **Equation Mat**

Materials:

▶ Blackline master **Equation Mat (Multiplication)** is located in the *Teacher's Resource Manual*, **page 33.**

▶ Blank cards

▶ Marking pens

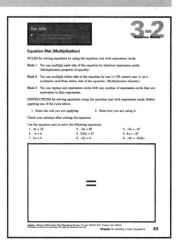

(Multiplication). Demonstrate each rule as you make expression cards and proceed with the solution. Before applying a rule, state the rule you are applying and why. Tell the students that they will be expected to do the same.

5. Proceed with the example by writing $\frac{1}{3}$ on each of two additional cards. Place a $\frac{1}{3}$ card on each side of the equal sign of the equation (Rule 1 on the equation mat). Ask the students to identify the relationships between $\frac{1}{3}$ and 3. They are reciprocals or multiplicative inverses: $\frac{1}{3} \cdot 3 = 1$. Because 3 and $\frac{1}{3}$ are multiplicative inverses of each other, they can be removed from the left side of the equation (Rule 2). What is left is x = 4, the solution to the equation.

6. Check the solution by substituting the value 4 for x in the original equation, 3x = 12. The new equation is 3(4) = 12, or 12 = 12, so the solution is correct.

7. Repeat the procedure with the equation 4x = 20. Multiply both sides by $\frac{1}{4}$. $\frac{1}{4} \cdot 4x = \frac{1}{4} \cdot 20$ (Rule 1). Solve to show that x = 5 (Rules 2 and 3).

8. Ask the students to solve next equation on the blackline master: –5x = 20. Have them make two cards for –1 and two cards for $\frac{1}{5}$. Then (–1)(–5)x = (–1)20 or 5x = –20 (Rule 3); and $\frac{1}{5} \cdot 5x = \frac{1}{5}(-20)$ (Rule 2) or 1x = –4 (Rule 3). Check: –5(–4) = 20.

9. Have the student groups continue solving equations from the blackline master using the equation mat, making new cards as necessary and following the rules and instructions.

Practice Activities

Multiplication and Division Equation Bingo

Directions:

1. Give each student a blank 4 × 4 bingo card.

2. Have the students write the following numbers randomly in the 16 squares (no free spaces): –3, 18, –8, 21, –13, 9, –9, 25, –72, 36, –15, 6, –30, 8, 0, 4.

3. Write the following problems one at a time on the overhead or

Materials:

▶ Blackline master for a **4 × 4 bingo card** is in the Appendix.

▶ Game markers to cover squares

board. Each student should use a marker to cover the square with the number that is the correct answer to each problem. Problems **(with answers)**—do not write answers on the board:

x = −3 **(−3)** $\frac{1}{2}$x = 3 **(6)** $\frac{1}{3}$x = −3 **(−9)**   2x = 16 **(8)**

.2x = −6 **(−30)**   .4x = 10 **(25)**   −2x = 16 **(−8)** $\frac{x}{3}$ = 6 **(18)**

$\frac{x}{-6}$ = 12 **(−72)**   5x = 105 **(21)**   118x = 0 **(0)** $\frac{2x}{3}$ = 6 **(9)**

−x = 13 **(−13)**   4x = 16 **(4)** $\frac{-3x}{5}$ = 9 **(−15)** $\frac{x}{-4}$ = −9 **(36)**

4. The first student to get four markers in a row says, "Bingo!" You should then check the student's answers. If they are correct, he or she wins the game.

5. Repeat, using the remaining problems or make new ones with the answers from step 3.

Guided Maze

Directions:

1. Give a copy of the blackline master **Guided Maze** to each student.

2. Write the following equations on the board or overhead:

   1. 3x = −21   2. 6x = 3   3. −4x = −32

   4. −x = 6   5. $\frac{1}{2}$x = 2   6. 4x = 3.2

   7. 5x = 15   8. $\frac{x}{4}$ = 3   9. −48 = 12x

   10. −.7x = 10.5

3. Write the following chart on the board or overhead:

L	**R**
$\frac{1}{3}$	7
−6	3
−7	150
−8	4
1	8
.8	.5
2	1.5
12	6
−15	−1
−4	15

?on →

Teacher's Tip:

Worksheet 2 for this objective, **page 3-7**, supports this activity with practice exercises.

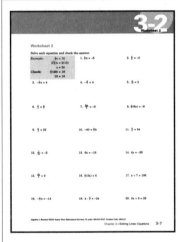

Materials:

▶ Blackline master **Guided Maze** is located in the *Teacher's Resource Manual*, **page 34**.

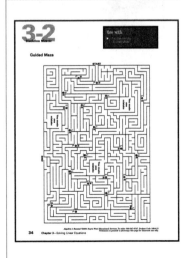

4. Have the students work the first equation given in #2 and find the answer in the L (left) or R (right) column in #3. The answer for this equation is in the "L" column. The students should then start the maze. When they get to the ❶, they should follow the "L" route, since the answer to the equation was in the "L" column. If the students work each problem correctly and follow the path, they will be able to get through the maze.

Problem-Solving Activities

Solving and Writing Equations

Directions:

Give each student a copy of the blackline master **Solving and Writing Equations**. Have the students work individually to solve the problems, which are reprinted below.

1. Solve the following equation for x.

$$6x = 30 \qquad x = \text{_____}$$

2. Write five equations whose solution is the same as that for $6x = 30$.

3. Solve the following equation for x.

$$4x = 6 \qquad x = \text{_____}$$

4. Write five equations whose solution is the same as that for $4x = 6$.

5. Which of the following equations have solutions that are integers?

   a. $\frac{1}{2}x = 4$ b. $4x = 2$

   c. $7x = 20$ d. $-3x = 42$

   e. $30x = 100$ f. $25x = 100$

Materials:

▶ Blackline master **Solving and Writing Equations** is located in the *Teacher's Resource Manual*, **page 35.**

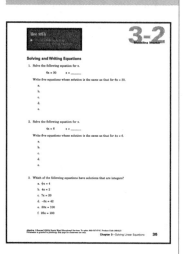

Phone Calls

Directions:

Give each student a copy of the blackline master **Phone Calls**.
Have the students work individually to solve the problems, which are
reprinted below.

1. A telephone company has a long-distance calling card that
   charges 7¢ per minute for any call anytime. Write an equation for
   the cost (c) of a call that lasts (m) minutes. c = _____

2. For the charges in #1, how much will a 10-minute phone call
   cost? (Solve for c when m = 10 minutes.)

3. How long can you talk if you want to spend only $3.50? [Solve for
   m when the total cost (c) is $3.50.]

4. How long could you talk for $5.00? Write your equation and solve
   for m.

5. Write the equation for the cost of phone calls if the charge is 10¢
   per minute.

6. How long could you talk at 10¢ per minute if you wanted to
   spend only $5.00? Write the equation and solve for m.

7. Write the equation for a plan where the cost of a phone call is
   14¢ per minute.

Materials:

► Blackline master
  Phone Calls is
  located in the
  *Teacher's Resource
  Manual,* **page 36.**

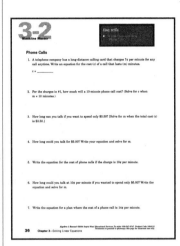

3-3 *Objective:* **Solve linear equations using one or more operations.**

Sample Test: Solve the following equations.

1. $3x + 6 = -12$

    Solution: x = –6

2. $5 - x = 7$

    Solution: x = –2

3. $3x + 4 = x - 2$

    Solution: x = –3

Concept Development Activities

Algebra Tiles

Part I: Algebra Tiles for General Linear Equations

Directions:

1. Group the students into pairs. Provide a set of algebra tiles for every two students.

2. Discuss what each piece in the set of algebra tiles represents:

   $\square$ = units

   $\boxed{}$ = variable x

   $\boxed{\begin{array}{c} \\ x \\ \ \ \ \ x \end{array}}$ = a square with dimensions of x, or x^2.

   The x^2 pieces will not be used in this activity, so have the students put them back in the container.

3. The $\boxed{}$ is usually referred to as a variable or as x. It is the unknown, and the object is to find out what number it represents.

4. Discuss that the variables piece has a different color on each side. One side is black ▬▬▬▬ (which represents x, a positive or negative number), and the other is red ▬▬▬▬ (which represents –x, the opposite of x). The units piece also has a different color on each side. One side is black ■ (which will represent +1), and the other is yellow ☐ (which will represent –1).

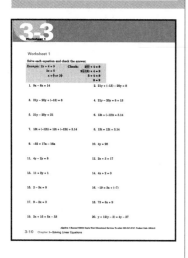

5. Review the concept of "zero pairs" by demonstrating that $3 + (-3)$ is represented by three black and three yellow tiles. Each black and yellow pair represents a zero pair because $+1 + (-1) = 0$. Therefore,  represents three zero pairs, or 0.

6. Write the equation $2x + 3 = 7$ on the board or overhead. Have the students model the equation using the algebra tiles.

7. Ask the students how they would solve the equation for x. Ask, "What is the value for x that makes the sentence true?" The usual steps are, first, to take away 3 from each side or add -3 to each side.

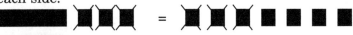

$$2x + 3 + (-3) = 7 - 3$$
$$2x = 4$$

The next step is to divide the four remaining tiles into two sets.

   so $1x = 2$

$$2x = 4$$
$$\frac{2x}{2} = \frac{4}{2}$$
$$x = 2$$

8. Show the students the work they did using the algebra tiles to solve the equations.

$$2x + 3 = 7$$
$$2x + 3 - 3 = 7 - 3$$
$$2x = 4$$
$$\frac{2x}{2} = \frac{4}{2}$$
$$x = 2$$

9. Model and write the steps for solving other equations.
   Examples: $3x - 1 = 5$ $2x - 4 = -8$ $4x + 1 = -11$

10. Be sure to summarize the algebra steps using the properties of equality to solve the equations.

Part II: Algebra Tiles for Equations With Variables on Each Side of the Equality

Note: This part should be done after the students have practiced solving simple linear equations with variables on one side.

Directions:

1. Write the equation $2x + 3 = x + 8$ on the board or overhead. Ask the students to use their algebra tiles to make a model of the problem.

2. Ask the students how to solve the problem. Write the steps as the students describe how they would solve the equation. For example, first take away 3 from each side or add –3 to each side

$$2x + 3 = x + 8$$
$$2x + 3 - 3 = x + 8 - 3$$
$$2x = x + 5$$

Next, take away an x from each side.

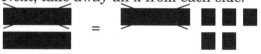

$$2x = x + 5$$
$$2x - x = x - x + 5$$
$$x = 5$$

3. Present other examples of equations with variables on each side for the students to solve using the algebra tiles.
   Examples: $3x + 4 = x - 5$ $4x - 6 = x + 6$ $6 - x = x + 8$

4. Have the students write a paragraph describing how to solve an equation with variables on each side.

5. Discuss different ideas the students generate and determine whether these ideas will always work. Note that it is usually necessary to add or subtract the constant before multiplying or dividing by the coefficient of the variable.

Principal Operator

Directions:

Teacher's Tip:

Worksheet 2 for this objective, **page 3-11**, supports this activity with practice exercises.

1. Explain to the class that in an algebraic expression, the last operation to be performed is called the principal operator. For example, the expression $3x + 6$ is an indicated sum. The principal operator is addition.

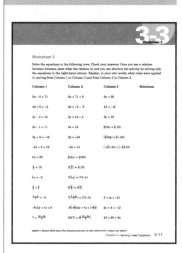

2. Ask students to name the principal operator in the following examples:

   $3y - 4$ **(subtraction)**

   $4(x + 2)$ **(multiplication)**

   $(6x + 5) + x$ **(addition)**

   $\frac{3x - 6}{2}$ **(division)**

   $\frac{3x}{2} + 5$ **(addition)**

   $(2x - 4)2$ **(multiplication)**

3. Explain that an algebraic equation can be solved by undoing the principal operator with the inverse operation. *Example:*

   $4x - 3 = 9$ (principal operator is subtraction; undo by adding 3)

   $4x - 3 + 3 = 9 + 3$

   $4x = 12$ (principal operator is now multiplication; undo by dividing by 4)

   $\frac{4x}{4} = \frac{12}{4}$

   $x = 3$

4. Give the class another example: $\frac{x - 1}{2} = 7$

   The principal operator is division; undo by multiplying by 2:

   $2 \cdot \frac{x - 1}{2} = 7 \cdot 2$

   $x - 1 = 14$

   Undo subtraction by adding 1:

   $x - 1 + 1 = 14 + 1$

   $x = 15$

5. Work through several other examples with the class. First ask what the principal operator is. Then ask how to undo the operation.

   $3x - 4 = 14$ $\frac{1}{2}x + 3 = 11$ $x - 27 = 14$

   $6 = 2x - 4$ $5 = \frac{x + 6}{3}$ $6(x + 1) = 24$

   $3(2x + 6) + 4 = 52$ $\frac{8 + 2x - 4}{3} = -2$

Materials:

▶ Blackline master **Equation Mat (Addition and Multiplication)** is located in the *Teacher's Resource Manual,* **page 37.**

▶ Blank cards

▶ Marking pens

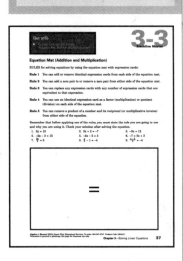

Equation Mat (Addition and Multiplication)

Directions:

1. Have the class form groups of three to five students. Distribute a copy of the blackline master **Equation Mat (Addition and Multiplication)** and blank cards to each group.

2. Explain that the equation mat can help the students understand the solution of equations. Like a balance scale, an operation on one side of the equal sign must also be performed on the other side of the equal sign for the equation to "balance."

3. If the students used the equation mat with addition and subtraction, they will be familiar with making the cards and applying the rules. Review the rules for addition and subtraction:

   Rule 1 You can add or remove identical expression cards from each side of the equation mat.

   Rule 2 You can add a zero pair to or remove a zero pair from either side of the equation mat.

   Rule 3 You can replace any expression cards with any number of expression cards that are equivalent to that expression.

4. Explain that you will now teach them two more rules that are used when solving equations with one variable. The new rules refer to multiplication and division and can be stated as follows:

   Rule 4 You can use an identical expression card as a factor (multiplication) or quotient (division) on each side of the equation mat.

   Rule 5 You can remove a product of a number and its reciprocal (or multiplicative inverse) from either side of the equation.

5. Give the students the example $3y = 15$. Write each element in the equation, 3, y, and 15, on a separate card. Ask the student groups to do the same using three blank cards. (The equations in this activity have been selected so that many of the same cards may be used with the solution of various equations.) Before applying a rule, state the rule you are applying and why. Tell the students that they will be expected to do the same. Each group must also check the solution before solving another equation from the blackline master.

6. Proceed with the example by writing $\frac{1}{3}$ on each of two additional cards. Place a $\frac{1}{3}$ card on each side of the equal sign of the equation (Rule 4 on the equation mat). Explain that 3 and $\frac{1}{3}$ are multiplicative inverses of each other, so they can be removed from the left side of the equation (Rule 5). What is left is y = 5, the solution to the equation.

7. Check the solution by substituting the value 5 for y in the original equation, 3y = 15. The new equation is 3(5) = 15, or 15 = 15, so the solution is correct.

8. Repeat the procedure with the next equation on the blackline master, 3x + 2 = –7. Have the students make cards for –2 and use Rule 1. Then have them use the cards for $\frac{1}{3}$ from the preceding equation (Rule 4) and use Rule 5 to solve the equation. Ask them to check their solutions.

9. Have the student groups continue solving equations from the blackline master using the equation mat, making new cards as necessary and following the rules and instructions. (Again, note that the equations in this activity have been selected so that many of the same cards may be used with the solution of various equations.)

Practice Activities

Do Not Use chalkboards
Students show work on
a pc of paper (so they can check)

Equation Bingo

Directions:

1. Give each student a blank 4 × 4 bingo card.

2. Read aloud the following 16 solutions and ask the students to write each one at random in the 16 squares on their grids: 6, –7, 9, 5, –8, –1, 4, 7, –63, –80, 0, –31, 15, 1, no solution, 42.

3. Write the following equations on the board or overhead one at a time in random order. Allow time for students to solve each equation and cover the answer on their bingo card before you write the next equation:

   5x = 3x + 12 **(6)**   9y + 42 = 3y **(–7)**

   5m + 1 = 7m – 17 **(9)**   –7x = 10 – 9x **(5)**

Teacher's Tip:

Worksheet 3 for this objective, **page 3-12**, supports this activity with practice exercises.

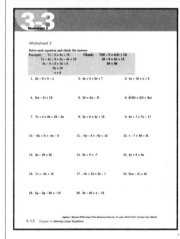

Materials:

▶ Blackline master for a **4 × 4 bingo card** is in the Appendix.

▶ Game markers to cover squares

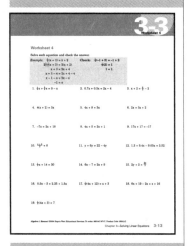

$8x + 32 = 4x$ **(–8)** $4z - 5 = 10z + 1$ **(–1)**

$6 - 3a = -14 + 2a$ **(4)** $0.7x + 0.3x = 2x - 7$ **(7)**

$21 = \frac{d}{-3}$ **(–63)** $-\frac{1}{4}x = 20$ **(–80)**

$2.2666x = 0$ **(0)** $\frac{3 + y}{7} = -4$ **(–31)**

$\frac{4x}{5} + 3 = x$ **(15)** $\frac{7 + y}{8} = y$ **(1)**

$\frac{1}{4}(12b - 20) = 3b + 8$ **(no sol.)** $\frac{7(x - 2)}{2} = 6 + 2x + 8 + x$ **(42)**

4. The students are to use paper and pencil to solve each equation. After solving an equation, they should cover the answer on their bingo card. The first student to cover four answers in a row, column, or diagonal shouts, "Bingo!" The caller should then check that student's solutions.

5. The game can be continued until other students get bingo. Additionally, you can make new problems for the game, bearing in mind that they must have the same solutions as the original problems.

Equation Rummy

Directions:

1. Have the students form groups of 3, 4, or 5 players. Provide each group with blank cards and marking pens.

2. Direct the students to write one equation per card from the blackline master **Equation Rummy**.

3. Each group should then shuffle and deal their cards. Players can be dealt 10, 8, or 6 cards, depending on the number of players in the group. The remaining cards are placed, face down, in a "draw" pile.

4. Players should solve the equations on the cards they have been dealt and should lay down any books of three cards that have the same solution. Once a book of three cards is on the table, any player, at his or her turn, can lay down cards with the same solution as for the book.

5. Play begins by each player, in turn, drawing a card from the "draw" pile and solving the equation on that card. Then that player can either form a book, add to an existing book, or discard

a card. The discards are available to any player who would like to draw one for his or her hand.

6. Play continues clockwise with each player taking a turn. Play ends when one player gets rid of all the cards in his or her hand. That player is declared the winner.

Make and Share Linear Equations

Directions:

1. Have the students select a number between −10 and +10. Have the students write the simple equation x = their number on a piece of paper, e.g., x = 3.

2. Write on the board or overhead ax + b = ?. Explain that the "a" and "b" can be any number the students choose for writing a linear equation, e.g., 4x + (−3) = ?; a = 4; b = −3. Have the students write an equation following this example.

3. Ask the students, "How do I find the solution?" The answer is to substitute their number for x (e.g., 3) into the equation: 4(3) + (−3) = ? so the ? = 9. Have the students write their equation (e.g., 4x − 3 = 9) on one sheet of paper and keep the solution (x = 3) on a different sheet of paper.

4. Repeat steps 1–3 to come up with two more equations using the form ax + b = ?, writing the equations and solutions on the sheets of paper.

5. Give the students the general form $\frac{x + a}{b}$ = ?. Have them create an equation of this form by selecting an "x" and numbers for a and b, then finding the ?. Read aloud some of their equations. Discuss how to ensure that the answer will be an integer if you wish.

6. Give the students the general form $\frac{1}{a}x + b$ = ?. Have the students create an equation for this form following the same procedures listed above.

7. Have the students exchange their papers with the equations on them. Have the students work the equations on the paper given to them and check the answers. Repeat exchanging papers as time allows. You may need to work some problems if the answers are different from the given answer.

Problem-Solving Activities

Create a Problem

Directions:

1. Write the equation ax + b = 12 on the board or overhead. Ask the class to find values for a, b, and x so the sentence will be true. Allow some time for the class to work out solutions. (a ≠ 0, b ≠ 0, x ≠ 0)

2. Group the students into pairs. Have the partners share their problems and check the answers. Ask: (1) How do you find out if the numbers that were chosen work? (2) Can there be different answers? (3) How many different answers can there be?

3. Make a list of some of the possible solutions.

   Example:

a	b	x
3	3	3
2	2	5
1	8	4
−2	2	−5

4. Write the equation ax + b = cx + d on the board or overhead. Ask the students, in their pairs, to find values for a, x, b, c, and d that will make the sentence true. Have them try to find three different sets of numbers that will make the sentence true.

5. Discuss some of the solutions and the "process" used to find the solutions. Solutions include:

a	b	c	d	x
3	−6	2	−2	4
2	8	3	11	−3
4	−2	3	−1	1

Chapter 3—Solving Linear Equations

Find the Number

Directions:

Give each student a copy of the blackline master **Find the Number**. Have the students work individually to solve the problems, which are reprinted below.

Write an equation to represent each stated problem. Solve the equation and check your solution.

1. A number decreased by twelve is twice the opposite of ten. Find the number.

2. The sum of two numbers is three times negative seven. If one of the numbers is negative twenty-four, what is the other number?

3. Two times the number forty-one added to twice another number is thirty-four. Find the other number.

4. Negative six times a number is negative forty-eight. What is that number?

5. Three-fourths of a number added to fourteen is twenty-three. Find that number.

6. What is a number that when multiplied by three and decreased by twice itself equals fifty?

7. If two and one-fourth of a number is the sum of negative four added to the opposite of one-half, what is the number?

8. Four times a number divided by three is five more than that number divided by two. Find the value of that number.

9. One-half added to three times a number is equal to one-half of the sum of seven added to eight times the number. What is that number?

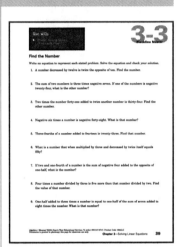

3-4 *Objective:* **Solve problems that can be represented as equations.**

Sample Test: Answer the following problems.

1. Bill has $32 in his savings account. If he saves $7.50 per week toward a new $113 skateboard, how long will it take him to purchase the new skateboard?

    Solution: 11 weeks (actually 10 weeks, 6 days)

2. In an industrial setting with three wind towers, the first wind tower is 20 feet taller than the second, and the second is twice the height of the third. If the third tower is 97 feet high, what are the heights of the first and second towers?

    Solution: The first tower is 214 feet high and the second tower is 194 feet high.

Concept Development Activities

Classroom Problems and Solutions

Directions:

1. Form an even number of cooperative work groups. In this way, the problems each group creates can be exchanged with another group for solution and verification.

2. Each group should select a student to write down the problems the group generates. The groups will generate problems that can be expressed as mathematical equations and can be solved by using the principles of equality. The challenge for each group is to develop the greatest number of high-quality algebraic sentences that can be represented as mathematical equations that use only one variable.

3. To give the students an idea of what is expected of them, share an example that relates to the class and, together with the students, develop a word sentence that can be written as an equation. For example, to determine the number of bilingual students in the room, you can let x equal the number of bilingual students. If there are 31 students in the classroom and 26 are not bilingual, then x + 26 = 31 is the equation, and x = 5. Two other examples of word sentences follow:

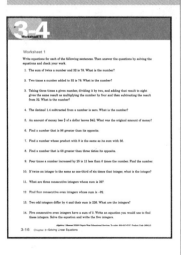

a. Ed is 4 inches taller than Janelle. If Janelle is 5 feet, 2 inches tall, how tall is Ed?

b. A classroom has seven rows of desks. Five of these rows have exactly 5 desks each. If the room contains 32 desks, how many desks are in the other two rows?

4. The critical attribute of this activity is to have the students check each answer to see that it correctly defines the variable condition. Note that the students may use equivalent equations that may not initially look the same. For example, in #3b, equivalent correct equations include $5(5) + x = 32$ and $32 - 5(5) = x$. Both yield $x = 7$.

5. This activity may be extended to school or home situations. A great homework activity is to direct each student to come to class with a sentence that describes a condition at home. The class may solve the problems together, or student pairs may exchange and solve problems. An example of such a sentence would be: "Nine people live in my house. There are twice as many children as adults. How many adults live in my house?"

Problems Involving Geometry

This activity is designed to promote discovery of the relationship of the angles of triangles. This relationship will be used to create sentences for which equations can be written and solved. Examples of such sentences are included on the blackline master **Problems Involving Geometry**.

Directions:

1. Students can work individually or in small groups.

2. This is an excellent time to review acute, right, obtuse, isosceles, and equilateral triangles, as shown on the blackline master. After the discussion, direct the students to draw at least three triangles (the size doesn't matter) and to label the angles sequentially: a, b, c, d, e, f, g, h, i. For example:

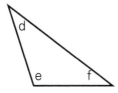

Answer Key for #3:
a. 5 feet, 6 inches
b. 7 desks

Answer Key for #5:
3 adults

Materials:

▶ Blackline master **Problems Involving Geometry** is located in the *Teacher's Resource Manual,* **page 40.**

▶ Paper from which to cut triangles

▶ Scissors

▶ Straightedge

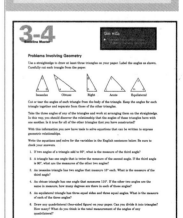

3-4
Concept/Practice

Cut triangles ont 1ST

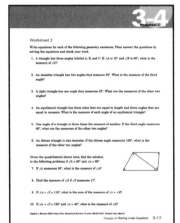
3. Ask the students to then cut off the three angles of each triangle and to arrange them on the straightedge. The students should be able to make a supposition that the three angles create a straight line, or add to 180 degrees. If they need to test this supposition with other instances, encourage them to do so.

4. Discuss the concept of the perimeters of triangles and quadrilaterals. Review the properties of the square, rectangle, and other quadrilaterals. Problem 6 of the blackline master **Problems Involving Geometry** guides the students to see that any quadrilateral is composed of two triangular shapes by connecting opposite vertices. Thus, the sum of the angles of a quadrilateral is $2 \times 180 = 360$ degrees.

Practice Activities

Writing Problems From Equations

Directions:

1. Have the students form small work groups. Each group is to write equations and then create sentences that represent those equations.

2. As an example, write the equation $3x = 45$ on the board or overhead transparency. Sentences that represent this equation include the following:

> Madison's father is three times as old as she is. How old is Madison if her father is 45?

and

> If an integer is multiplied by three, the product is forty-five. What is the integer?

Emphasize that many sentences can be used to represent any given equation.

3. Ask the students to try an example. Write the equation $4y + 2 = 14$ on the board or overhead transparency. Ask the students to come up with sentences that represent this equation. Two possibilities are:

> Fourteen is two more than four times a number. What is the number?

and

> There are two more oranges than four times the number of apples. There are fourteen oranges. How many apples are there?

Ask the students to read their sentences aloud to illustrate different ways of representing the same equation.

4. Have each student in the group write a simple equation and share it with each other. The other students then write a word sentence that represents that equation. As a group, the students should then analyze that sentence to see that it satisfies the conditions of the equation.

5. Some equations that can be used to help the students get started are given below:

$$2x - 7 = 5 \qquad \frac{n}{3} = -2 \qquad j + (j + 2) = 12 \qquad \frac{3}{4}y = 18$$

Writing and Solving Number Theory Sentences

A simple and fun activity for students is to generate equations from sentences about even or odd sequential integers. This activity will also assist you in providing a foundation for students to understand and solve equations from number theory sentences.

Directions:

1. Review what is meant by the set of integers as well as the set of even integers and the set of odd integers. Begin with the set of integers $\{\ldots -2, -1, 0, 1, 2, 3, \ldots\}$. Then ask questions related to this set and to the odd and even integer subsets to be sure the students have a good understanding of the set of integers, the set of even integers, and the set of odd integers.

   For example, write the set of integers on the board or an overhead transparency. Then have students analyze the following statements and make conclusions about them:

   a. If n represents one of these integers, how would you express the next sequential integer?

   b. If n represents any integer, write an expression for an even integer.

Answer Key for #1:
a. n + 1
b. 2n
c. (2n + 1) or (2n – 1)
d. {n, n+1, n+2, n+3}
e. {n, n+2, n+4}
f. {n, n+2, n+4, n+6}

c. If n is any integer in this set, what is an expression for any odd integer?

d. Write the set of four consecutive integers if the first one is n.

e. How would you write the set of three consecutive even integers if n is even?

f. How would you express the set of an odd integer n and the next three consecutive odd integers?

2. Have the students, in groups, convert the following eight sentences into equations and then solve them. They should check their answers for accuracy.

a. Find two consecutive integers whose sum is 31.

b. Find three consecutive even integers whose sum is 24.

c. What three consecutive odd integers add up to –27?

d. Find three consecutive integers whose sum is 27.

e. Can you identify three consecutive even integers whose sum is 219?

f. Find four consecutive odd integers whose sum is –8.

g. Explain why the three consecutive odd integers $(2x + 1)$, $(2x + 3)$, and $(2x + 5)$ cannot have a sum of 100.

h. Write an expression for the sum of three consecutive even integers if $3n - 1$ is the smallest integer of the three.

Answer Key for #2:
a. 15 and 16
b. 6, 8, and 10
c. –7, –9, and –11
d. 8, 9, and 10
e. No, the sum of even integers is always even.
f. –5, –3, –1, and 1
g. The sum of three odd integers is always odd.
h. $(3n - 1) + (3n + 1) + (3n + 3)$

Problem-Solving Activity

Writing Equivalent Equations and Finding
Their Solutions

Directions:

Materials:

► Blackline master
**Writing Equivalent
Equations and
Finding Their
Solutions** is located
in the *Teacher's
Resource Manual,*
page 41.

Give each student a copy of the blackline master **Writing Equivalent
Equations and Finding Their Solutions**. Have the students work
individually to solve the problems, which are reprinted below.

1. Explain, in your own words, the steps you would take to solve the
    problem $\frac{2x+4}{3} = 12$.

2. Write two equivalent equations for $\frac{2}{3}x + \frac{4}{3} = 12$ that lead to the
    solution of the equation.

3. Write two word sentences that are equivalent to, or the same as,
    "The difference of a number and 14 is 38." Use the word "subtracted"
    in one sentence and the word "decreased" in the other.

4. Explain how to solve $2p + 10 = 42$ if you have to undo the
    multiplication first.

5. Explain why undoing the multiplication first is inconvenient for
    solving the equation $7x - 4 = 24$.

6. If 14 times a number added to 127 is the same as the difference
    between 13 times that number and 899, what is that number?

7. A number is decreased by 35, then that quantity is multiplied by
    6, then the result is added to 87, and finally that result is divided
    by 3. The value of that expression is 49. Find that number.

8. You are eight years younger than your cousin Quinten. In four
    years you will be $\frac{2}{3}$ as old as he will be then. What are your ages
    now?

9. A city block is half as wide as it is long. If the distance around
    the block is 840 yards, what are the dimensions of the city block?

10. Your ongoing share of income for designing the Web page for a
    new company is $50 per week plus $.05 per transaction. How
    many transactions per week must the site conduct for you to earn
    an average of $15 per day from this Web page, assuming a
    5-day work week?

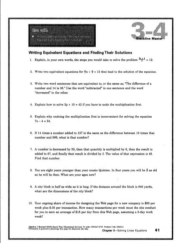

3-5 *Objective:* Solve a proportion with a missing part.

Sample Test:

1. Determine which pairs of the following ratios form proportions:

   a. $\frac{2}{3}, \frac{12}{18}$

   b. $\frac{15}{30}, \frac{1}{2}$

   c. $\frac{15}{21}, \frac{60}{105}$

   Solution: yes

   Solution: yes

   Solution: no

2. Solve each proportion:

   a. $\frac{2}{3} = \frac{8}{x}$

   b. $\frac{4}{w} = \frac{2}{10}$

   c. $\frac{x}{1.5} = \frac{2.4}{1.6}$

   Solution: x = 12

   Solution: w = 20

   Solution: x = 2.25

3. A juice beverage calls for 3 parts fruit juice concentrate to 12.5 parts water. What is the percent of concentrate in the final mixture?

   Solution: 24%

Concept Development Activities

Ratios and Chance

In developing understanding of how to solve proportions with a missing part and how to solve problems involving percentages, students must first understand the concept of a ratio, or the comparison of two numbers by division. A fun way to approach this topic is through information discovery of outcomes of events (probability).

Directions:

1. Divide the students into small groups and assign each group to a workstation. The number of workstations for this activity is determined by the number of students, the size of the groups, and the amount of materials available.

2. For the purposes of these directions, rolls of toilet paper are used as an example. The same steps should be followed for coins, dice, or thumbtacks. The students may come up with other objects to use.

3. Place one or more rolls of toilet paper at a workstation. Ask all of the students to gather around that workstation for this example. Tell the students that they are going to approximate how many

Materials:

▶ Coins, dice, rolls of toilet paper, thumbtacks, or other objects

Chapter 3—Solving Linear Equations

times a roll of toilet paper will land on its end when dropped. It is important to record the number of times the event was tried as well as the number of times it was successful. (Ask about unsuccessful outcomes.) The events must be replicated as closely as possible; for example, the height from which the object is dropped should be about the same each time.

4. Ask the students to record the outcomes. For example:

Roll Dropped	Landed on End
(event or attempt)	(successful outcome)
~~HHH~~ ~~HHH~~ ~~HHH~~ /	~~HHH~~

5. In this example, the rolls were dropped from table height a total of 16 times with 5 successful outcomes (roll landed on one of its ends).

6. Ask the students to determine the ratio (the comparison of two numbers as a fraction) of successes to total attempts. $\left(\frac{5}{16}\right)$ Point out that ratios can also be written with a colon, such as 5:16. Note that this example is only one experiment. Your result, although it may be close to this ratio, may differ.

7. Ask the students to return to their own workstations and begin work. Each station should have a specific assignment, such as the following:

    Thumbtacks: How many times is a tack likely to land on its top when dropped a certain number of times. What is the ratio of "top" to "trials"? What is the ratio of "point" to "trials"? What is the ratio of "top" to "point"?

    Coins: How many times does a coin come up "heads" in a certain number of tosses? What is the ratio of heads to tosses? Heads to tails? Tails to tosses?

    Dice: How many times does a specific number come up with a certain number of tosses of one die? What is that ratio? If two dice are used, how many times will the numbers rolled add to a certain sum? What are these ratios?

8. When the students begin to understand the ratios involved with their activities, have them increase the number of attempts. Then ask whether the ratios change significantly. The students should see that even though both ratios are not exactly the same, they are close to a mathematical probability of the event occurring.

Materials:

▶ Coins, dice, rolls of toilet paper, thumbtacks, or other objects

Teacher's Tip:

This activity refers back to the preceding Concept Development Activity, **Ratios and Chance**.

Teacher's Tip:

Worksheet 1 for this objective, **page 3-20**, supports this activity with practice exercises.

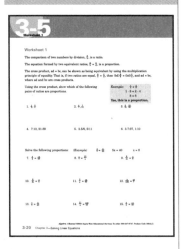

9. Close this activity by asking the students to write their ratios as fractions as well as by using a colon. Explain that a ratio can also be written as a decimal (as in a batting average or probability) or as a percentage. For workstations that have the same task, the ratios can be compared.

Solving a Proportion

Directions:

1. Remind the students of the exercise using toilet paper rolls from the previous Concept Development Activity, **Ratios and Chance**. In that exercise, the ratio of successful attempts to total events was $\frac{5}{16}$, or 5:16. Ask for the ratio of nonsuccessful occurrences to total events.

2. Now ask the students to suppose the exercise with the toilet paper rolls had illustrated that the success ratio was $\frac{4}{16}$. Ask how many successes would then be likely in four events. Show that you would use the equation $\frac{4}{16} = \frac{n}{4}$, so there is likely to be one success. $\left[\frac{4}{16} = \frac{n}{4}, \text{ or } 4\left(\frac{4}{16}\right) = 4\left(\frac{n}{4}\right), \text{ or } 1 = n\right]$

3. Explain that the equation $\frac{4}{16} = \frac{1}{4}$, or an equality stating that two ratios are equal, is a proportion. Show that by using the multiplication and division properties of equality, a proportion can be solved by using the cross product, as follows:

   If $\frac{a}{b} = \frac{c}{d}$, then $(bd)\frac{a}{b} = \frac{c}{d}(bd)$, or $ad = bc$. So the cross product, $ad = bc$, is an equivalent equation to the original proportion. It is called a cross product because you can obtain the multipliers by making a cross (or X) in the proportion: $\frac{a}{b}\times\frac{c}{d}$: $ad = bc$.

4. Ask what the probable successes of the toilet paper roll landing on end $\left(\frac{1}{4}\right)$ would be after 20 trials, 40 trials, and 100 trials.

5. Ask the students to return to the ratios that were generated in the previous **Ratios and Chance** activity. Have them write an equation to determine how many times a successful outcome would occur if they doubled the number of trials. Ask what it would be if they tripled the number of trials. Ask how many successes would be likely to happen if they tried it 100 times.

For example, if a coin was tossed 20 times and the real probability of heads occurring $\left(\frac{1}{2}\right)$ was discovered, then for 20 trials, $\frac{1}{2} = \frac{n}{20}$, or n = 10; for 60 trials, $\frac{1}{2} = \frac{n}{60}$, or n = 30; and for 100 trials, $\frac{1}{2} = \frac{n}{100}$, or n = 50.

6. Have students imagine a die being tossed 30 times and the 4 appearing for 5 of the 30 tosses, which is equivalent to odds of $\frac{1}{6}$. Ask how many times they would expect the 4 to appear if the die were tossed 60, 20, or 180 times.

7. Have the students imagine that 25 thumbtacks are dropped, and 8 of them land "point down." Ask how many "point down" tacks they would expect if 50, 100, or 250 thumbtacks were dropped.

8. For the same trial with 25 tacks as was used in #7, ask the students how many thumbtacks would land "point up" if 200 tacks were dropped.

Geometry Proportions

This activity informally introduces students to the proportionality of the sides of similar triangles. Rather than using the angles to create equations for solution, the students will discover that similar triangles have proportional sides.

Directions:

1. Divide the class into groups of two or three (or have the students work individually).

2. Ask each group to draw a triangle with one side measuring 2 inches and another side measuring $2\frac{1}{2}$ inches. Ask the groups to cut out the triangle and label the third side "a."

3. Now ask the the groups to draw another triangle that has the same angle between two sides as in #2, but to make the sides 4 inches and 5 inches long. Ask the groups to cut out this triangle and label the third side "b." When they cut out this triangle, they should recognize that the triangles are the same shape but different sizes.

4. Ask the groups to calculate the ratios of the corresponding sides of the two triangles: 2:4, $2\frac{1}{2}$:5.

Materials:

▶ Rulers

▶ Scissors

▶ Enough paper from which to cut at least three sets of two similar triangles

5. Ask the students if they could approximate "b," the third side of the second triangle, if they knew the approximate measure of "a," the third side of the first triangle. Have them write an equation that will solve for b if a is determined to be 3 inches.

6. Other examples may be used to create other triangle pairs that are the same shape but different sizes. Have the students construct any triangle that has angles of 40°, 60°, and 80°. Have them compare the ratio of the sides.

7. Give the student groups the following problem: A triangle has sides of 3, 4, and 5 inches. A triangle with similar shape but different size has a side of 9 inches that corresponds to the side of 3 inches of the original triangle. Find the measures of the sides that correspond to the 4- and 5-inch sides.

8. △ABC is similar to △DEF.

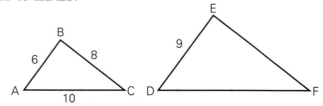

Find side $\overline{EF}$. _____

Find side $\overline{DF}$. _____

Practice Activities

Recipe Proportions

Directions:

1. Divide the students into small groups. Have each group bring in a recipe they want to use for this activity.

2. The following example can be used to introduce this activity:

> Gene's Italian Bread Recipe (3 loaves)
> 2 cups warm water
> 1 teaspoon dry yeast
> 2 tablespoons honey
> 2 teaspoons salt
> 6 cups flour

Materials:

▶ Recipes from various sources: for example, the cafeteria cook, a local baker, a home cookbook, cooking magazines, the food section of the local newspaper

What would be the recipe for making 6 loaves of bread?

Recipe converted to 6 loaves: $\dfrac{\text{original recipe}}{\text{new recipe}} = \dfrac{3 \text{ loaves}}{6 \text{ loaves}} = \dfrac{1}{2}$

For water: $\dfrac{1}{2} = \dfrac{2 \text{ cups}}{C \text{ cups}}$, so $C = 4$ cups

For yeast: $\dfrac{1}{2} = \dfrac{1 \text{ tsp}}{t \text{ tsp}}$, so $t = 2$ tsp

Other ingredients are determined similarly.

3. Assign each group a different quantity of loaves and have them adjust the recipe accordingly. Then have them turn their attention to their own recipes. If the recipe is one that serves fewer than 10 people, ask them to double the recipe. If the recipe is from the cafeteria, for example, and serves a large group of people, ask them to halve the recipe.

Equivalent Ratios and Solving Proportions

Directions:

Materials:
▶ Blank cards or 💿
▶ Markers

1. Divide the class into groups of three or four. Have each group make one set of 42 cards with the following numbers (one number per card):

$\frac{1}{2}$	$\frac{2}{4}$	3:6	50%	.5	5:10	$\frac{5}{10}$	
$\frac{3}{10}$	$\frac{6}{20}$	$\frac{9}{30}$	30%	.3	12:40	$\frac{15}{50}$	
$\frac{3}{5}$	$\frac{6}{10}$	.6	15:25	60%	60:100	$\frac{9}{15}$	
$\frac{3}{8}$	$\frac{6}{16}$	9:24	.375	$37\frac{1}{2}$%	$\frac{12}{32}$	$\frac{18}{48}$	
$\frac{5}{8}$	5:8	.625	$\frac{25}{40}$	62.5%	625:1000	15:24	
$\frac{1}{4}$	$\frac{3}{12}$	25%	100:400	.25	$\frac{25}{100}$	250:1000	

2. Have each group designate a dealer, who will shuffle the cards and deal six cards to each player (including himself or herself). The extra cards in the deck should be placed face down in a pile on the table.

3. Play proceeds from the dealer's left clockwise. Each player draws one card from the face-down pile on the table. The object is for the players to find sets of two, three, four, or more cards in their hands that are proportional (equivalent). When it is a player's turn, he or she places the matching cards face up on the table

Materials:

▶ Blackline master **Proportion Game Chart** is located in the *Teacher's Resource Manual*, **page 42.**

▶ Dice

▶ Game marker pieces

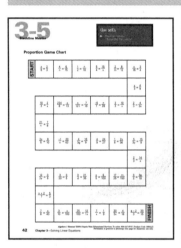

Teacher's Tip:

Worksheet 2 for this objective, **page 3-21**, supports this activity with practice exercises.

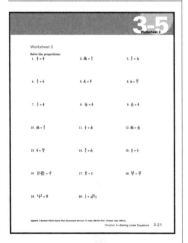

and explains why the cards are proportional. If a player does not have a proportion, the play is passed to the player's left.

4. The first player to get rid of all of his or her cards (to go "out") is the winner. Play then continues until the other players each go out or all the cards in the stack have been drawn. The remaining players are ranked according to the number of cards they have remaining in their hands at the end of play.

5. Modifications can be made to the game. One is that the proportions can be placed in the center of the playing area, and all players can, during their turns, play additional proportional cards on these matches.

Solve the Proportion

Directions:

1. Divide the class into groups of about four students.

2. Give a copy of the blackline master **Proportion Game Chart** to each group. Give each group one die. If possible, use dice numbered 1, 2, 3, 1, 2, 3, which will provide more practice for each student.

3. The members of each group should take turns rolling the die. The student who rolls the largest number starts the game. The group continues taking turns clockwise.

4. Everyone in the group puts a game marker on the start space. The first player rolls the die and moves his or her marker the number of spaces showing on the die. The student writes the problem in the space on which he or she lands on a piece of paper and then works the problem, which is checked by the group. If the answer is correct, the next player takes a turn. If it is incorrect, the student returns to the previous spot.

5. Play continues until the first player gets to the finish space.

6. Students may work a problem that had previously been done by another player. This is okay. However, they should not look at work done by the earlier player.

7. This activity can be repeated several times.

Problem-Solving Activity

Body Proportions ⚙

Directions:

Give each student a copy of the blackline master **Body Proportions**. Have the students work individually to solve the problems, which are reprinted below.

1. Explain that the height of the average human body, if divided into 16 units of measure, is approximately proportioned in the following ratios:

Head	2:16
Neck to shoulder	1:16
Body	6:16
Thigh	3:16
Calf	3:16
Ankle and foot	1:16

2. Explain that the following approximate proportions have also been determined:

Shoulder to waist	2:16
Arm	5:16
Shoulder to elbow	2:16
Elbow to wrist	2:16
Hand	1:16

3. Have the students determine how close these ratios are to the actual proportions in their bodies. Have them measure their heights and compute the proportions. For example, if a student's height is 64 inches, then that student's neck height should be calculated as $\frac{1}{16} = \frac{x}{64}$, or x = 4 inches.

4. After the computations are completed, have the students determine how closely their measurements conform to the proportions.

Materials:

▶ Blackline master **Body Proportions** is located in the *Teacher's Resource Manual*, **page 43**.

▶ Tape measures

▶ Rulers

3-6 *Objective:* Use proportions to solve percent problems.

Sample Test: Solve the equations.

1. 35% of 28 is _____. **Solution: 9.8**

2. 21 is 6% of _____. **Solution: 350**

3. What percent of $45 is $5.40? **Solution: 12%**

4. Create the proportion to determine the savings if a purchase of a $36 item is made with a 7% discount.
    Solution: $\frac{7}{100} = \frac{n}{36}$, or $.07 = \frac{n}{36}$.

Concept Development Activities

Percent as Ratio

This activity is designed to introduce percent, a ratio that compares a number to 100, in preparation for solving proportions involving percentages.

Directions:

1. Ask the students what they think a percent is. List as many plausible answers as reasonable.

2. List areas for discussion that have units of 100 and lend themselves to percent calculations. For example, one dollar = 100 cents; a football field is 100 yards in length; or a flagpole, building, or area can be 100 units in measure.

3. Ask the students to generate questions involving percentage for other class members to answer. This can be done in pairs with one student asking a partner the question and the partner responding. Then the roles can be reversed. Examples of such questions are:

    What percent of one dollar is a dime?

    $n\% = \frac{n}{100}, = \frac{10 \text{ cents}}{100 \text{ cents}}, = \frac{1}{10} = .1$, or 10%

Teacher's Tip:

Worksheet 1 for this objective, **page 3-24**, supports this activity with practice exercises.

3-6
Worksheet 1

Find the solutions to the following problems.
1. What percent of a dollar is one nickel?

2. What is the decimal equivalent of 5 cents?

3. If n is .47, what is .47 as a percent?

4. ⅝ represents what percent? What decimal?

5. N is 78% of 100. What is the value of N?

6. What is the decimal equivalent of 78%?

7. The top 36 feet of a 100-foot high flagpole is repainted. What percentage of the pole is repainted? If ⅗ of the flagpole is repainted, what decimal is represented? What percent of the pole is yet to be painted? What decimal represents that percent? How many feet of the pole are yet to be painted?

8. What percent of one dollar is 100 cents? What decimal represents 100% of one dollar?

9. The Statue of Liberty is approximately 300 feet high, including the base upon which the statue stands. If the base is 150 feet high, what percent of the total height is the statue itself?

Algebra 1 Manual ©2004 Sopris West Educational Services. To order: 800-547-6747. Product Code 180312
3-24   Chapter 3—Solving Linear Equations

A 32-yard gain is what percent of a football field?

$n\% = \frac{n}{100}, = \frac{32 \text{ yd.}}{100 \text{ yd.}}, = \frac{32}{100} = .32$, **or 32%**

Twenty-five cents is what percent of a dollar?

$n\% = \frac{n}{100}, = \frac{25\cent}{100\cent}, = .25$, **or 25%**

A business occupies 9 floors of a 100-story building. What percent of the building is occupied by that business?

$n\% = \frac{n}{100}, = \frac{9 \text{ floors}}{100 \text{ floors}}, = .09$, **or 9%**

The decimal $.50 is what percent of a dollar?

$n\% = \frac{n}{100}, = \$.50 = \frac{50\cent}{100\cent}, = .5$, **or 50%**

A quarterback breaks away for a 40-yard run. What percentage of the playing field was gained?

$n\% = \frac{n}{100}, = \frac{40 \text{ yd.}}{100 \text{ yd.}}, = \frac{4}{10} = .4$, **or 40%**

4. Using these and other examples generated, ask the students to write proportions that represent these questions. With the examples based upon 100 units, the proportions seem trivial, but they are important and easy for students to understand.

5. *Note:* When working with percents, discuss the corresponding decimal value, such as 32 cents is $.32, or 9% is $\frac{9}{100} = .09$.

Percent as Proportion

Directions:

1. Review the discoveries from the preceding activity, **Percent as Ratio**. Review that $n\% = \frac{n}{100}$ and that n represents the decimal n-hundredths.

2. Ask the students to construct and complete the following table:

n	1	3	5	10	17	25	43	72	98	100	125
$\frac{n}{100}$											
n%											
n as decimal											

Teacher's Tip:

Worksheet 2 for this objective, **page 3-25**, supports this activity with practice exercises.

3. Note that just as any n above was written as a percentage, any number can be written as a percentage by using the solution of a proportion in which the ratios are $\frac{\text{part}}{\text{whole}}$. So $n\% = \frac{n}{100} = \frac{\text{part}}{\text{whole}}$. For example,

   a. $\frac{2}{5}$ is what percentage? $\frac{2}{5} = n\%$, or $\frac{2}{5} = \frac{n}{100}$, so $2(100) = 5n$. Then $n = 40$, and $\frac{n}{100} = \frac{40}{100} = .40$, so $n = 40\%$.

   b. $\frac{2}{3}$ is what percentage? $\frac{2}{3} = n\%$, or $\frac{2}{3} = \frac{n}{100}$, so $2(100) = 3n$. Then $n = 66\frac{2}{3}$, and $\frac{n}{100} = .666$, so $n = 66.7\%$.

   c. 1.25 is what percentage? $1.25 = n\%$, or $\frac{125}{100} = \frac{n}{100}$, so $n = 125$, and $\frac{n}{100} = 1.25$, so $n = 125\%$.

4. Explain that most percentage problems can be written as proportions, since any percent can be written as a ratio: $\frac{n}{100}$. *Examples:* $40\% = \frac{40}{100}$; $15\% = \frac{15}{100}$; $6\% = \frac{6}{100}$. The remaining numbers are a part of the whole and the whole amount. For example: Your savings of \$1,000 earns 6% interest. How much interest would you earn for one year? That is, 6% of 1,000 is _____. The proportion is $\frac{n}{100} = \frac{\text{part}}{\text{whole}}$. In our example, $\frac{6}{100} = \frac{x}{1000}$. $100 \cdot x = 6,000$, so $x = 60$ or \$60 interest.

   Discuss other examples such as: 20% of _____ is 50 and _____% of 30 is 3.

5. Direct the students to write the proportions for the following problems: $\frac{n}{100} = \frac{\text{part}}{\text{whole}}$

Problem:	Proportion:
a. 13% of 200 = n	$\frac{13}{100} = \frac{n}{200}$
b. 45% of 120 = n	$\frac{45}{100} = \frac{n}{120}$
c. 16 = 20% of n	$\frac{16}{n} = \frac{20}{100}$
d. n% of 20 = 5	$\frac{n}{100} = \frac{5}{20}$
e. 6 = 15% of n	$\frac{6}{n} = \frac{15}{100}$
f. n% of 150 = 27	$\frac{n}{100} = \frac{27}{150}$

Answer Key for #4:

$\frac{20}{100} = \frac{50}{x}$

$20x = 5000$

$x = 250$

$\frac{n}{100} = \frac{3}{30}$

$300 = 30n$

$10 = n$ or 10%

Practice Activities

Percent as Proportion, Dominoes

Directions:

1. Divide the students into groups of two to four players. Give each group a copy of the blackline master **Dominoes for Percents as Proportions**.

2. Have the students cut the dominoes out of each sheet of paper.

3. Each player in a group should draw a total of 8, 6, or 5 dominoes all at one time, depending on whether there are 2, 3, or 4 players in the group.

4. One student is designated as the first player, and play continues to the left. The first player to draw a "double" lays that domino down. A double is a domino with the correct solution for the stated problem. (Students may use paper and pencil to solve the domino problems.)

   An example of a double is:

   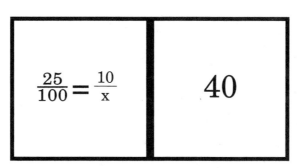

5. The players then, in turn, attempt to play a domino that matches with one end of the played dominoes. Any player not having a play draws one domino from the extra dominoes (they are face down) and may play the drawn domino if it is playable.

6. If a player plays a domino that does not connect correctly, he or she must take back the domino, draw a domino from the stack, and pass his or her turn.

7. Play can stop with the first person to use all of his or her dominos being declared the winner, or play can continue until all plays are exhausted.

Materials:

▶ Blackline master **Dominoes for Percents as Proportions** is located in the *Teacher's Resource Manual*, **pages 44–46**.

▶ Scissors

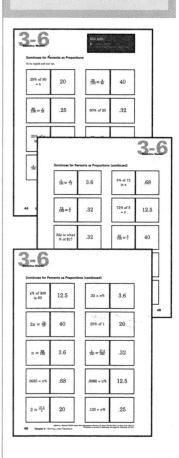

8. A typical game array after a few plays might look like the example below. Note that doubles are played across the other dominoes, not end-to-end.

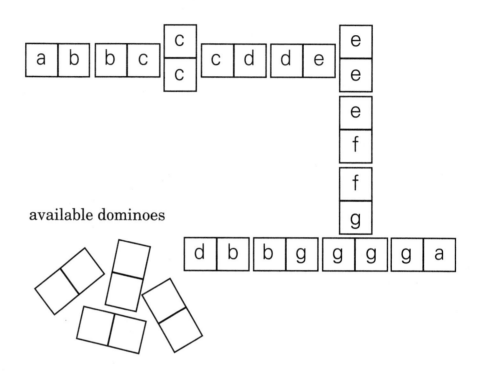

available dominoes

Variation: Give the dominoes to an individual student and see if he or she can put all pieces in a domino configuration.

Newspaper Hunt

Directions:

1. Students are to find an article, advertisement, graph, or table that uses percentages. They can do this at home, in the library, or in class with newspapers and magazines that you provide.

2. Have the students copy the information involving the percentages and bring it to class if they are doing the work at home or the library.

Materials:

▶ Daily newspapers, *USA Today*, financial magazines

3. Have the students form groups of four. Using typical numbers with the percentages they find, have the students make up problems and present their problems to the other groups to solve.

4. Some articles may give data only as percentages. Discuss what is meant by the percentages and how they were computed. Students can make up problems based on the information.

Problem-Solving Activity

Everyday Problems

Directions:

Give each student a copy of the blackline master **Everyday Problems**. Have the students work individually to solve the problems, which are reprinted below.

Find the solutions to the following problems:

1. In a sale, a disk player that usually costs $120 is advertised for 30% off. How much is the sale price?

2. A racing bicycle that regularly sells for $1,500 is advertised for $1,200. What is the percent of discount?

3. A shirt that regularly sells for $22 is on sale for $18. A special sale is advertised at 40% off the regular price or 25% off the sale price. Which is the better deal?

4. Last year 15,600 people attended a particular rock concert. This year, the attendance was down 6%. About how many people attended the concert this year?

5. Members of a ski club are given 20% off their lift ticket price. What is the regular price of a lift ticket if a member is given an eight dollar discount?

6. The list price for a pair of in-line skates is $60, but they are on sale for $48. What is the percent of discount?

7. If you earn $6.50/hour at the Star Drive-in and are given a raise to $7.02, what is the percent of increase in wages that you were awarded?

Teacher's Tip:

Worksheet 3 for this objective, **page 3-26**, supports this activity with practice exercises.

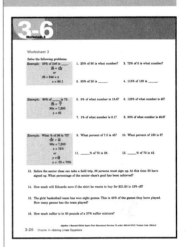

Materials:

▶ Blackline master **Everyday Problems** is located in the *Teacher's Resource Manual*, **pages 47–48**.

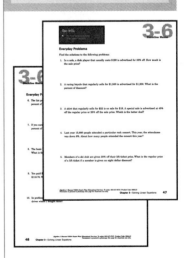

8. The basic monthly payment for Pablo's car is $425. With interest, that payment is $476. What is the interest rate?

9. You paid $138 for a new driver to use with your golf clubs. I bought the same driver for $118.70. What percent more did you pay for your driver than I paid for mine?

10. In problem 9, what percent of your $138 price could you have saved by buying your driver where I bought mine?

Graphing Relations and Functions

4-1 Graph ordered pairs and relations.

4-2 Identify the domain, range, and the inverse of a relation.

4-3 Determine the range for a given domain of a relation.

4-4 Graph linear equations.

4-5 Determine whether a relation is a function and find a value for a given function.

4-1 *Objective:* Graph ordered pairs and relations.

Sample Test:

1. Give the letter of the point in Quadrant III; in Quadrant II.

   Solution: C; B

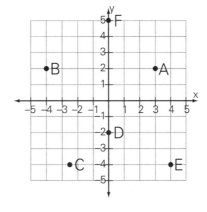

2. Give the ordered pair for letter A; for letter C.

   Solution: A (3, 2); C (2½, –4)

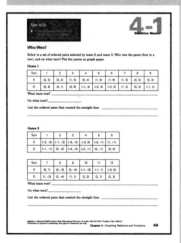

Concept Development Activities

Quadrants

Directions:

1. Split the classroom into four sections with an imaginary vertical line and an imaginary horizontal line. Ask the students to give as many sets of names to these quadrants as they can (for example, Northeast, Northwest, Southeast, and Southwest).

2. Assign each section a quadrant number: Quadrant I, Quadrant II, Quadrant III, and Quadrant IV.

3. Ask the students to draw the quadrants on graph paper, using the whole sheet. For each quadrant, they should draw the items it contains (for example, tables, chairs, desks, etc.).

4. Have the class decide on a scale for the coordinate plane. Using this scale, ask the students to give an ordered pair for each of the different items in the room.

5. Discuss with the class why each student has different answers and what could be done to standardize the graphs, which are essentially maps of the room.

Tic-Tac-Toe, Four in a Row

Directions:

1. Make a grid on an overhead graph transparency, marking 0 to +10 on the x- and y-axes.

2. Divide the class into two groups. Designate one group "team X" and one group "team O." Call on a person from team X, and ask him or her to give you two numbers between 1 and 10. The first number will be the "x" value and the second will be the "y" value of a point.

3. Plot the point represented by the two numbers on the transparency. Emphasize the plotting of the points by counting out loud "1, 2, 3, 4" as you move across the x-axis and "1, 2, 3, 4" as you move up the y-axis. Put an "X" on the point represented by the ordered pair of numbers.

4. Call on a person from the O team and repeat steps 2 and 3. Put an "O" on the point represented by the ordered pair of numbers.

5. Explain to the class that the purpose of this activity is to be the first team to place four of its own points in a row at grid intersection points (as opposed to between grid lines). The four in a row can be horizontal, vertical, or diagonal.

6. Alternate calling on team X and team O for ordered pairs. Write the ordered pairs on the board in a chart with headings "X" and "O" before graphing, so the students can see the ordered pairs being plotted. A team spokesperson may need to be appointed by each team.

7. Continue until one team gets four points in a row. Ask the winning team to name the ordered pairs that formed the row and list them on the board.

8. Next, make a grid marked from –5 to +5 on the x- and y-axes. Start by giving the O team the point (–1, 2). This will force the teams to use all of the grid with positive and negative coordinates.

9. Several games may need to be played so the students have the idea of how to get four points in a row and how to block their opponent.

10. Now divide the class into pairs, and have each pair play against another pair. Have each team write the ordered pair before plotting it. Circulate around the class to be sure the students are naming and plotting the ordered pairs correctly.

11. Distribute a copy of the blackline master **Who Won?** to each student to complete for classwork or homework.

Practice Activities

Name Coordinates

Directions:

1. Have the students make a coordinate plane on the graph paper with the same scale in all four quadrants.

2. Have the students draw their two initials on the graph paper using only straight lines and containing as many intersecting

Teacher's Tip:

Worksheet 1 for this objective, **page 4-2**, supports this activity with practice exercises.

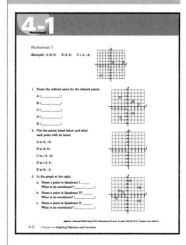

Teacher's Tips:

▶ A variation of this activity is for teams to get five points in a row.

▶ You pick the starting point for both teams.

Materials:

▶ Blackline master for **graph paper** is in the Appendix.

▶ Ruler

Practice

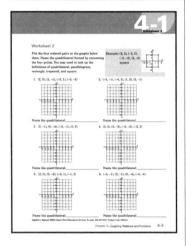

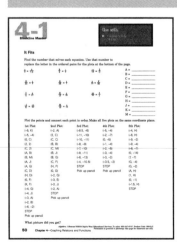

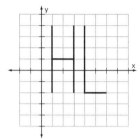
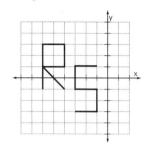

lines (integer coordinates) as possible. Ask half the students to use Quadrants I and IV and the other half to use Quadrants II and III.

Examples:

3. Ask each student to list the coordinates of the intersection points of their initials on notebook paper, making a separate list for each initial. The students should not indicate what the letters are. The points should be sequential, listed in the order used to draw each letter.

4. Ask the students to exchange their lists with students from the other half of the class.

5. The students should then use their own graph paper to plot the points in the list they received and connect the points in the order given. They can then check each other's work by looking at the initials and comparing them to their original graphs.

It Fits

Directions:

1. Distribute a copy of the blackline master **It Fits** to each student.

2. Review how to solve proportional equations. Have the students solve each proportion on the blackline master and indicate the value for each letter.

Materials:

▶ Blackline master **It Fits** is located in the *Teacher's Resource Manual*, **page 50.**

▶ Blackline master for **graph paper** is in the Appendix.

3. Ask the students to use the values to find the ordered pairs at the bottom of the page. The students should then use these ordered pairs to make a drawing by connecting the points in the order represented by the ordered pairs.

4. After the students have plotted the points and completed their pictures on the graph paper, have them compare their pictures with one another. If the pictures are different, have the students check their ordered pairs and check the letter solutions to the equations.

Chapter 4—Graphing Relations and Functions

Problem-Solving Activity

Quadrant Graphing

Directions:

1. Ask the students to draw a coordinate plane on a full sheet of graph paper and label the quadrants. Distribute a copy of the blackline master **Quadrant Graphing** to each student.

2. Review the concept that a line must be drawn with arrows at both ends to show that it goes on forever in both directions. Ask the students to complete the exercises on the blackline master.

3. After the students finish the exercises, discuss each of their four lines. Ask the following questions for each line. (This could be done as a whole class or in small groups.)

   a. What is always true about the x-coordinate for that line?

   b. What is never true about the x-coordinate?

   c. What is sometimes true about the x-coordinate?

   d. What is always true about the y-coordinate?

   e. What is never true about the y-coordinate?

   f. What is sometimes true about the y-coordinate?

4. Direct students to notice the following:

   a. Whether the x- and y-coordinates are always positive or negative

   b. Whether the x- and y-coordinates increase or decrease in value

   c. Whether the line is parallel to an axis or sloped in one direction

Materials:

▶ Blackline master **Quadrant Graphing** is located in the *Teacher's Resource Manual*, **page 51.**

▶ Blackline master for **graph paper** is in the Appendix.

4-2 *Objective:* **Identify the domain, range, and the inverse of a relation.**

Sample Test: Use the relation {(2, 3), (4, −1), (3, 0), (4, −3), (−2, −2)} to answer the following questions:

1. Give the domain of the relation.   **Solution: {2, 4, 3, 4, −2}**

2. Give the range of the relation.   **Solution: {3, −1, 0, −3, −2}**

3. Give the inverse of the relation.

   Solution: {(3, 2), (−1, 4), (0, 3), (−3, 4), (−2, −2)]

Concept Development Activities

Relationships

Directions:

1. Ask the students to list six ordered pairs on their papers and to define this list by giving it the name "relation."

2. Now ask the students to list only the x-coordinate of each ordered pair and to name this list the "domain."

3. Do the same for the y-coordinates. Have the students name this list the "range."

4. Now present the name "inverse," and ask the students to give you a definition of inverse and to write the inverse relations.

5. Help the students develop this knowledge by creating a relationship of two brothers (have students suggest names for the brothers). Tell them one brother is three years older than the other. Make a table of the brothers' ages when the younger brother is 5, 6, 7, 8, 9, and 10 years old. **{(5, 8), (6, 9)...}**

6. Walk the students through the ideas of domain and range by using this table.

7. Talk about what the inverse would mean in this case, and then give the domain of the inverse relation and the range of the inverse relation. The inverse gives the ordered pairs of the older compared to the younger at the different ages. **{(8, 5), (9, 6)...}**

Materials:

▶ Blackline master for **graph paper** is in the Appendix.

Earnings ☀

Directions:

1. Have the students write the following sentence at the top of their lined papers: "The clerk at the video store earns $6.00 per hour."

2. Ask the students to write the ordered pairs that represent the hours and the amount earned up to 5 hours. Talk about which should be the x-coordinate and which should be the y-coordinate. Discuss that a relation is a set of ordered pairs.

3. Have the students graph the ordered pairs on the graph paper. Use the hours worked as the x-axis and the amount earned as the y-axis.

4. Discuss the domain and range of the relation.

5. Ask the students to make a table based on the graph that shows the relation between hours worked and amount earned up to 5 hours. Include some fractional points. *Example:* $2\frac{1}{2}$ hours, $15 or $(2\frac{1}{2}, 15)$

6. Ask the students to write a description of the information given in the visual presentation under the graph. Have them finish by giving the graph a title and axis labels.

7. Discuss which of the above ways to identify a relation would be the easiest for an employer to read and show to a new employee.

8. Ask the students to write the inverse relation and discuss how it is formed. Discuss what the inverse relation represents.

Materials:

▶ Blackline master for **graph paper** is in the Appendix.

▶ Lined paper

Teacher's Tip:

Worksheet 1 for this objective, **page 4-6**, supports this activity with practice exercises.

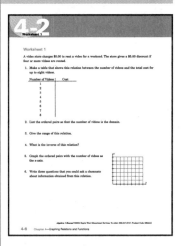

Teacher's Tip:

A variation of this activity could be a weekly or monthly earnings.

Practice

Practice Activities

Relation Matching

Directions:

1. Make copies of the blackline master **Relation Matching**, and give one to each student.

2. Ask the students to match the number with the correct letter on the blackline master and to represent the correct answers as a relation (a set of ordered pairs).

3. Have the students list the numbers 1 through 16 as the x-coordinates and the letters A through P as the y-coordinates and show a table of this relation.

4. Grade the activity using either the relation (set of ordered pairs) or the table.

5. Share the correct answers with the class by allowing the students to correct any they missed. Then have the students go back to their original answers and correct them by writing each incorrect word and next to it the complete correct answer. For example, if the student missed #9, he or she would write "Range—the set of all second coordinates from the ordered pairs."

Relation Bingo

Directions:

1. Give each student a 4 × 4 bingo card and a copy of the blackline master **Relation Matching**. Choose one of the columns on the blackline master and have the students randomly fill in the squares on the bingo card with the items in that column. Have the students put away the blackline master so they cannot see the definitions in the other column.

2. Read a definition from the other column, or write it on the board or overhead. Have the students cover the matching descriptors on their bingo cards with markers. The first student to cover four answers in a row, column, or diagonal shouts, "Bingo!" You should then check that student's solution to confirm the bingo.

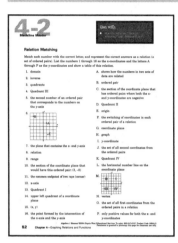

Problem-Solving Activity

The Budget Movie Tickets 💡

Directions:

1. Divide the students into groups of two or three.

2. Ask each group to graph how they think the price of movie tickets has gone up from the year they were born to the present. Give them the starting price of $2.60 in 1980. Students will need to estimate the prices.

3. When they are finished, give one copy of the blackline master **The Budget Movie Tickets** to each student and have the students construct a graph of the data. Ask the students to compare the costs listed with those on their graph.

4. Ask the students to complete the blackline master individually and then discuss the answers with the other members of their group.

5. Ask the students to extend their year scales to the year 2010 and then extend their graphs to estimate what movie tickets will cost by the year 2010.

6. Have each group report back to the class what their estimate is and why they think so. Talk about how their graph helped them with the estimate.

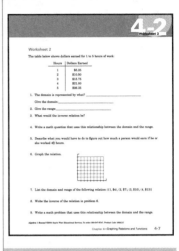

Materials:

▶ Blackline master **The Budget Movie Tickets** is located in the *Teacher's Resource Manual*, **page 53.**

4-3 *Objective:* Determine the range for a given domain of a relation.

Sample Test:

1. Find the ordered pairs that satisfy the relation y = 2x + 1 when the domain is {−1, 0, 1, 2}.

   Solution: {(−1, −1), (0, 1), (1, 3), (2, 5)}

2. Complete the table of values for x + y = −2.

x	x + y = −2	y	(x, y)
−2			
0			
2			
4			

   Solution:

x	x + y = −2	y	(x, y)
−2	**−2 + y = −2**	**0**	**(−2, 0)**
0	**0 + y = −2**	**−2**	**(0, −2)**
2	**2 + y = −2**	**−4**	**(2, −4)**
4	**4 + y = −2**	**−6**	**(4, −6)**

Concept Development Activities

Domain and Range Development

Directions:

1. Review with students that the domain is the set of the first value in the ordered pairs of a relation. The range is the set of second values.

2. Have the students make two columns on their papers:

x	y
Domain	Range

3. Discuss the meanings of independent and dependent. Use life examples first, then the math example that the value (or solution) of one depends on the value of the other. Ask the students to guess which one—domain or range—would be independent or dependent.

4. Give the following examples to the students. For each example, ask which variable depends on the other. Ask the students to write it out in a sentence.

Example 1: Distance is the rate of speed times the time traveled. If the rate is 55 mph, what is the distance?

Explain that D = r times t, or D = 55 · t in this case. Ask the students to write which variable depends on the other. The students would write: "Distance depends on the time."

Ask, "What is D (the distance) for 2 hours, 4 hours, 10 hours?" (2, _____), (4, _____), (10, _____).

Explain that the domain is {2, 4, 10}. Ask, "What is the range?"

Example 2: If you work at a job and receive $5.25 per hour, then dollars earned is $5.25 times the number of hours worked. d = 5.25 times h. The students would write: "Dollars depend on the hours."

Have the students complete the table and the following exercises for d when given h:

The domain is {____, ____, ____, ____}
The range is {____, ____, ____, ____}

h	d
8 hr.	$_____
12 hr.	$_____
20 hr.	$_____
40 hr.	$_____

Discuss that the domain is the independent variable and the range is the dependent variable. The range depends on what is chosen for the substitution or domain.

5. Summarize that the domain consists of possible values that can be substituted into the equation. The range consists of the possible resulting values.

Making Tables

Directions:

1. Write an equation on the board or overhead. For example, 2x + y = 6.

2. Ask the class to name some values that could be used for x. Ask, "How many values are there that we could use for x?" **(Infinitely many)**

Answer Key for #4:
Range for Example 1:
{110, 220, 550}

Example 2:
Domain: {8, 12, 20, 40}
Range: {42, 63, 105, 210}

Teacher's Tip:

Worksheet 1 for this objective, **page 4-10**, supports this activity with practice exercises.

4-3
Worksheet 1

Worksheet 1
Example: y = ½x + 2
If x = –6, then y = ½(–6) + 2
    y = –4 + 2
    y = –2

Find the values for y if y = ½x + 2.
1. a. If x = 2, then y = _____   b. If x = 0, then y = _____
   c. If x = 6, then y = _____   d. If x = –2, then y = _____
   e. The value we use for x is called the domain. The domain for this equation is _____

2. Complete the table below for the equation y = 2x – 4. The domain is {–2, 0, 2, 4, 6}.

x	y = 2x – 4	y	(x, y)
(Example) –2	y = 2(–2) – 4	–8	(–2, –8)
0			
2			
4			
6			

3. Find the values for y for the equation x + y = 8. The domain is {–2, –1, 0, 2, 4}.

x	x + y = 8	y	(x, y)
(Example) 0	0 + y = 8	8	(0, 8)
–2			
–1			
2			
4			

4-10   Chapter 4—Graphing Relations and Functions

3. Tell the class that because no one could ever find or use all of the values, you will restrict the domain and use only some values for x. Discuss that if you use only the integers from −4 to +2, the domain would be {−4, −3, −2, −1, 0, 1, 2}.

4. Ask the students how they can find the y values. Discuss the responses the students offer.

5. Introduce a table as a good way to find the y values. Write the following tables on the board or an overhead transparency.

One type of table has the equation above and the x and y values below. For example, 2x + y = 6

x	y
−4	
−3	
−2	
−1	
0	
1	
2	

Substitute for x and find y.

6. Another example is a table that has more organization:

x	2x + y = 6	y	(x, y)
−4			
−3			
−2			
−1			
0			
1			
2			

Have the students substitute for x and solve the equation for y. They should then list the values for y and write the ordered pairs (x, y).

7. Have the students try both examples of tables for y = x − 2 when the domain is {−2, −1, 0, 2, 6}.

Answer Key for #5:
2x + y = 6

x	y
−4	14
−3	12
−2	10
−1	8
0	6
1	4
2	2

Answer Key for #6:

x	2x + y = 6	y	(x, y)
−4	2(−4) + y = 6	14	(−4, 14)
−3	2(−3) + y = 6	12	(−3, 12)
−2	2(−2) + y = 6	10	(−2, 10)
−1	2(−1) + y = 6	8	(−1, 8)
0	2(0) + y = 6	6	(0, 6)
1	2(1) + y = 6	4	(1, 4)
2	2(2) + y = 6	2	(2, 2)

Answer Key for #7:
y = x − 2

x	y
−2	−4
−1	−3
0	−2
2	0
6	4

x	y = x − 2	y	(x, y)
−2	y = −2 − 2	−4	(−2, −4)
−1	y = −1 − 2	−3	(−1, −3)
0	y = 0 − 2	−2	(0, −2)
2	y = 2 − 2	0	(2, 0)
6	y = 6 − 2	4	(6, 4)

Practice Activities

Forming Equations

Directions:

1. Have the students form groups of three and designate themselves as Student 1, 2, or 3.

2. Ask Student 1 to give a domain value, Student 2 to give a range value, and Student 3 to give an equation for which that ordered pair would be a solution. For example,

Student 1	Domain = 3
Student 2	Range = 4
Student 3	$x + y = 7$ (or $y = x + 1$, etc.)

3. Have the students rotate positions so that every student does each of the three tasks.

4. Ask the students to make a table showing their solutions to the equation $2x + y = 6$. Have Student 1 give four values for the domain, have Student 2 substitute the value for x and find y, and have Student 3 give the ordered pair (x, y).

x	$2x + y = 6$	y	(x, y)

5. Next, the students should make a table for the relation $y = -2x + 6$. Rotate student positions for giving the domain, finding the range, and giving the ordered pair.

x	$y = -2x + 6$	y	(x, y)

6. Give the students the relation $x \cdot y = 12$. Ask each student to find four ordered pairs that would satisfy the equation. Have groups discuss the possible solutions.

   (___, ___), (___, ___), (___, ___), (___, ___)

Teacher's Tip:

Worksheet 2 for this objective, **page 4-11**, supports this activity with practice exercises.

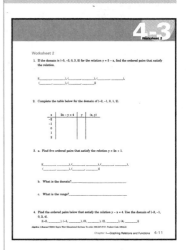

Answer Key for #4:
Some possible answers. Answers will depend on the domain given.

x	$2x + y = 6$	y	(x, y)
0	$2 \cdot 0 + y = 6$	6	(0, 6)
1	$2 \cdot 1 + y = 6$	4	(1, 4)
-1	$2 \cdot (-1) + y = 6$	8	(-1, 8)
2	$2 \cdot 2 + y = 6$	2	(2, 2)
-2	$2 \cdot (-2) + y = 6$	10	(-2, 10)

Answer Key:
5. Students will find the same answers as number 4 since the equations are the same.
6. Some possible answers. Cannot have zero! {(1, 12), (-1, -12), (2, 6), (-2, -6), (3, 4), (-3, -4)...}

4-3

Practice

Materials:

► Blank 3 × 5 cards

Teacher's Tip:

Worksheet 3 for this objective, **page 4-12**, supports this activity with practice exercises.

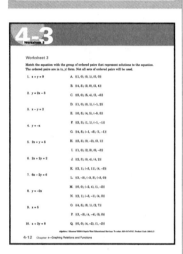

Find Your Partners

Directions:

1. Have each student make a set of three cards:

   a. On the first card, the student should write an equation.

   b. The second card should have the equation solved for y in terms of x.

   c. The third card should have solutions as ordered pairs to the equation (three ordered pairs).

   Examples of sets of cards are the following:

Card 1	**Card 2**	**Card 3**
$x + y = 4$	$y = 4 - x$	$\{(2, 2), (3, 1), (4, 0)\}$
$2x + y = 3$	$y = 3 - 2x$	$\{(0, 3), (1, 1), (3, -3)\}$
$x - y = 6$	$y = x - 6$	$\{(7, 1), (0, -6), (6, 0)\}$
$2x + 2y = 4$	$y = 2 - x$	$\{(1, 1), (0, 2), (3, -1)\}$
$3x - y = 0$	$y = 3x + 0$	$\{(1, 3), (0, 0), (-2, -6)\}$
$x = y$	$y = x$	$\{(-1, -1), (0, 0), (3, 3)\}$

2. Collect all the cards. Then give each student one card. This will provide enough material to use the activity for two or three days. Hand out the cards randomly or as students come into class.

3. Have the class stand up. Instruct each student to find the other two students who have equivalent cards to form groups of three.

4. As groups finish finding their partners, have them exchange cards with others in their group and check one another's cards.

5. Since not all of the cards have been used, some cards may not have matches. Students could write new solutions for the cards or hold onto the cards until the following day or until all cards have been used.

6. Each group can make a set of three new cards if you wish to continue. Or the group members can write three new solutions written as ordered pairs.

Domain and Range Game

Directions:

1. Divide the class into two groups. Each group will work together for a team score.

2. Write an equation on the board—for example, $y = x - 4$.

3. The first group should give a domain value (for example, 8). The second group should give the range using the first group's value (in this case, 4).

4. The first group must immediately say whether they agree or disagree with the range. Have only one student answer each time, going straight down the line of students. Each student is responsible for the group score when it is his or her group's turn.

5. Follow this procedure with three more equations and then rotate the tasks for the groups.

6. Use the following scoring scheme:

    If the second group gives the correct range   +2 points
    If the first group says "wrong" and the range is correct,
       or if it says "correct" and the range is wrong   −1 point
    If the first group is correct in its check   +1 point

7. Depending on the class, you may want to mix difficult and easy equations.

8. After the students work with linear equations, you could give equations such as:

    $x \cdot y = 6$ or $x \cdot y = -6$ $x \cdot y = 0$
    $\frac{x}{y} = 2$ $y = x^2 + 2$

> **Teacher's Tip:**
>
> **Variation:** Write the equation in linear form and have the students in both groups solve the equation for y in terms of x and then give the domain and the range.

Materials:

▶ Blackline master for **graph paper** is in the Appendix.

Problem-Solving Activity

How Much Do You Weigh? 💡

Directions:

1. Tell the students that a person who weighs 100 pounds on Earth would weigh 140 pounds on Neptune due to the difference in the force of gravity.

2. Have the students work in groups to guess how much a person who weighs 150 pounds on Earth would weigh on Neptune. Give them some other weights to guess.

3. Explain that knowing an equation would give them the force of gravity on Neptune, and they would be able then to figure anyone's weight on Neptune. See if the students can come up with, "What times 100 would give us 140?"

4. Have the groups find answers to the equation and check them. Work with the groups until they each have the concept.

5. Discuss that they now know that any Earth weight (e) times 1.4 will give the weight on Neptune (n). Have the groups develop this as a math sentence. **(Neptune weight is 1.4 times Earth weight)** Have the students write the equation for n in terms of e. **(n = 1.4e)**

6. Have the students individually make a table of any five Earth weights. Then have them complete the table with Neptune weights by using the equation they developed. For example:

Weight on Earth (e)	100				
Weight on Neptune (n)	140				

$n = 1.4e$

7. Students should give the relation of ordered pairs for the weights in their tables. Ask them then to graph these ordered pairs. Talk about the scale for both the x- and y-axes and have the students use the same scale within each group.

8. Give some weights on Neptune and ask for the Earth weights. *Examples:* 280, 84, 42, 770.

4-4 *Objective:* **Graph linear equations.**

Sample Test:

1. a. Find the ordered pairs that satisfy the relation $y - 2x = -4$ for the domain of $\{-1, 0, 2, 4\}$.

   Solution: {(–1, –6), (0, –4), (2, 0), (4, 4)}

   b. Graph the line $y - 2x = -4$.

   Solution:

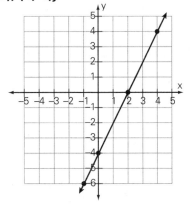

2. Complete the table and construct the graph for $y = x - 3$.

x	y = x – 3	y	(x, y)
–1			
0			
2			
4			
6			

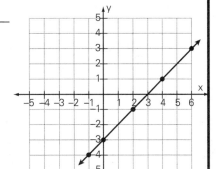

   Solution:

x	y = x – 3	y	(x, y)
–1	y = –1 – 3	–4	(–1, –4)
0	y = 0 – 3	–3	(0, –3)
2	y = 2 – 3	–1	(2, –1)
4	y = 4 – 3	1	(4, 1)
6	y = 6 – 3	3	(6, 3)

3. Graph the line that has the relation $\{(-2, 3), (0, 5), (-5, 0)\}$.

   Solution:

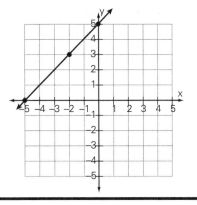

Concept Development Activities

Making Line Graphs

Directions:

1. Write the equation y = 2x + 1 on the board or overhead transparency.

2. Ask the students how to make a graph of the equation. Review the concepts that (1) you need ordered pairs to build a graph, (2) making a table of values will give ordered pairs that satisfy the equation, (3) you need to choose appropriate scales and parts of the grid to make the graph.

3. Copy and distribute the blackline master **Making Line Graphs** to each student.

4. Refer to the table for y = 2x + 1 and ask the students to complete the table. Discuss the completed table and correct ordered pairs.

5. Ask "How can we make a graph from the table?" Have the students complete the graph. Have a student show his or her graph and explain how it was constructed.

6. Now have the students complete problem 1 on the blackline master. Review that a set of ordered pairs needs to be determined either by selecting some values for x and solving for y or by making a table. Students can use any method or table as long as it determines correct ordered pairs.

7. Have the students construct the graph. Review the process. Continue with problems 2–4.

8. Discuss that all of these equations are *straight lines*. Ask why the students think they are straight lines. Discuss that any equation that can be written in the form ax + by = c is a linear equation and the graph is a straight line.

Materials:

► Blackline master **Making Line Graphs** is located in the *Teacher's Resource Manual,* **pages 54–55.**

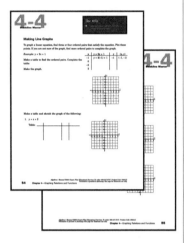

Teacher's Tip:

Worksheet 1 for this objective, **pages 4-16 and 4-17**, supports this activity with practice exercises.

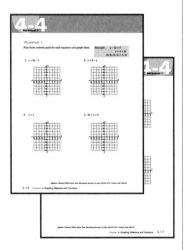

Graphing Lines

Directions:

1. Give each student a copy of the blackline master **Graphing Lines**.

2. Remind the students that to enter an equation into the calculator, it must be solved for y in terms of x. This format also makes it easier to find ordered pairs by hand.

3. Have the students work in groups of three to complete the blackline master.

4. Ask the groups to bring back to the whole class any interesting or unusual findings. *Examples:* the equation x = 0 or y = –2. Discuss why the graphs are different from one another and name other graphs that would look similar. *Examples:* x = 0 and x = 5.

Materials:

▶ Blackline master **Graphing Lines** is located in the *Teacher's Resource Manual*, **pages 56–57.**

▶ Blackline master for **graph paper** is in the Appendix.

▶ Graphing calculator

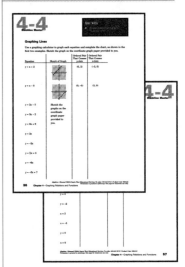

Teacher's Tip:

This activity is best done with a graphing calculator. Students can also complete this activity by hand, but you may want to reduce the number of problems in that case.

Materials:

▶ Blackline master for **graph paper** is in the Appendix.

Teacher's Tip:

Worksheets 2 and 3 for this objective, **pages 4-18 through 4-20**, support this activity with practice exercises.

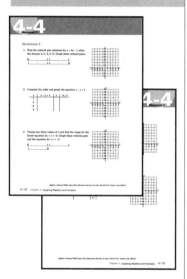

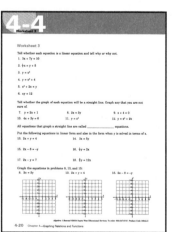

Linear and Nonlinear Equation Forms 💡

Directions:

1. Have the students work in groups of two or three. Give the students two equations, one linear and one nonlinear. For example, $x + y = 8$ and $xy = 8$.

2. Ask the groups to set up equation tables and to find at least five ordered pairs for each equation. The equation tables should look like the following:

x	x + y = 8	y	(x, y)

x	xy = 8	y	(x, y)

Remind the students to use both positive and negative numbers and to always check to see what zero gives.

3. Talk about how the equation tables are the same and how they are different.

4. Now ask the students to graph the two equations. Talk about how the graphs are the same and how they are different.

5. Ask the students to think about how many ordered pairs they would need in order to know how a graph will look.

6. Give two more equations—one linear and one nonlinear—to the groups. For example, $y = 2x - 1$ and $y = x^2 - 1$. Have the students set up equation tables and find ordered pairs. Remind the students to use positive and negative values in their equation tables.

7. Talk about how the equation tables are the same and how they are different.

8. Ask the students to graph the two equations. Talk about how the graphs are the same and how they are different.

9. You may want to do this same activity a few more times until the students can come up with the difference between a linear and a nonlinear equation and the differences in the graphs.

10. Now ask the students to write what they see as the general form of a linear equation (what it must have and what it must not have). **(ax + by = c where a, b, and c are any real numbers)**

11. Ask the groups to decide how many ordered pairs they would need to know to be certain about what a graph looks like.

12. Ask each group to come up with a linear and a nonlinear equation to give to another group to graph.

13. Finish the groups' discovery by together coming up with the general form of a linear equation (ax + by = c) and that form solved for y in terms of x. Also reinforce the idea of the infinite number of ordered pairs that work and lie in that straight line.

Practice Activities

Make and Share

Directions:

1. Write the following equations on the board or overhead transparency:

    y = ax + b where a and b are integers

    ax + by = c where a and b are integers

    x = ay + b where a and b are integers

2. Explain that a, b, and c can be any integers. Ask the students to write an equation in the form y = ax + b. *Example:* y = −2x + 8 where a = −2 and b = 8.

    Discuss the equations and check to see if the students are following the directions.

3. Ask the students to write an equation for ax + by = c and x = ay + b on their paper. Quickly check the students' equations.

4. Ask the students to make graphs of their equations on graph paper.

5. Form groups of four students. Have the students within each group exchange papers with the equations written on them (not the graphs). Have the students make graphs of the equations they now have. Rotate the equation pages again and have the students construct the graphs. Rotate the equation pages for the last time. Each student should have a graph for all the equations in the group.

6. Have the students compare their graphs and determine which graphs are correct if there are any differences. All the students in a group should be able to make any graph from an equation written by the group.

x-Axis and y-Axis

Directions:

1. Give each student a copy of the blackline master **x-Axis and y-Axis.** Have the students form groups of three or four.

2. The students should work the problems on the blackline master individually, and when they are finished, they should discuss in their groups the answers and the x-intercept and y-intercept. Discuss that it is recommended to have another point, in addition to the intercepts, to be sure that all three points lay on the line.

3. Tell the groups to share how they know where these points are and how this knowledge can help in graphing equations.

4. Have each group make up linear equations to give to the other groups. Each group should find where the graph crosses the x-axis and y-axis for the equations the group has been given.

Materials:

▶ Blackline master **x-Axis and y-Axis** is located in the *Teacher's Resource Manual,* **page 58.**

▶ Blackline master for **graph paper** is in the Appendix.

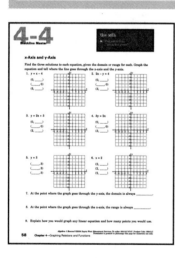

Problem-Solving Activities

Straight or Curved?

Directions:

1. Have the students work in small groups. Give each group a copy of the blackline master **Straight or Curved?** and plenty of graph paper to make graphs big enough to see the line.

2. The object is to determine whether the situations will graph a straight line after setting up an equation, a table, and a solution set of at least four ordered pairs.

3. Remind the students that they should first identify the independent variable (the one to which they will give many values) and then the dependent variable that they are trying to find.

4. After the groups are finished, have them write what they think the general form (or rule) is to graph a straight line (a linear equation).

5. Discuss the groups' findings with the class and compare the equations and graphs of the groups.

Materials:

▶ Blackline master **Straight or Curved?** is located in the *Teacher's Resource Manual*, **page 59.**

▶ Blackline master for **graph paper** is in the Appendix.

Materials:

▶ Blackline master **Name Your Equation** is located in the *Teacher's Resource Manual*, **page 60.**

▶ Blackline master for **graph paper** is in the Appendix.

▶ Graphing calculators

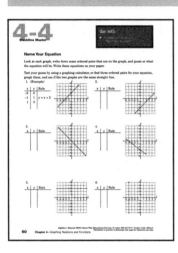

Name Your Equation 💡

Directions:

1. Distribute a copy of the blackline master **Name Your Equation** to each student.

2. Have the students list some ordered pairs that satisfy each graph and then guess at an equation for the graph and write it down. This is the type of activity necessary in science.

3. Pair up the students to check each other's equations. The students should try to convince their partners that they are correct by presenting facts about the graph and the equation.

4. The students can check the equations by using graphing calculators, or the partners can find three ordered pairs for each equation and graph these points to see if the graph matches the one chosen by the student.

5. Discuss the types of graphs that are easy to identify by their equations, such as $y = x$, $y = 3$, and $x = -2$.

6. Discuss the different equation forms that graphed the same line. Help the students check to see if they are equivalent.

4-5 *Objective:* **Determine whether a relation is a function and find a value for a given function.**

Sample Test:

1. Which of the following relations is a function?

   a. {(–1, 3), (0, 2), (–3, 6), (2, –4)}

   c. {(0, 0), (–1, 2), (0, 4), (2, –3), (–2, 4)}

   Solution: a

   b.
x	y
–2	2
3	6
–1	3
–2	4
–3	–6

2. a. If f(x) = 2x – 1, find the value of f(5).

   Solution: f(5) = 2(5) – 1 = 9

   b. If f(x) = 3x – 8, find the value of f(2).

   Solution: f(2) = 3(2) – 8 = –2

   c. If f(x) = x² + 1, find the value of f(–2).

   Solution: f(–2) = (–2)² + 1 = 5

Concept Development Activities

Relations as Functions 💡

Directions:

1. Review with the students the idea that in a relation the value of one variable depends on the value of another variable. This gives us a set of ordered pairs that are related.

2. Talk about a function, explaining that it is a special kind of relation in which each first value of the ordered pairs may be paired with one and only one second value.

3. See if the students can come up with a situation in which this would be true and one in which it would not be true. For example, if a person on top of a building drops a coin from the roof, the

Teacher's Tip:

Worksheet 1 for this objective, **page 4-24**, supports this activity with practice exercises.

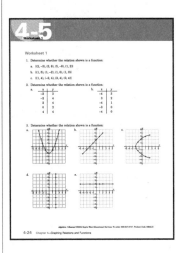

distance the coin falls is a function of the time the coin is in the air. For each distance there is one time. Describe this situation to the class. Let D(t) stand for the distance in feet, and let the time, t, in seconds go from 1 to 4. The function is $D(t) = 16t^2$.

Have the students complete the following table on their own paper.

t (seconds)	Distance Fallen (feet)
1	
2	
3	
4	

4. Then talk about a situation in which the relation would not be a function. For example, the ticket price for a light rail train usually depends on the zones. The stops within a certain zone are all priced the same, even though their distances vary, as shown in the following table:

Station	Miles	Zone	Price of Ticket	Student Work Ordered Pair
Mt. Station	12	5	$6.00	
Highland	14	5	$6.00	
Church Road	13	4	$5.50	
East Road	12	4	$5.50	
Newtown	10	2	$4.50	

Have the students list the ordered pairs (miles, price) and discuss.

5. Have the students practice writing relations as functions. Emphasize that one quantity is a function of the other, and that is why the notation is of the form f(x) instead of another letter, such as y. An example could be the idea of the post office. The price is a function of the number of 37-cent stamps you buy. Set up a table for the price P(x) = $.37x:

Number of Stamps	Price ($)
1	$ .37
2	$ .74
3	$1.11
4	$1.48
5	$1.85

6. Have the students set up a table for the function f(x) = 2x + 3 for which the values of x are {3, 2, −1, 0}.

7. Discuss how each of the functions described in this activity are the same and how they are different.

8. Other relations that could be discussed are earnings/hour, phone rates/minute, cost/pound, etc.

Function Graphs

Directions:

1. Have students form groups of two or three. Copy the blackline master **Function Graphs** and give one copy to each group.

2. Have the groups look at the graphs of relations on the blackline master. Explain that those graphs that have a "yes" are graphs of functions. The graphs that have a "no" are *not* graphs of functions.

3. Have the groups determine what is the same about each of the graphs that are functions and how those graphs differ from the ones that are not functions. **[Those that are not functions can have two dependent (y) values for the same independent (x) value.]**

4. Have each group write out the general definition of a function using the concepts of domain and range. Let the groups share these definitions with the class. Look for common elements.

5. Present the table to the right. Have the groups graph it and then state whether the relation is a function. Ask them to write the function in the words of a relationship.

Number of People	Days Needed for Job
2	6
3	4
4	3

(The number of days needed to complete the job is a function of the number of people working on it.)

6. Now have each group develop three or four relations to give to another group to complete and graph to determine if they are functions. Ask the groups to state the functions in the words of a relationship.

Materials:

▶ Blackline master **Function Graphs** is located in the *Teacher's Resource Manual*, **page 61.**

▶ Blackline master for **graph paper** is in the Appendix.

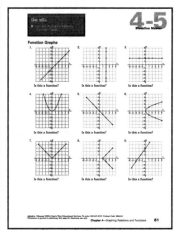

4-5

Teacher's Tip:

Worksheet 2 for this objective, **page 4-25**, supports this activity with practice exercises.

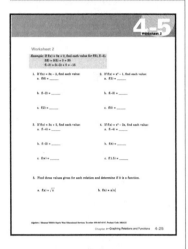

Teacher's Tip:

To extend this activity, have students graph the two functions in #4 to see where the two lines intersect.

Answer Key for #4:
f(–2)

Answer Key for #5:
3.5, 23, 59, 153.5, and 153.5

The Function Value 💡

Directions:

1. Review with the students that x represents the domain and y represents the range of the relation in a function. Then discuss that instead of using y, we use f(x) to emphasize that one quantity is a function of the other quantity.

2. Present the function f(x) = 3x − 2 and have the students find the value in the range that depends on 4 in the domain. This is written as:

$$f(4) = 3x - 2$$
$$= 3(4) - 2$$
$$= 10$$

   The value in the range would thus be 10. The ordered pair is (4, 10).

3. Repeat #2 using functions that the students offer.

4. Give the students the following two functions:

$$f(x) = x^2 - 5 \quad \text{and} \quad f(x) = x + 1$$

   Ask them to look at the following values to determine which value the two functions have in common: f(–2), f(2), f(–1), and f(1).

5. Give the students the following scenario: Pop Fligh hits a pitch that is 3.5 feet high. As the ball travels toward the outfield, its height can be represented by the following function:

   $$f(x) = -0.005x^2 + 2x + 3.5.$$

   First have the students draw a picture of what is happening.

   Then ask them to find each value to complete the chart to the right.

Feet From Home Plate	Height of the Ball in Feet
0	
10	
30	
100	
300	

6. From the information they found, ask the students to team up to figure out where a player should stand to catch a fly ball hit by Pop if they can catch a ball 10 feet in the air. Ask them why the heights for 100 and 300 feet the same.

Concept/Practice

7. Ask the students what other information they can figure out from the values. *Example:* Could the ball go over a 10-foot fence 400 feet from the plate?

Answer Key for #7: No, the ball would be only $3\frac{1}{2}$ feet off the ground.

Practice Activities

Function Board

Directions:

1. Have the students form groups of three. Give one copy of the blackline master **Function Board** to each group.

2. Make dice from the blank cubes with the six sides numbered 1, 2, 3, 1, 2, 3. Give one die to each group.

3. Have each student select a marker as a game piece and place it on start. The students should roll the die to determine who will go first (whoever rolls the largest number). Play will continue clockwise.

4. Play proceeds as follows: The first player rolls the die and moves that many spaces. The student looks at the ordered pairs in the box and tells whether the relation is a function and why or why not. The other players determine if he or she is correct.

5. If the player is correct, the player's marker stays on that spot. If the player is incorrect, the marker is moved back to the player's previous spot.

6. Play continues until someone reaches the "end."

7. Circulate among the students and explain the rule if there is a conflict.

Materials:

► Blackline master **Function Board** is located in the *Teacher's Resource Manual,* **page 62.**

► Game markers

► Blank wooden cubes

Chapter 4—Graphing Relations and Functions   **4-29**

Practice/Problem-Solving 4-5

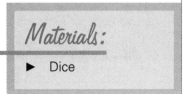

Materials:

▶ Dice

Domain Roll

Directions:

1. Have the class form groups of four. Give each group one die.

2. Write the equation $f(x) = 2x - 3$ on the board.

3. Each person in each group should roll the die and use that number for the x value. For example, if a student rolls a 3, $f(3) = 2(3) - 3 = 3$.

4. Each student should solve the equation for his or her value, and the group should check the answer. If it is correct, the student gets one point. Each group keeps a tally for its players.

5. Continue with these other equations. The equations may be used more than once.

$f(x) = 2x + 3$	$f(x) = -3x + 1$	$f(x) = 6 - x$	$f(x) = 3x + 2 - x$
$f(x) = -3 + 3x$	$f(x) = x^2$	$f(x) = 12 - x^2$	$f(x) = 7x + 2$

If you have more time, make up other equations.

Materials:

▶ Blackline master **Wind Chill Temperature** is located in the *Teacher's Resource Manual,* **page 63.**

▶ Blackline master for **graph paper** is in the Appendix.

▶ Graphing calculators

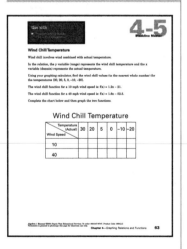

Problem-Solving Activity

Wind Chill Temperature

Directions:

1. Introduce the blackline master **Wind Chill Temperature** by explaining that wind chill temperature refers to the still-air temperature that would have the same cooling effect on your skin as the combination of the actual temperature and wind. Thus, a very windy day that had an actual temperature of 20 degrees could have a wind chill temperature well below zero.

2. Explain that the relation between wind chill temperature and actual temperature depends on the wind speed. Each wind speed will have a different relation. Let the y variable (range) represent the wind chill temperature and the x variable (domain) represent the actual temperature.

4-30 | Chapter 4—Graphing Relations and Functions

3. Instruct students to use a graphing calculator as they work on the wind chill temperature chart. Guide them through the activity as described in the following steps.

4. Expain that the wind chill temperature relation for a 10 mph wind is $f(x) = 1.2x - 21$, where x is the temperature. Ask the students to find values for the following actual temperatures: {30, 20, 5, 0, –10, –20}. Explain that they should round the temperature off to the nearest whole number for the wind chill temperature chart.

5. Now present the wind chill temperature relation for a 40 mph wind: $f(x) = 1.6x - 52.5$. Ask the students to find values for the same actual temperatures: {30, 20, 5, 0, –10, –20}.

6. Discuss with the students the change in temperature when the wind is blowing faster or when the temperature is warmer or colder.

7. Have the students use their graphing calculators to graph these two functions. Discuss the results they can determine from the graphs.

> **Teacher's Tip:**
>
> Have students research the relation for other wind speeds and calculate the temperatures.

Chapter 5

Analyzing Linear Equations

5-1 Determine the slope of a line from a graph or given two points on the line.

5-2 Write the equation of a line in standard form given two points on the graph of the line.

5-3 Draw a best-fit line and find the equation of the best-fit line for a scatter plot.

5-4 Write linear equations in the slope-intercept form to find the slope, x-intercept, and y-intercept, and sketch the graph.

5-5 Use the slope of lines to determine if two lines are parallel or perpendicular.

5-1 *Objective:* **Determine the slope of a line from a graph or given two points on the line.**

Sample Test: Find the slope of the line for each problem.

1. The slope of the line in the graph is _____.

   Solution: m = 2

2. For a line that passes through the points (2, –2), (–2, –1), the slope is _____.

   Solution: $m = -\frac{1}{4}$

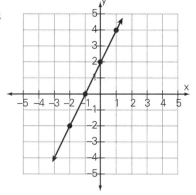

Materials:

▶ Blackline master for **graph paper** is in the Appendix.

▶ Overhead graph paper transparencies

▶ Rulers

Concept Development Activities

Ruler Slope

Directions:

1. Each student needs a ruler. Have the students work in pairs.

2. Have the students mark off a distance of 4″ on a piece of paper.

3. Have the students put the end of one ruler on the first mark and raise the ruler up and down. Discuss the steepness of the ruler.

   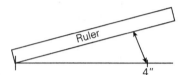

   Example: "If I were a skier going down this hill, which steepness (slope) would make me go faster?" Explain that the steepness is called the "slope" of the line.

4. Have the students put one end of the ruler on the first mark and then put another ruler perpendicular on the second mark. Instruct them to raise the first ruler up 1″, as in the figure.

   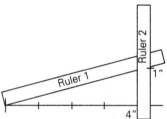

   Ask how high ruler 1 is at the 4″ mark on the paper. (**1″**) Explain that the slope is the distance ruler 1 rises compared to the distance away from the vertex. Ask how high the ruler rises. (**1″**) Ask how far it is from the vertex. (**4″**) Explain that the slope is $\frac{1}{4}$. That is, the line rises one unit for every 4 units $\left(\frac{+1}{+4}\right)$. Some math texts call this the "run."

5. Now have the students raise the ruler 2″ at the 4″ mark. Be sure the students understand that the slope of this hill (line) is $\frac{\text{rise}}{\text{run}}$. The slope is $\frac{+2}{+4}$, or $\frac{1}{2}$. It goes upward 1 unit vertically for every 2 units horizontally.

   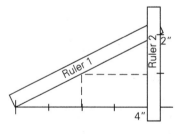

6. Make graphs of these lines on the overhead projector using Quadrant I.

   a. From the origin (0, 0), go over 4 units (4, 0) and then move up 1 unit (4, 1). Draw the line. The slope is $\frac{\text{rise}}{\text{run}} = \frac{+1}{+4} = \frac{(4, 0) \text{ to } (4, 1)}{(0, 0) \text{ to } (4, 0)}$.

b. For the second line, start at the origin $(0, 0)$, go over 4 units $(4, 0)$, and then move up 2 units $(4, 2)$. The slope is $\frac{+2}{+4} = \frac{(4, 0) \text{ to } (4, 2)}{(0, 0) \text{ to } (4, 0)}$ or $\frac{+1}{+2}$ when simplified.

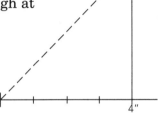

7. Ask the students to make a line that is 3″ high at the 4″ mark. The slope is $\frac{+3}{+4} = \frac{(4, 0) \text{ to } (4, 3)}{(0, 0) \text{ to } (4, 0)}$.

Then have the students make a line that is 4″ high at the 4″ mark. The ratio is $\frac{+4}{+4}$ $\left(\frac{\text{rise}}{\text{run}}\right)$, or the slope is 1 $\left(\frac{+1}{+1}\right)$.

8. On the overhead, graph a line that goes through $(0, 0)$ and $(4, 4)$. Show the students that for every unit the line goes up, it goes over 1 unit (slope of $\frac{1}{1}$, or 1). Compute the slope $\frac{(4, 0) \text{ to } (4, 4)}{(0, 0) \text{ to } (4, 0)} = \frac{+4}{+4} = +1$.

9. Ask, "How would we get a slope of +2?" Have the students use their rulers as in steps 4 and 5, raising ruler 1 to 8″ high at the 4″ mark. Then graph the line through $(0, 0)$, $(4, 8)$ on the overhead. Show that for every 2 units the line moves up, it moves horizontally 1 unit. The rise is 2 units, and the run is 1 unit. Show the students that the slope can be computed with any two points on the line. To illustrate this, select the points $(1, 2)$ and $(2, 4)$ on the graph.

Example:

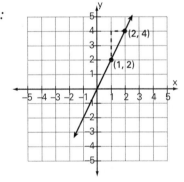

Show the students the $\frac{\text{rise}}{\text{run}}$ from the point $(1, 2)$ to the point $(2, 4)$ by going up (vertical) +2 units (rise) and go over (horizontal) +1 unit. Thus, $\frac{\text{rise}}{\text{run}} = \frac{+2}{+1}$. The slope is $\frac{+2}{+1}$ or +2.

10. Have the students draw a slope of 3. They may draw a line through $(0, 0)$ and $(4, 12)$, for example.

Ask, "What do you think the slope would be for a vertical line?" Possible answers: "Straight down." "No slope." "You would fall." Explain that the slope is undefined $\left(\text{e.g., } \frac{\text{rise}}{\text{run}} = \frac{+4}{0}\right)$.

Discuss the slope of a horizontal line at 4″. Help the students see that if the line is flat, there is no rise $\left(\frac{\text{rise}}{\text{run}} = \frac{0}{+4}\right)$, and the slope is 0.

11. On the overhead graph paper, draw some lines that go through the origin and discuss the slope of each line.

Discover the Slope

Directions:

1. Give a copy of the blackline master **Graphs and Related Numbers** to each student.

2. Explain that each graph has a number associated with it (in parentheses). Ask the students to study the blackline master and write down questions that can be answered "yes" or "no" that they want to ask to figure out the relationship between the number in parentheses and the graph.

3. Divide the students into groups of four or five and have the members of each group compare their questions. From the questions of the group members, have each group select up to three questions that the group will ask you.

4. Go from group to group answering each group's first question. Each group should then decide which question they want to ask next. Continue going to the groups until each group has asked all of its questions.

5. Give the groups of students 10 minutes to discuss their ideas and try to find the relationship between the number and the graph. They may also formulate additional questions.

6. Continue answering questions that can be answered "yes" or "no." Then ask each group to determine the relationship, agree on the wording, and write it down.

7. After all or most groups believe they have discovered the relationship, take each group's conjectures and discuss them one at a time. There can be several correct observations relating the numbers to the graphs because there are several ways to find the slope.

8. Form at least one generalization of finding the slope, e.g., $\frac{\text{rise}}{\text{run}}$ or $\frac{\text{vertical change}}{\text{horizontal change}}$.

Materials:

▶ Blackline master **Graphs and Related Numbers** is located in the *Teacher's Resource Manual,* **page 64.**

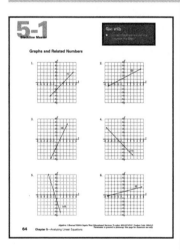

Graph Paper Slope

Directions:

1. Review the plotting of points by using the overhead projector. Mark the x- and y-axes and ask the students to name some points. Plot the points they name, for example, (3, 2), (–2, 2), (3, –4), (–5, –2).

2. On the overhead projector, draw the graph of y = x. Do not tell the students the equation. Have the students discuss observations about the graph. For example, say:

   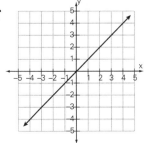

   a. "Name some points on this graph."
      (2, 2), (–3, –3), (4, 4)...

   b. "What do you notice about this graph?"

   Students should see that it bisects the x- and y-axes at a 45° angle, or that the graph goes up 1 unit for each 1 unit it goes over. $\frac{\text{rise}}{\text{run}} = \frac{1}{1}$ or $\frac{4}{4}$, etc.

3. Give a copy of the blackline master **Graphs** to each student. Graph 1 is the graph on the overhead. Have the students locate the point (1, 1). Have the students go up 1 unit to (1, 2). Ask, "How far over is the line?" **(1 unit)** Be sure the students see that this graph has a slope of 1. $\frac{\text{rise}}{\text{run}} = \frac{+1}{+1} = +1$.

4. Have the students look at graph 2. Ask, "Do you think the slope is greater or less than for graph 1?" Ask the students to name a point on the graph, such as (–2, –1). Ask, "How do I get to another point where the graph intersects a vertex?" Have the students draw the vertical line first to see how far the graph *rises*. Draw the line from (–2, –1) to (–2, 1). Then have the students draw the horizontal line from (–2, 1) to (2, 1). Have them count the units to find the slope. The "rise" is up, which is "+" 2. The "run" is to the right, which is "+" 4. $\frac{+2}{+4} = +\frac{1}{2}$.

5. Direct the students' attention to graph 3. Ask, "Do you think the slope is greater or less than for graph 1?" Ask, "What do you think the slope of graph 3 is?" See if the students can understand that the change in y is up

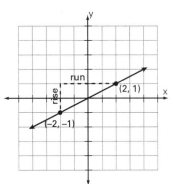

Materials:

► Blackline master **Graphs** is located in the *Teacher's Resource Manual,* **page 65.**

► Blackline master for **graph paper** is in the Appendix.

► Overhead graph paper transparencies

► Rulers

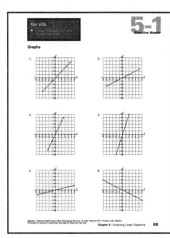

Teacher's Tip:

Worksheet 1 for this
objective, **page 5-2**,
supports this activity
with practice exercises.

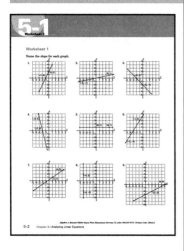

2 and the change in x is to the right, 1. The slope is $\frac{\text{rise}}{\text{run}} = \frac{+2}{+1}$ or
+2. Have the students draw the rise and run lines.

6. Next, have the students look at graph 4 and find the slope. Have
   the students draw the rise and run lines between two points on
   the graph. $\frac{\text{rise}}{\text{run}} = \frac{+3}{+1} = +3$

7. Then have the students find the slope of graph 5. $\frac{\text{rise}}{\text{run}}$ is +1 to +4,
   or $+\frac{1}{4}$.

8. Ask the students if they notice anything different about graph 6.
   (It slants in the opposite direction.) Graphs 1–5 slant from left to
   right going upward. Graph 6 slants from left to right going
   downward. Ask the students what they think the slope of graph 6
   is. Explain that in graphs 1–5, they went up, which is a positive
   direction on the y-axis, and to the right, which is a positive
   direction on the x-axis. For example, in graph 3, the change in y
   was +2 and the change in x was +1, so the slope was $\frac{+2}{+1} = +2$.

   Pointing to graph 6, ask, "If we go up the y-axis 1 unit (+1) from
   any point on the graph, how do we get to another point on the
   graph?" Help the students see that they would go to the left
   (negative on the x-axis) 2 units. So, $\frac{\text{change in y}}{\text{change in x}}$ or $\frac{\text{rise}}{\text{run}}$ is $\frac{1}{-2}$ or $-\frac{1}{2}$.
   Graphs 2 and 6 slope the same but in different directions. Graph
   2 slopes in the positive direction and graph 6 slopes in the
   negative direction. For graph 6, $\frac{\text{rise}}{\text{run}} = \frac{+1}{-2} = -\frac{1}{2}$.

Materials:

► Blackline master for
  graph paper is in
  the Appendix.

► Overhead graph
  paper transparencies

Two-Point Slope

Directions:

1. On the board or the overhead, sketch some number lines. Locate
   two points on one of the lines and ask, "How far is it from ____ to
   ____?"

   Example: 8 − 2 = 6

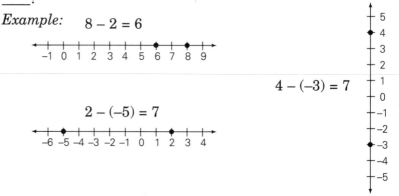

   4 − (−3) = 7

   2 − (−5) = 7

2. After several examples, ask the students to give a rule (conjecture) on how to find the distance between any two points on a number line. For example, subtract the numbers.

3. Sketch the graph of the line containing the points (1, 2) and (5, 5) on the overhead. Label the points (1, 2) and (5, 5) on the graph.

4. Review the definition of slope as the change in y compared to the change in x, or $\frac{\text{rise}}{\text{run}}$.

5. Ask the students how you can find the slope of a line containing the points (1, 2) and (5, 5).

6. Most students will want to count (change in y = 3 and change in x = 4). Show them that they can also find the change in y and the change in x by subtracting, because the x- and y-axes are number lines.

   Rise is from 2 to 5; (5 − 2) = 3.

   Run is from 1 to 5; (5 − 1) = 4.

   Slope is $\frac{\text{change in y}}{\text{change in x}} = \frac{\text{rise}}{\text{run}}$.

   Thus, we can find the slope without graphing if we know two points: $\frac{\text{change in y}}{\text{change in x}} = \frac{5-2}{5-1} = \frac{3}{4}$ or $\frac{(y_2 - y_1)}{(x_2 - x_1)}$ for points (x_1, y_1) and (x_2, y_2).

7. Go over another example. Give the students the points (2, 3) and (4, 7). Ask what they think the slope will be. Show that the rule is true no matter which points are selected for (x_1, y_1) and (x_2, y_2). If $(x_2, y_2) = (4, 7)$ and (x_1, y_1) is (2, 3), the slope (designated by "m") $= \frac{(y_2 - y_1)}{(x_2 - x_1)} = \frac{(7-3)}{(4-2)} = \frac{+4}{+2} = +2$. The slope is +2. It would be +2 regardless of which points are selected.

8. Now, graph a line containing the points (2, 3) and (4, 7) on the overhead and repeat the steps in #6 above. Show the students that they are just finding the distance on the number line for each component (x, y).

9. Repeat the process using two other points on the line. For example, (−1, 2), (7, 6) or (−3, −4), (1, 0). Have the students find the slope and then draw the graph. Show that the slope is the same regardless of which points are selected for (x_1, y_1) and (x_2, y_2).

Teacher's Tip:

Worksheet 2 for this objective, **page 5-3**, supports this activity with practice exercises.

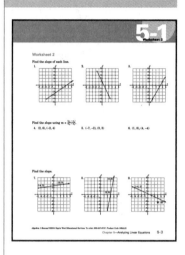

Materials:

▶ Blackline master for **graph paper** is in the Appendix.

▶ Four dice of two different colors (example: red and white) for each pair of students

▶ Paper bag

Practice Activities

Pick the Slope

Directions:

1. Pair the students up and give each pair four dice—two of one color (representing negative numbers) and two of another color (representing positive numbers)—in a paper bag. For this example, red dice are negative and white dice are positive.

2. Have one student in each pair reach into the bag and select two dice.

3. The student should roll the dice. If, for example, the student selected two red dice and rolled a 1 and 4, the student should write down the point (−1, −4).

4. The student should put the dice back in the bag and let the other student draw and roll two dice. If, for example, the student selected one white die and one red die (one positive and one negative) and rolled a 4 with the white die and a 2 with the red die, the student would write (4, −2).

5. One student should sketch a graph on graph paper of a line containing the two points and find the slope.

6. The other student should find the slope by using the formula. The students should then compare answers and check their work.

7. *Note:* Many of the answers will involve fractional slopes. Discuss that fractional slope is a good description of $\frac{\text{rise}}{\text{run}}$.

8. Have the students reverse roles for finding the slope and continue the practice.

Find the Slope

Directions:

1. Have each student sketch a coordinate plane on graph paper and label the x- and y-axes from −10 to 10.

2. Instruct each student to select any two points on the coordinate plane and label them. The students should then use their rulers

Materials:

▶ Blackline master for **graph paper** is in the Appendix.

▶ Rulers

Chapter 5—Analyzing Linear Equations

to draw the line that connects the points. For an example, see the graph at the right.

3. In groups of four, have the students work together to find the slope of each graph the four students drew. Have them estimate the slope from the graph and then compute the slope by using the formula $m = \frac{(y_2 - y_1)}{(x_2 - x_1)}$. Instruct the students to not write their computations on the graphs.

4. Have each group exchange the four graphs with another group and find the slopes. Groups should continue exchanging the graphs until time expires or all groups have found the slopes for all of the graphs.

Problem-Solving Activity

Newspaper or Magazine Slope 💡

Directions:

1. Have each student find a linear graph in a newspaper or magazine.

2. Have the students name two points that are on the graph and write an explanation of what the points mean. An example might be sales over particular years.

3. The students should then find the slope of the line represented in the graph. After they have done so, ask them to write an explanation of what they think the slope has to do with the data on the graph. For example, a slope of $\frac{1}{4}$ for a line depicting sales over particular years would mean that sales were increasing by $\frac{1}{4}$ each year.

Teacher's Tip:

Worksheet 3 for this objective, **page 5-4**, supports this activity with practice exercises.

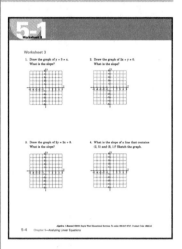

Materials:

▶ Newspapers and/or magazines that have linear graphs

Teacher's Tip:

Because this is a multiple step process, having students show their work will be important for diagnosis as well as for awarding partial credit.

Materials:

► Overhead graph paper transparencies

5-2 *Objective:* Write the equation of a line in standard form given two points on the graph of the line.

Sample Test: Write the equation of this line and then simplify the equation to the standard form. Show your work.

Solution: $x - 3y = -5$

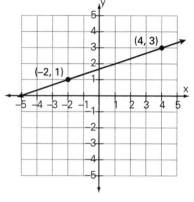

Concept Development Activities

Why Find the Equation?

Directions:

1. Tell the students this story about Andy.

    Story: When Andy was 10 years old, his parents started giving him an allowance. He decided that he was going to save $2 a week from his allowance so he could buy items that cost more than he received in his allowance. Andy had $4 when he started. At the end of **one week,** he had $2 more for a total of **$6. (1, 6) (one week—$6 saved)** At the end of four weeks, he had saved $12 **(4, 12)**, etc.

2. Sketch the graph on the overhead without naming a lot of points. [Use (1, 6) and (4, 12).] Keep the scales 1:1 on the x- and y-axes.

3. Explain that if you were to know the equation for this line, you could calculate how much Andy would have saved after 20 weeks or 52 weeks.

4. Explain that information collected in science, business, or medicine can often be graphed as a line. Finding the equation of the line is an important step in making predictions.

5. Ask, "Is there anything we know about the graph of this line?" Some possible answers: It starts at 4. It has a positive slope. We can find the slope. It keeps getting larger.

6. Review how to find the slope.

   a. From the graph: If the scales have been kept at 1:1, the students can see that the graph rises 2 for each week. (The slope is 2.)

   b. Using the two points: $m = \frac{(y_2 - y_1)}{(x_2 - x_1)}$; $m = \frac{(12 - 6)}{(4 - 1)} = \frac{6}{3} = 2$.

7. Explain that you can find the equation of this line by using the slope equation. To show the students that it does not make any difference which point is chosen when finding the equation, go through the procedure twice, using one point the first time and the other point the next time.

   Example:
   $$m = \frac{(y_2 - y_1)}{(x_2 - x_1)}$$
   $$2 = \frac{(y - 6)}{(x - 1)}$$
   $$2(x - 1) = \frac{(y - 6)}{(x - 1)} (x - 1), \text{ or}$$
   $$y - 6 = 2(x - 1)$$

   y-coordinate   m or slope   x-coordinate

   Explain that this is called the *point-slope form* of the equation $(y = mx + b)$. Next, simplify the equation.

   $y - 6 = 2x - 2 \rightarrow y - 2x - 6 = -2 \rightarrow$ **$y - 2x = 4$** $\rightarrow -2x + y = 4$.

   Explain that this simplified equation is called the *standard form* of the equation $(ax + by = c)$.

8. Now use the other point:

   $y - 12 = 2(x - 4) \rightarrow y - 12 = 2x - 8 \rightarrow y - 2x - 12 = -8 \rightarrow$
   $y - 2x = 4 \rightarrow -2x + y = 4$, the standard form.

   The equations are equivalent, regardless of the point chosen.

9. Now work through an example of a line containing the points (3, 5) and (4, 6).

Answer Key for #9:
$m = \frac{(6 - 5)}{(4 - 3)} = \frac{1}{1} = 1$

Concept Development

Materials:

► Blackline master **What Is the Equation?** is located in the *Teacher's Resource Manual,* **page 66.**

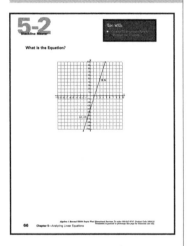

Teacher's Tip:

Worksheet 1 for this objective, **pages 5-7 and 5-8,** supports this activity with practice exercises.

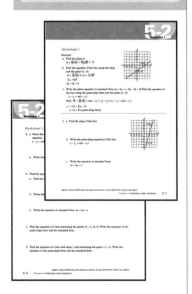

Discover the Equation

Directions:

1. Give each student a copy of the blackline master **What Is the Equation?**

2. Discuss with the students why it is important to find the equations of graphs. (See steps 1–4 of the Concept Development Activity **Why Find the Equation?**) Explain that you want to find the equation of the line on the blackline master. **(Answer, in standard form, is 3x – y = 4.)**

3. Have each student write three questions about the graph that may help in finding the equation.

4. Divide the students into groups of four or five. Have them review the questions and discuss which questions they want to ask you first. Circulate among the groups and answer three questions from each group. Give the groups some time to work on finding the equation. If a group finds the equation, ask them if they can find the equation another way.

5. After the groups have worked for a while, circulate and answer more questions from the groups.

6. Note that there are several ways that the equations can be found, including the following.

   a. Make a table of values and then use "guess and check" to determine the equation.

   Example: $y = 3x - 4$

x	y
3	5
0	-4
-1	-7

   b. Guess at rules until the equation is found. For example:

   $x + 2 = y$ **(No)** $x - 6 = y$ **(No)** $y = x - 4$ **(No)**

   $y = 2x - 1$ **(No)** $y = 3x - 4$ **(Yes)**

7. If a group finds an algebra method, have them present it to the class.

8. If no group finds an algebra method, present the point-slope method of finding the equations. Students should find the method interesting and simple if they have worked on finding the equation with no success.

To find the equation with the point-slope method, explain that you first find the slope: $m = \frac{(y_2 - y_1)}{(x_2 - x_1)} = \frac{[5 - (-7)]}{[3 - (-1)]} = \frac{12}{4} = 3.$

Now comes the point that most students won't think of: You substitute a point back into the slope equation. This is the point-slope method: $m = \frac{(y_2 - y_1)}{(x_2 - x_1)}$

$$3 = \frac{(y - 5)}{(x - 3)}$$
$$3(x - 3) = \frac{(y - 5)}{(x - 3)}(x - 3)$$
$$3(x - 3) = y - 5$$

or $y - 5 = 3(x - 3)$. This is the *point-slope form.*

Now write the equation in *standard form,* $ax + by = c.$
$$y - 5 = 3x - 9$$
$$-5 = 3x - 9 - y$$
$$4 = 3x - y, \text{ or } 3x - y = 4, \text{ or } -3x + y = -4$$

9. Work several other problems on the overhead to find the equations. Start by plotting the points $(0, -3)$ and $(1, 6)$ on an overhead graph. Sketch the line and show the students how to find the equation.

   a. $m = \frac{(y_2 - y_1)}{(x_2 - x_1)} = \frac{[6 - (-3)]}{(1 - 0)} = \frac{9}{1} = 9$

   b. Substitute a point back into the slope equation:

   $m = \frac{(y_2 - y_1)}{(x_2 - x_1)} \rightarrow 9 = \frac{[y_2 - (-3)]}{(x_2 - 0)}$ (the subscripts can be dropped)

   $9 = \frac{y + 3}{x} \rightarrow 9x = y + 3 \rightarrow 9x - y = 3, \text{ or } -9x + y = -3$

10. Answer any questions. Then let the students find equations in standard form for the following points:

   Examples: $(2, -1), (6, 7)$
                  $(4, 2), (-2, 5)$

Answer Key for #10:
2x – y = 5
x + 2y = 8

Practice

Materials:

► Transparency on which you have copied the equations in step 3

Practice Activities

Find Another Equation

Directions:

1. On the board, write:

    $2x + y = 6$ and $-2x + y = 8$

2. Show the equations from step 3 on the overhead projector. Instruct the students to simplify each equation and put it in standard form. Tell them that the answer will be either (A) $2x + y = 6$ or (B) $-2x + y = 8$.

    Thus, the students are given the answer—either equation A or B. They are to use algebra skills to find the standard equation.

    The purpose of this activity is to help students work from the point-slope form to the standard form.

Answer Key for #3:

a. A	b. A	c. B
d. B	e. A	f. A
g. A	h. B	i. B
j. B		

3. a. $y + 2 = -2(x - 4)$ b. $y - 6 = -2x$
    c. $y - 12 = 2(x - 2)$ d. $y - 4 = 2(x + 2)$
    e. $y - 8 = -2(x + 1)$ f. $y + 4 = -2(x - 5)$
    g. $2x = 6 - y$ h. $2y - 12 = 4x + 4$
    i. $y - 0 = 2(x + 4)$ j. $2x + 8 = y$

Match Them

Directions:

1. Give a copy of the blackline master **Match Them** to each student.

2. The students are to draw a line on the blacklline master from the "Points or Point and Slope" column to the correct slope to the correct point-slope equation and finally to the correct standard equation.

3. The advantage of this practice activity is that the answers are given. The students need to apply the formulas and use algebra to find the correct equations. This activity should also help reinforce the names of the equations (point-slope and standard).

4. **Variation:** Cut out the first and second columns and have the students match the points to the slopes. Cut out the third and fourth columns and have the students match the point-slope equations to the equivalent standard equations.

Materials:

▶ Blackline master **Match Them** is located in the *Teacher's Resource Manual*, **page 67.**

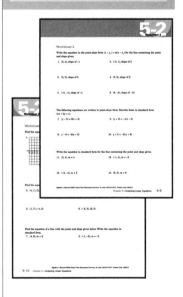

Teacher's Tip:

Worksheets 2 and 3 for this objective, **pages 5-9 and 5-10**, support this activity with practice exercises.

Materials:

► Blackline master **Airplane Miles** is located in the *Teacher's Resource Manual,* **page 68.**

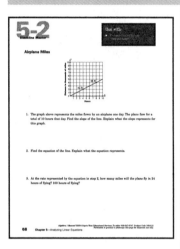

Problem-Solving Activities

Airplane Miles

Directions:

1. Give each student a copy of the blackline master **Airplane Miles**. Have the students work individually to solve the problems.

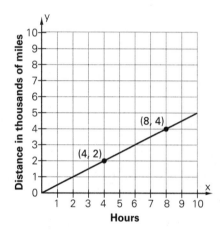

2. Explain that the graph on the blackline master represents the miles flown by an airplane in one day. The plane flew for a total of 10 hours that day. Have the students find the slope of the line and explain what the slope represents for this graph.

3. Have the students find the equation of the line and explain what the equation represents.

4. Ask, "At the rate represented by the equation in step 2, how many miles will the plane fly in 24 hours of flying? 100 hours of flying?"

Average Girls' Height

Directions:

1. Give each student a copy of the blackline master **Average Girls' Height**. Have the students work individually to solve the problems.

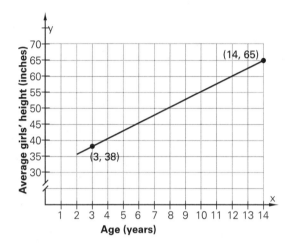

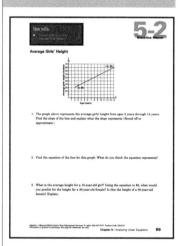

2. Explain that the graph on the blackline master represents the average girls' height from ages 2 years through 14 years. Have the students find the slope of the line and explain what the slope represents. (When finding the slope, they should round off or approximate.)

3. Next, have the students find the equation of the line for this graph. Ask, "What do you think the equation represents?"

4. Ask what the average height for a 10-year-old girl is. Have the students use the equation they generated in #3 to predict for the height for a 30-year-old female. Ask, "Is this the height of a 30-year-old female?" Have students explain their responses.

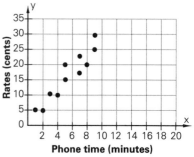

5-3 *Objective:* **Draw a best-fit line and find the equation of the best-fit line for a scatter plot.**

Sample Test: Draw a best-fit line for the data and determine the equation of the line.

Solution: Answers will vary, but closest equation is $3x - y = 0$

Concept Development Activities

Predictions

Directions:

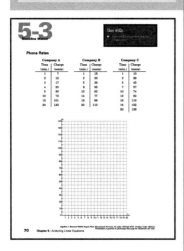

1. Give one copy of the blackline master **Phone Rates** to each student.

2. Discuss that this information represents the cost of making long-distance calls from different long-distance phone companies. Have different students explain each table.

3. Explain that from the information they will be able to "predict" the cost of a call for any length of time. The prediction will not be exact. However, it will be close and give a good estimate on costs. The prediction should represent an average cost.

4. Have the class make a picture of the data by plotting the information on the graph provided.

5. Ask the class how they can get an *average* cost and make predictions. Allow time for a discussion of various ideas. Try to get the students to concentrate on the tables and the graph. Some ideas that need to be discussed include the following:

   a. You can find the average charges for different "times." For example, the charges for 1 minute are 7¢, 15¢, and 10¢; the average is 10.7¢. Which point on the graph is closest to the average? **(10¢, the middle one)** The average for 10 minutes is 69.7¢, which is again in the middle—close to 72¢, but in the middle. The average for 20 minutes is 126.3¢.

Materials:

▶ Blackline master **Phone Rates** is located in the *Teacher's Resource Manual,* **page 70.**

▶ Ruler

b. The graph to represent the average or best fit would go through the middle of the set of points.

c. Ask if the line using (1, 15) and (20, 136) would be a good average or "fit." **(No, it is above the data, not in the middle.)** Ask if a line using (1, 7) and (14, 77) would be a good "fit." **(No, it is too low and not in the middle.)**

Teacher's Tip:

Worksheet 1 for this objective, **page 5-13**, supports this activity with practice exercises.

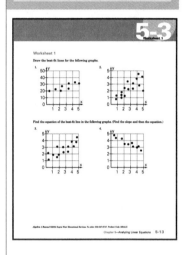

6. Ask the students to use a ruler and draw the "best-fit" line.

7. Circulate in the class to see if the students are drawing the line in the middle.

8. Have the students read the cost for 7 minutes from their graphed line. It should be around 47¢. A 7-minute call on the average would cost about 47¢.

9. Ask the class, "How can we make predictions for a 30-minute call or a 60-minute call? We need a rule or formula." The formula is the equation of the line!

10. Have the students select two points on their graph that are close to the vertices on the best-fit line. For example, (1, 11) and (5, 35). Have them find the equation. $m = \frac{35 - 11}{5 - 1} = \frac{24}{4} \approx 6$. Then, using the point-slope form: $y - 11 = 6(x - 1)$
$$y - 11 = 6x - 6$$
$$-5 = 6x - y$$
or $6x - y = -5$.

11. Collect several equations from the class. The slope should be around 6.

12. Check some rates with the class.

7-minute call (step 8)	$6(7) - y = -5$	$-y = -47$	$y \approx 47¢$
30-minute call	$6(30) - y = -5$	$-y = -185$	$y \approx 185¢$
60-minute call	$6(60) - y = -5$	$-y = -365$	$y \approx 365¢$

13. Discuss the advantages of using a best-fit line.

Include: a. gives an average of data

b. allows predictions for equations

c. not exact for any one set of data

d. simplifies the process and saves a lot of computations

e. summarizes the data into an equation if there is a correlation between the points

Concept Development

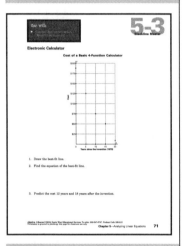

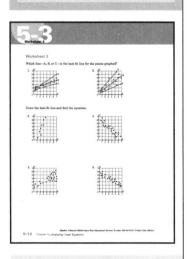

Answer Key for #4: $75.60, $23.40

Best-Fit Line Equation

Directions:

1. Give a copy of the blackline master **Electronic Calculator** to each student.

2. Have the students draw the best-fit line by following these steps:

   a. Ask, "Can you connect all the points with one line?"

   b. Instruct the students to draw a line so that some points are above the line and some points are below it—the average would be more in the middle of the points. Have them make a light dashed line first.

   c. Have the students check the dashed line to see if it comes close to the middle points. They should redraw if necessary and then complete the line.

3. Instruct the students to find the equation of the best-fit line by following these steps:

   a. Locate two points on the best-fit line for which they can name the coordinates, for example (0, 180) and (15, 50). Name the points.

   b. Find the slope of the line by using $m = \frac{(y_2 - y_1)}{(x_2 - x_1)}$.
   Example: $\frac{180 - 50}{0 - 15} = \frac{130}{-15} = -8.7$

   c. Write the equation by using the point-slope equation: $y - y_1 = m(x - x_1)$. *Example:* $y - 50 = -8.7(x - 15)$

   d. Simplify to the standard form: $8.7x + y = 180.5$, or $8.7x + y = 180$, depending on the point used since the slope is rounded off.

4. Ask, "About what would be the cost 12 years after the invention? 18 years after?"

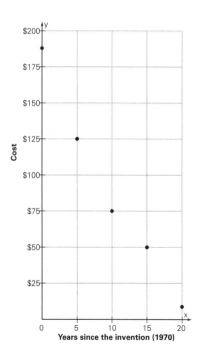

Practice Activity

Match the Graph

Directions:

1. Make enough copies of the blackline master **Graphs and Equations** for the class. Then use a paper cutter (a few sheets at a time) to cut out the squares, or give one copy of the blackline master to each student to cut out using scissors.

2. The students are to make four sets of cards, each consisting of one card for each category: points, best-fit line, slope, and equation. They will need to work individually to determine the slopes and the equations from the points and lines.

3. **Variation:** Give the students only the points cards. Have them draw the best-fit line, compute the slope, and find the equation. Then give them the other cards to see how closely their answers match up.

4. **Variation:** Give each student a best-fit line card. Have the students find the points card that goes with the line. Then have the students compute the slope and find the equation by using the best-fit line card.

Materials:

▶ Blackline master **Graphs and Equations** is located in the *Teacher's Resource Manual,* **page 72.**

▶ Paper cutter or scisors

▶ Rulers

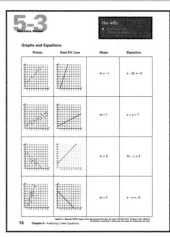

Teacher's Tip:

Worksheet 3 for this objective, **page 5-15,** supports this activity with practice exercises.

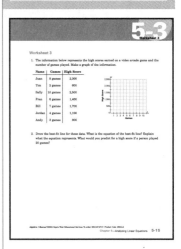

Materials:

▶ Blackline master for **graph paper** is in the Appendix.

▶ Dice

Dice Experiment 1: Separate Rolls

Directions:

1. Divide the students into groups of five.

2. Explain that each student is going to roll one die 10 times and plot each roll on a graph.

3. Have the first student roll the die. Suppose the student gets a 4. The student would plot the point (1, 4) on the graph. The student would then roll a second time. Suppose he or she gets a 5. The point (2, 5) would be plotted. The same process is followed through 10 rolls for each person in the group. All of the group's points are plotted on the same graph.

   Example:

   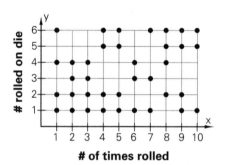

4. Have each group show their graph. Ask, "Is there a correlation so we could draw a best-fit line?" Only in rare cases will there be. These are *random* chances for 1–6 and there should be *no* correlation.

5. Discuss that not all data have a correlation, and in some experiences there is no correlation between events. When scientists collect data and there is no correlation, they can eliminate this outcome from their ideas and try something else.

Boys' Heights

Directions:

1. Discuss with the class that a doctor's office has a chart on average growth, weight, and height of boys and girls. Ask, "How do you think this chart was developed?"

   From the discussion, present the idea that a large set of data was collected by ages to find an average. Indicate that this would be a good class project. Explain that the class will now work on creating a chart to get average boys' heights at various ages.

2. Discuss how the class can collect the data and for what age levels. Get as large a sample of population and various ages as the class can collect. If, for example, a student could visit an elementary class, he or she would need a tape measure to measure the boys' heights and would need to get their ages. Have the class make a table of ages and heights.

3. After the table is made (ages to heights), have each student graph the points for each boy (age to height).

4. Divide students into groups of four or five. Have the students compare their graphs of the data. Ask the students which graph(s) they feel represent the data best (scattered diagram).

5. Have each group make a best-fit line and find the equation of the line.

6. Get reports from each group and compare the equations.

7. Try some of the average age points for the data to see how they compare to the average from the equations.

8. Have the groups make predictions for some boys' heights not covered on the chart.

9. Discuss the limits (no more growth) of the equation for average height of boys.

5-4 *Objective:* Write linear equations in the slope-intercept form to find the slope, x-intercept, and y-intercept, and sketch the graph.

Materials:

▶ Blackline master for **graph paper** is in the Appendix.

Teacher's Tip:

Worksheets 1 and 2 for this objective, **pages 5-18 and 5-19**, support this activity with practice exercises.

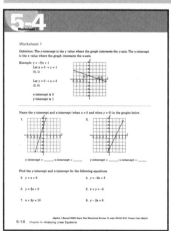

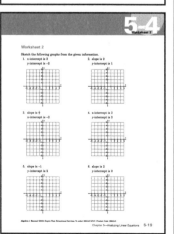

Sample Test:

Write the equation $2x - y = 7$ in slope-intercept form. What is the slope of the line? What is the y-intercept of the line? Sketch the graph.

Solution: $y = 2x - 7$; slope is 2; y-intercept is −7

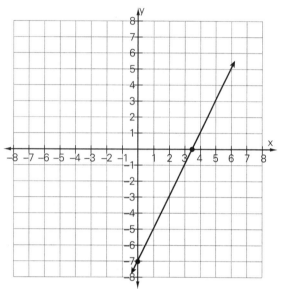

Concept Development Activities

x-Intercept and y-Intercept

Directions:

1. Ask the class, "What are the fewest points I need to draw the graph of a linear equation (a line)?" **(two points)** Ask, "How can I find two points very easily? For example, in the equation $y = 3x + 6$, how can I get two points quickly?"

2. Some discussion may be necessary and different answers will be presented. Most students will agree that if you let $x = 0$ $(y = 3 \cdot 0 + 6)$, the y value is 6 and easy to get. **(0, 6)**

3. Demonstrate this concept with a few more examples. For $y = 2x - 4$, when $x = 0$, $y = -4$, so the point is $(0, -4)$. Graph the point $(0, -4)$ on the overhead. This is the point where the graph intersects the y-axis. Explain that the point is called the *y-intercept.* Explain that you can find the *x-intercept,* or the point where the line crosses the x-axis, by letting $y = 0$. For $y = 2x - 4$, if $y = 0$, $0 = 2x - 4 \rightarrow 4 = 2x \rightarrow 2 = x$, or $x = 2$. **(2, 0)** Graph the point $(2, 0)$.

4. Draw a graph, for example, $y = x + 5$, on the overhead. Ask, "Where does the graph intersect the x-axis?" **(x = –5)** Be sure the students see that the x-intercept is –5.

5. Discuss that to find the x-intercept, we let $y = 0$. Show this on the graph. If $y = 0$, the point will be on the x-axis. To find the y-intercept, we let $x = 0$. Show this on the graph. If $x = 0$, the point will fall on the y-axis. Try a sample equation, $y = x + 3$. If $x = 0$, y will be 3. Plot (0, 3). This is the point of intersection for the y-axis. The y-intercept is 3. Find the x-intercept by letting $y = 0$. $0 = x + 3 \rightarrow x = -3$, so (–3, 0) is the intersection point on the x-axis. The x-intercept is –3.

Discover Slope-Intercept Form

Directions:

1. Divide the students into groups of five.

2. Write the following equations on the board or overhead:

   $y = x \qquad y = \frac{1}{2}x \qquad y = -x \qquad y = 2x \qquad y = -2x$

3. For each group, have each group member graph a different one of these equations so that all five equations will be graphed.

4. Have the students write the equation they graphed on their graph.

5. Ask each group to answer the following questions:

   a. What is the same about the equations?

   b. What is different about the equations?

   c. How do the graphs compare?

   d. How does the slope compare to the equation?

6. Ask the students to predict the slope of each of the following equations:

   $y = 5x \qquad -2x = y \qquad y = \frac{1}{3}x$

7. Have the students see if they can find the slope of the following equations using algebra (i.e., solving for y):

   $x = y \qquad 3y = 12x \qquad x - y = 0 \qquad 2y = x$

Materials:

▶ Blackline master for **graph paper** is in the Appendix.

Answer Key for #5:
a. $y = mx$
b. the coefficient of x (m)
c. different steepnesses (slopes); all go through origin
d. $y = x$, slope 1; $y = \frac{1}{2}x$, slope $\frac{1}{2}$; the slope is m, or the coefficient of x when written $y = mx$

Answer Key for #6:
$5, -2, \frac{1}{3}$

Answer Key for #7:
$1, 4, 1, \frac{1}{2}$

Materials:

▶ Graphing calculators (minimum of 5)

Answer Key:
2. All are in the form of $y = mx$; the only difference is the m for each equation.
3. Slope is steeper for the larger m. Some slopes are negative and others are positive; all graphs go through the origin.

Graphing Calculator Slope

Directions:

1. Divide the students into groups of five. In each group, have each group member graph one of the following equations on their graphing calculators:

$y = \frac{1}{2}x$ $y = x$ $y = 2x$ $y = -x$ $y = -2x$

2. Write the equations on paper or on the board. Ask, "What is the same about these equations?"

3. Now have the students compare the graphs on the calculators for each equation. Ask, "What is different and the same about each graph?"

4. Ask the students to predict the graph of each of the following equations:

$y = 3x$ $y = -3x$ $y = .1x$ $y = 6x$ $y = -\frac{1}{2}x$

Then have the students make the graphs on their calculators.

Materials:

▶ Blackline master for **graph paper** is in the Appendix.

Discover the Constant 💡

Directions:

1. Write the following equations on the overhead or the board:

A	B	C	D	E
$y = x$	$y = -x$	$y = 2x$	$y = \frac{1}{2}x$	$y = -\frac{1}{2}x$
$y = x + 3$	$y = -x + 2$	$y = 2x + 2$	$y = \frac{1}{2}x + 3$	$y = -\frac{1}{2}x + 2$
$y = x - 2$	$y = -x - 3$	$y = 2x - 1$	$y = \frac{1}{2}x - 4$	$y = -\frac{1}{2}x - 2$
$y = x + 6$	$y = -x + 5$	$y = 2x - 6$	$y = \frac{1}{2}x - 1$	$y = -\frac{1}{2}x + 5$

2. With the students divided into groups of five, assign each student the task of graphing one of the columns of equations A through E, so that each group graphs all five columns. The students should graph all four equations in their column on the same set of coordinates and label each line with the equation.

Example:

$y = -x$

$y = -x + 2$

$y = -x - 3$

$y = -x + 5$

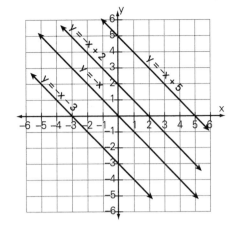

Teacher's Tip:

Worksheets 3 and 4
for this objective,
pages 5-20 and 5-21,
support this activity
with practice exercises.

3. Ask each group to discuss and answer the following questions.
    Students need to compare the graphs made by each group
    member.

    a. What is the same about the graphs within each column?

    b. What is different about the graphs within each column?

    c. Explain how you can graph the equation $y = 3x + 2$.

    d. Explain how you can graph the equation $y = mx + b$. This is
        called the *slope-intercept form*.

    e. Graph the equation $y = 2x - 3$ without making a table of
        values. Ask, "What is the slope? What is the y-intercept?"

    f. In the equation $y = -3x + 6$, what is the slope of the line?
        Where does the line intersect the y-axis?

    g. In the equation $y = mx + b$, what is the slope? Where does it
        intersect the y-axis?

Answer Key for #3:
a. The lines are parallel;
   they all have the same
   slope.
b. The numbers being
   added or subtracted
   (the constants); the x-
   and y-intercepts are
   different.
c. slope is 3, y-intercept
   is 2
d. slope is m, y-intercept
   is b
e. slope is 2, y-intercept
   is –3
f. The slope is –3; the y
   intercept is 6.
g. The slope is m and
   the y-intercept is b.

Concept Development

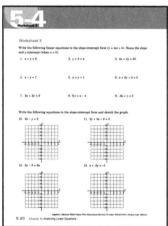

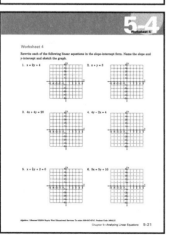

Graphing Calculator Constant

Directions:

1. Divide the students into groups of four. Each student should have a graphing calculator. Ask each student to graph one of the following equations on their calculators, so that each group graphs all of the equations.

   $$y = x \qquad y = x + 3 \qquad y = x - 2 \qquad y = x + 6$$

2. Have the group members compare their graphs and equations. **Optional:** Have the group members sketch the graphs on graph paper, labeling each line with its equation.

3. Ask each group to discuss and answer the following questions:

   a. What is the same about the graphs of the four equations?

   b. What is different about the graphs of the four equations?

4. If necessary for students to understand the relationship of the equation and slope-intercept, assign some more equations to graph, such as the following. Each group should select a column and graph the four equations.

$y = -x$	$y = 2x$	$y = \frac{1}{2}x$	$y = -\frac{1}{2}x$
$y = -x + 2$	$y = 2x + 2$	$y = \frac{1}{2}x + 3$	$y = -\frac{1}{2}x + 2$
$y = -x - 3$	$y = 2x - 1$	$y = \frac{1}{2}x - 4$	$y = -\frac{1}{2}x - 2$
$y = -x + 5$	$y = 2x - 6$	$y = \frac{1}{2}x - 1$	$y = -\frac{1}{2}x + 5$

   Repeat steps 1 through 3 above.

5. Ask the students to explain how to graph the equation $y = 3x + 2$. Have the students sketch the graph on graph paper before they graph it on the graphing calculator. Have the students compare the graphs and see if they are the same. Remind the students that the form $y = mx + b$ is called the *slope-intercept form.*

6. Have the students sketch the following graphs on graph paper:

   $$y = x - 3 \qquad y = 2x + 1 \qquad y = -2x - 2$$

   Discuss the slope and y-intercept of each graph. Be sure the students understand that these equations are written in the slope-intercept form ($y = mx + b$).

Slope-Intercept Form

Directions:

Materials:

► Blackline master for
graph paper is in
the Appendix.

► Overhead graph
paper transparencies

1. This activity is to be used after students have already explored
   the y = mx + b form of equations. These concepts are developed in
   the Concept Development Activities **Discover the Constant** and
   Graphing Calculator Constant.

2. Review how to graph an equation that is in the slope-intercept
   form. *Example:* y = 3x − 1. The y-intercept is −1 and the slope is
   3. Graph this equation on the overhead or board. To graph the
   equation, find the y-intercept (−1) at point (0, −1) and use the
   slope of +3: rise +3, run +1. Another method is to find the
   x-intercept $\left(\frac{1}{3}\right)$ and plot that point.

3. Have the students plot the graphs of y = x − 2 and y = −2x + 4
   using the y = mx + b form (slope is m and y-intercept is b).

4. Discuss how easy it is to graph equations if they are written in
   the slope-intercept form. Have students name the slope and
   y-intercept for the following equations (y = mx + b):

   a. y = 3x + 1   b. y = −2x + 6
   c. y = $\frac{1}{2}$x + 4   d. y = .3x + 4.3

   Answer Key for #4:
   a. m = 3, b = 1
   b. m = −2, b = 6
   c. m = $\frac{1}{2}$, b = 4
   d. m = .3, b = 4.3

5. Explain that not all linear equations are written in the
   slope-intercept form. Ask the students, "How can we take an
   equation such as x + y = 4 and write it in the slope-intercept
   form?"

   Answer Key for #5:
   m = −1, b = 4

$$x + y = 4$$
$$x + y − x = 4 − x$$
$$y = 4 − x,$$
$$\text{or } y = − x + 4$$

   Ask, "What is the slope? What is the y-intercept?"

   Answer Key for #6:
   a. y = 2x − 3; m = 2, b = −3
   b. y = x − 2; m = 1, b = −2
   c. y = −x + 4; m = −1,
      b = 4
   d. y = −$\frac{1}{2}$x + 3; m = −$\frac{1}{2}$,
      b = 3
   e. y = −2x + 6; m = −2,
      b = 6
   f. y = $\frac{1}{3}$x − 3; m = $\frac{1}{3}$, b = −3

6. Have the students use the addition and multiplication properties
   of equality to rewrite the following equations in the slope-intercept
   form. Then have them name the slope and the y-intercept for
   each equation.

   a. 2x − y = 3   b. y − x + 2 = 0   c. 2x + 2y = 8
   d. 2y + x = 6   e. 4x + 2y = 12   f. x − 3y = 9

7. Discuss the techniques used above to rewrite the equations in the slope-intercept form. After the equations have been rewritten into the slope-intercept form, have students graph the equations on the overhead or board. Remind them to find the y-intercept and then use the slope to find another point.

Practice Activities

Name the y-Intercept or Slope

Directions:

1. Give a copy of the blackline master **Equation Board** to every three or four students.

2. Have each group write the following equations on the front side of blank cards, one per card, and the slopes (m) and y-intercepts (b) for the equations on the back side of the cards.

Equation (front)	Slope (back)	y-Intercept (back)
$y = -2x + 7$	$m = -2$	$b = 7$
$x + y = 9$	$m = -1$	$b = 9$
$2x - y = 3$	$m = 2$	$b = -3$
$y = \frac{1}{2}x - 6$	$m = \frac{1}{2}$	$b = -6$
$6 + x = y$	$m = 1$	$b = 6$
$3 + 2y = x$	$m = \frac{1}{2}$	$b = -\frac{3}{2}$
$6x + 6y = 6$	$m = -1$	$b = 1$
$2x + y = 0$	$m = -2$	$b = 0$
$x + 3y = 6$	$m = -\frac{1}{3}$	$b = 2$
$y = .5x + 3.5$	$m = .5$, or $\frac{1}{2}$	$b = 3.5$
$.5x - y = 2$	$m = .5$, or $\frac{1}{2}$	$b = -2$
$x + .5y = 1$	$m = -2$	$b = 2$
$y + 4 = x + 2$	$m = 1$	$b = -2$
$3x + 2y = 4$	$m = -\frac{3}{2}$, or $-1\frac{1}{2}$	$b = 2$
$y + 7 = 19 - x$	$m = -1$	$b = 12$
$3y - 4 = 6x + 8$	$m = 2$	$b = 4$
$2y - x = y + 6$	$m = 1$	$b = 6$
$2y + x = 5 - x$	$m = -1$	$b = \frac{5}{2}$
$y + 3 = 2x + 4$	$m = 2$	$b = 1$
$x + y = -3$	$m = -1$	$b = -3$
$2x + y = 6$	$m = -2$	$b = 6$

Materials:

▶ Blackline master **Equation Board** is located in the *Teacher's Resource Manual*, **page 73.**

▶ Game markers to cover squares

▶ Blank wooden cubes, labeled 1, 2, 3, 1, 2, 3 on the six faces, for each group

▶ Blank cards or 💿

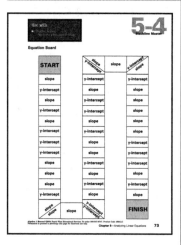

$y + 2y = 6x - 3$	$m = 2$	$b = -1$
$9 + x = y$	$m = 1$	$b = 9$
$\frac{1}{2}y + 2x = -4$	$m = -4$	$b = -8$
$3x + 3y = y + x - 6$	$m = -1$	$b = -3$
$.6y - 1.2x = 2.4$	$m = 2$	$b = 4$
$.5x + .3y = .2y + .4$	$m = -5$	$b = 4$
$2x - 3y = 9 - 4y$	$m = -2$	$b = 9$
$6y - 12 = 18x + 6$	$m = 3$	$b = 3$
$x - 2y + 7 = 3$	$m = \frac{1}{2}$	$b = 2$

3. Each student will need a marker (bean, chip, game marker, etc.) to use on the game board. Each group will need a deck of equation cards, placed equation-side up in a pile.

4. The first student, determined by the roll of a die, should take the top card, read the equation, and then write the equation on his or her paper in slope-intercept form. The student should then roll the die and moves 1, 2, or 3 spaces on the game board. The space on which the marker lands indicates the required information (slope or y-intercept).

5. The student should provide the information and then turn the card over to see if he or she is correct. If incorrect, the student moves back to the last space he or she occupied. The card is placed at the bottom of the deck, equation side facing up.

6. Students take turns rolling, providing the information, and checking the answers on the back of the cards.

7. The activity is over when *all* students reach the finish line.

Materials:

▶ The deck of cards from Practice Activity **Name the y-Intercept or Slope** or

▶ Blackline master for **graph paper** is in the Appendix.

Graph It

Directions:

1. Divide students into groups of three or four. Give each group 10 to 12 of the cards, which the groups should place in a pile with the equation side up.

2. Instruct each student to draw a card from the deck and leave it face up. The students are to put the equation in the slope-intercept form, name the slope and the y-intercept, and sketch the graph.

3. After all the students are finished with their graphs, they should check their work by turning the equation card over and checking to see if the graph they drew has the correct y-intercept and slope.

4. Each student should sketch three or four graphs.

Materials:

▶ Blackline master for **graph paper** is in the Appendix.

Student Exchange

Directions:

1. Give each student a piece of graph paper.

2. Have the students write an equation in standard form ($ax + by = c$) on the top of the paper (for example, $2x + y = 7$).

3. Have the students exchange papers. On the paper they receive, the students are to put the equation in slope-intercept form, name the slope and y-intercept, and sketch the graph. Circulate among the students and check their work.

4. Give each student a new piece of graph paper and have them write another equation in standard form.

5. Have the students exchange papers and repeat step 3 above.

6. Repeat as time allows.

Problem-Solving Activity

Long-Distance and Checking 💡

Directions:

Give each student a copy of the blackline master **Long-Distance and Checking**. Have the students work individually to solve the problems, which are reprinted below.

1. The long-distance phone rates for company D are computed by using the formula R = .07t + .26, where R is the rate and t is the time in minutes. (*Hint:* Rewrite equations as cents instead of dollars.)

   a. What is the slope of the line represented by this equation?

   b. What does the slope represent?

   c. What is the R-intercept for this line?

   d. What does the R-intercept represent?

   e. Sketch the graph of the equation.

   f. What is the rate for a 20-minute phone call?

   g. What is the rate for a 30-minute phone call?

2. The service charge for a checking account at bank K is figured by the following formula: S = .1c + 2.00, where S is the service charge and c is the number of checks written.

   a. What is the slope of the line represented by this equation?

   b. What does the slope represent?

   c. What is the S-intercept for this line?

   d. What does the S-intercept represent?

   e. Sketch the graph of the equation.

   f. What is the service charge if you write 6 checks?

   g. What is the service charge if you write 15 checks?

5-5 *Objective:* Use the slope of lines to determine if two lines are parallel or perpendicular.

Sample Test: Indicate whether the graphs of the two equations would be parallel, perpendicular, or neither.

a. $2x + y = 4$
    $y = -2x - 4$

b. $x + 3 = y$
    $y + x = 4$

c. $2y = 4x + 10$
    $2y = x - 6$

Solution: parallel

Solution: perpendicular

Solution: neither

Concept Development Activities

Discover Parallel and Perpendicular Line Graphs

Directions:

1. Divide the students into groups of three or four.

2. **Parallel lines:** Give the following directions to the students:

   a. Write an equation of the form $y = mx + b$, where m and b are integers.

   b. Sketch the graph of the equation in step a.

   c. Draw any line parallel to the graphed line and find the equation for the parallel line.

   d. Analyze the two equations and write a rule telling when the graphs of two linear equations will be parallel lines. **(Slopes are the same.)**

3. Have two or three groups present their rule and give examples. **(Same slope, different intercepts.)** Discuss the accuracy of the generalizations.

4. **Perpendicular lines:** Give the following directions to the students:

   a. Write an equation of the form $y = mx + b$, where m and b are integers.

   b. Sketch the graph of the equation in step a.

   c. Draw any line perpendicular to the graphed line with the

intersection at (0, b), the y-intercept. (You may need to review right angles and perpendicular lines.) Find the equation for the perpendicular line.

d. Analyze the two equations and write a rule telling when the graphs of two linear equations will be perpendicular lines. **(Slopes are negative reciprocals, or the product of the slopes is –1.)**

5. Have two or three groups present their rule and give examples. **(Negative reciprocal of the slope.)** Discuss the rules and see if they will work for all cases.

Which Are Parallel?

Directions:

1. Write the following three equations on the board or overhead for the students to graph:

    a. $y = 2x + 3$ b. $y = 2x$ c. $y = x + 2$

    Have the students label each graph with its equation.

2. After the students have sketched all three graphs, ask, "Which two graphs are parallel lines?"

3. Ask, "Can you tell if the graphs of two linear equations will be parallel without making the graphs?"

4. See if the students can identify which of the following equations will have parallel lines as graphs.

    a. $y = x + 4$ b. $y = -x + 3$ c. $y = x - 1$

5. Have several students give their choices. Then have the students sketch the graphs to see if they are correct.

6. Ask the students to name an equation that would have a parallel graph to each of the following equations:

    a. $y = 3x$ b. $y = -x + 2$ c. $y = \frac{1}{2}x + 4$

7. Sketch some of the graphs from students' equations to show that the graphs are or are not parallel.

Materials:

▶ Blackline master for **graph paper** is in the Appendix.

▶ Overhead graph paper transparencies

Teacher's Tip:

Worksheet 1 for this objective, **page 5-24**, supports this activity with practice exercises.

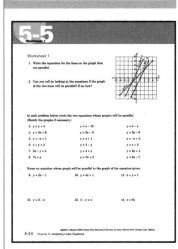

Answer Key:
2. a and b
3. Yes, same slope, different intercepts
4. a and c
6. a. $y = 3x + b$, $b \neq 0$
   b. $y = -x + b$, $b \neq 2$
   c. $y = \frac{1}{2}x + b$, $b \neq 4$

Concept Development

Materials:

▶ Blackline master for **graph paper** is in the Appendix.

▶ Overhead graph paper transparencies

Teacher's Tip:

Worksheet 2 for this objective, **page 5-25**, supports this activity with practice exercises.

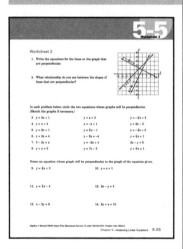

Answer Key:
2. a and c
3. Yes, the slopes are negative reciprocals, or the product of the slopes is –1.
4. a and c and a and b
6. a. $y = -x + b$
   b. $y = -2x + b$
   c. $y = -\frac{1}{4}x + b$
   d. $y = \frac{1}{2}x + b$

Which Are Perpendicular?

Directions:

1. Write the following three equations on the board or overhead for the students to graph:

   a. $y = 2x + 1$ b. $y = x + 1$ c. $y = -\frac{1}{2}x + 2$

   Have the students label each graph with its equation.

2. After the students have sketched all three graphs, ask, "Which two graphs are perpendicular lines?"

3. Ask, "Can you tell if the graphs of two linear equations will be perpendicular without making the graphs?"

4. See if the students can identify which of the following equations will have perpendicular lines as graphs.

   a. $y = 3x + 2$ b. $y = -\frac{1}{3}x + 1$ c. $y = \frac{1}{3}x - 1$

5. Have several students give their choices. Then have the students sketch the graphs to see if they are correct.

6. Ask the students to name an equation that would have a perpendicular graph to each of the following equations:

   a. $y = x - 1$ b. $y = \frac{1}{2}x + 3$
   c. $y = 4x + 6$ d. $y = -2x + 1$

7. Sketch some of the graphs from students' equations to show that the graphs are or are not perpendicular.

Graphing Calculator: Parallel and Perpendicular

Directions:

Materials:

▶ Graphing calculators (minimum of 5)

1. Using graphing calculators, have the students make the graphs of the following two equations on the same axes:

   $y = 2x - 1$ $\qquad\qquad$ $y = 2x + 3$

2. Ask the students what they notice about the graphs. **(They are parallel, do not intersect.)** Ask the students why they think the graphs of these equations are parallel. **(Same slope, different intercepts.)**

   Answer Key for #4:
   a. $y = 3x + b,\ b \neq 1$
   b. $y = x + b,\ b \neq 0$
   c. $y = -\frac{1}{2}x + b,\ b \neq 2$

3. Give the students the equation $y = -x + 1$ to graph using graphing calculators. Have the students write an equation of a line they think will be parallel to it. Then, using the graphing calculators, have them put the graph on the same axes to check their equation.

4. Have the students name an equation parallel to each of the following equations:

   a. $y = 3x + 1$ $\qquad$ b. $y = x$ $\qquad$ c. $y = -\frac{1}{2}x + 2$

   Have the students graph each pair on their graphing calculators to see if they are correct.

5. Now have the students make the graphs of the following two equations on the same axes, using the graphing calculators:

   $y = 2x + 1$ $\qquad\qquad$ $y = -\frac{1}{2}x - 2$

6. Ask the students what they notice about the graphs. **(They are perpendicular.)** Ask the students why they think the graphs of these equations are perpendicular. **(Slopes are negative reciprocals, or the product of the slopes is –1.)**

7. Give the students the equation $y = x + 3$ to graph using graphing calculators. Have the students write an equation of a line they think will be perpendicular to it. Then, using the graphing calculators, have them put the graph on the same axes to check their equation.

Concept/Practice

Answer Key for #8:
a. $y = -\frac{1}{3}x + b$
b. $y = x + b$
c. $y = 2x + b$
d. $y = -\frac{1}{2}x + b$

Materials:

▶ Blackline master for **graph paper** is in the Appendix.

8. Have the students name an equation they think will have perpendicular graphs to each of the following equations:

a. $y = 3x + 1$ b. $y = -x + 2$

c. $y = -\frac{1}{2}x + 1$ d. $y = 2x + 14$

Have the students graph each pair on a graphing calculator to see if they are correct.

Practice Activities

Name the Equation

Directions:

1. Have the students take a ruled piece of paper and make two vertical lines dividing the paper into three columns. They should label the first column "Equation," the second column "Parallel Equation," and the third column "Perpendicular Equation."

2. Have the students write the two equations $y = x + 3$ and $y = 2x - 1$ on separate lines in the "Equation" column.

3. Have the students write equations in the other two columns that satisfy the headings. For example:

Equation	Parallel Equation	Perpendicular Equation
$y = x + 3$	$y = x - 1$	$y = -x + 2$

4. Discuss correct responses and why they are correct for the first two problems. Graph some equations if there is disagreement on correct responses.

5. Now write the two equations $2x + y = 4$ and $y + 6 = 3x$ in the "Equation" column. Review writing equations in slope-intercept form. Then have the students write equations in the other two columns that satisfy the headings.

6. Now write the equation $y = -2x + 1$ on the next row in the "Parallel Equation" column. Have the students complete the other two columns. *Example:*

Equation	Parallel Equation	Perpendicular Equation
$y = -2x + 4$	$y = -2x + 1$	$y = \frac{1}{2}x + 3$

5-38   Chapter 5—Analyzing Linear Equations

7. Next, write the equation y = 3x + 1 in the "Perpendicular Equation" column. Have the students complete the other two columns. *Example:*

Equation	Parallel Equation	Perpendicular Equation
$y = -\frac{1}{3}x + 1$	$y = -\frac{1}{3}x + 4$	$y = 3x + 1$

8. Give the students the following equations in the columns indicated and have them complete the table. They should write all the answers in slope-intercept form.

x + 1 = y	perpendicular column
x + y = 6	equation column
y − 2x = 3	parallel column
2y + x = 5	perpendicular column
$\frac{1}{2}$y + x = 3	equation column
y + 6 = 2x + 1	parallel column
2x + y = x − 1	equation column
y + 3 = $\frac{1}{2}$x − 1	perpendicular column
2x + 2y = 6	parallel column

Parallel—Perpendicular Cards

Directions:

1. Write the following equations on a piece of paper. Give one copy of the list to each student with equations the student is to copy onto cards circled.

2. Divide the students into groups of three or four. Each group should have a deck containing all of the equations.

3. Equations for the cards:

y = x + 3	y = x − 2	y = −x + 4
x + 2y = 4	x = 6 − 2y	3 + y = 2x
x + y = 1	x = 3 − y	y = x + 2
2x − y = 3	y = 2x	2 − 2y = x
y = $\frac{1}{2}$x + 1	2y − x = 2	y = −2x
2y − x = 4	x = 6 + 2y	y + 2x = 1
y − 3x = 2	3x = 4 + y	3y + x = 6
3x + y = 0	4 − 3x = y	x = 9 + 3y
x + 3y = 6	3y = 2 − x	y − 3x = 2
y = $\frac{2}{3}$x + 1	3y − x = 3	y + 3x = 2

Materials:

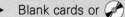

► Blank cards or 💿

Teacher's Tip:

Worksheet 3 for this objective, **page 5-26**, supports this activity with practice exercises.

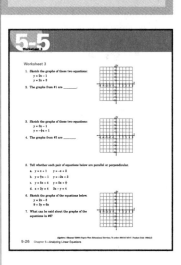

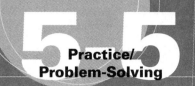
4. Have each group shuffle the cards and deal four cards to each student.

5. Each student should lay one of his or her cards down in front of them. The dealer starts play. The dealer's task is to play one of the remaining three cards on one of the four equations showing. Students can play a card where the equation will be parallel or perpendicular to the equation showing. Students will need paper and pencil to put the equations in slope-intercept form.

6. The student whose turn it is needs to state if the equation's graph is parallel or perpendicular to the one given, and why.

7. The group needs to check that the card played is correct.

8. If a student cannot play or is incorrect, that student should draw a card from the deck.

9. Play continues clockwise.

10. The first player to play all of his or her cards is the winner.

Problem-Solving Activities

Slope-Intercept

Directions:

Give each student a copy of the blackline master **Slope-Intercept**. Have the students work individually to solve the problems, which are reprinted below.

1. Write the equation of the line that passes through the point $(1, 2)$ and is parallel to the graph of $x + y = 8$. Write the equation in slope-intercept form.

2. Write an equation in the slope-intercept form of the line that passes through the point $(2, 0)$ and is perpendicular to the graph of $2x + y = 3$.

3. Write an equation in slope-intercept form of the line that passes through the point $(2, 2)$ and is parallel to the graph of $3 + y = x$.

4. Write the equations of two lines that are perpendicular and each contains the point $(2, 4)$.

Materials:

► Blackline master **Slope-Intercept** is located in the *Teacher's Resource Manual*, **page 75**.

Two Ships

Directions:

Give each student a copy of the blackline master **Two Ships**. Have the students work individually to solve the problems, which are reprinted below.

1. Two ships are traveling to the same destination. To be safe, the ships are given parallel routes so they will not collide if one goes faster than the other. Ship A has the route shown in the graph. What is the equation for a good route for ship B?

2. If two ships are going to cross each other's path, the best way is to cross at a 90° angle so the time is minimized when they could collide. If ship C is going to intersect ship A's path (shown in the graph) at (6, 5), what is the equation of the route ship C should follow through the point (6, 5)?

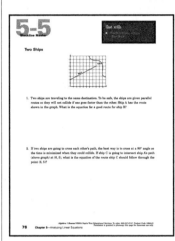
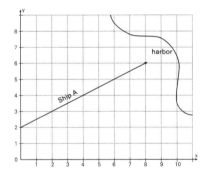

Solving Linear Inequalities

6-1 Solve and graph the solution set of inequalities with addition and subtraction.

6-2 Solve and graph the solution set of inequalities with multiplication and division.

6-3 Solve and graph the solution set of inequalities using more than one operation.

6-4 Solve and graph the solution set of compound inequalities and inequalities involving absolute value.

6-5 Graph inequalities in the coordinate plane.

6-1 *Objective:* **Solve and graph the solution set of inequalities with addition and subtraction.**

Sample Test: Solve each inequality and graph the solution on the number line provided.

1. $x + 9 < 6$

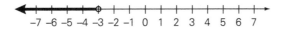

   Solution: x < –3

2. $a - 8 > 2$

   Solution: a > 10

3. $h + 12 \leq 15$

   Solution: h ≤ 3

4. $g - 7 \geq -13$

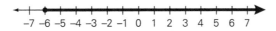

   Solution: g ≥ –6

Concept Development

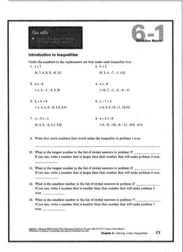

Concept Development Activities

Introduction to Inequalities ☀

Directions:

1. Give one copy of the blackline master **Introduction to Inequalities** to each student.

2. Review the symbols >, ≥, <, and ≤.

3. Select a student to read the directions and problem 1 from the blackline master.

4. Explain to the students that the set of numbers below each problem is the replacement set (the set of numbers used to check for solutions).

5. Ask a student if the first number in the replacement set satisfies the inequality (makes the inequality true). Have the students circle the number if it satisfies the inequality.

6. Continue with another student and the second number in the replacement set, a third student and the third number, and continue until you have checked every number in the replacement set.

7. Have the students complete problems 2–8. Discuss the answers.

8. Form pairs of students to complete problems 9–13. Discuss the answers.

9. Continue with an explanation of why on the number line we use an open circle for < and > **(not an exact number at the beginning)** and a filled circle for ≥ and ≤ **(an exact number at beginning).** This discussion will serve as an introduction to the next Concept Development Activity, **Introduction to Inequality Graphs**.

Introduction to Inequality Graphs

Directions:

1. Draw a number line on the board or project it on the overhead, and label it as follows:

2. Write the sentence "x < 3" under the number line. Ask a student to read the sentence. **(x is less than 3.)**

3. Review the symbols >, <, ≥, and ≤.

4. Ask a student what number is represented by point A. **(–2)** Ask if that point (–2) satisfies the sentence x < 3. **(Yes, –2 < 3.)**

5. Ask another student what number is represented by point B. **(1)** Ask if that point (1) satisfies the sentence x < 3. **(Yes, 1 < 3.)**

6. Now ask the same questions about point C **(3; No, 3 < 3 is false.)** and point D. **(5; No, 5 < 3 is false.)**

7. Ask the students to name other numbers that satisfy the sentence x < 3. Of course, infinitely many numbers are less than 3.

8. Hopefully, someone will name 2 as a number that satisfies the sentence. If not, suggest 2 as an answer. Ask if 2 is the largest number that satisfies the sentence x < 3. Discuss that 2 is the largest integer that satisfies x < 3 but that there are other real numbers larger than 2 that satisfy x < 3. See if the students can name some. **($2\frac{1}{2}$, $2\frac{3}{4}$, 2.9, 2.99)**

9. Draw a number line like the one below under the original number line.

10. Ask the class, "What is the largest number that you can think of that satisfies x < 3?" Some students will probably respond with something like 2.9999. Ask, "Is this less than 3?" **(Yes)** "How about 2.9999999—is it less than 3?" **(Yes)**

11. Ask, "How can we picture this?" Discuss the use of the open circle for x < 3. Show how to picture x < 3. Reinforce that the open circle means all numbers up to 3 but not including 3.

12. Follow similar steps to discuss the graphs of x > –4, x ≤ –2, and x ≥ 1. Show the linear graphs and write the corresponding inequalities below them.

Teacher's Tip:

Worksheet 1 for this objective, **page 6-2**, supports this activity with practice exercises.

Materials:

▶ Blackline master for **number lines** is in the Appendix.

▶ Overhead number line transparency

Number Line Demonstration

Directions:

1. Using the overhead projector, place two points on the number line. For example, use –8 and 5.

2. Discuss which number is larger, which number is smaller, and how far apart the numbers are. **(5 is larger, –8 is smaller, and they are 13 units apart.)**

3. Ask the students to write an inequality sentence for all numbers between –8 and 5. **(5 > x > –8 or –8 < x < 5)**

4. Choose a student to give an answer for #3. If that student used the < inequality, ask if anyone used a different inequality in their answer. If no one offers another answer, ask whether an answer using the > inequality would also be correct (or vice versa, if the student used the > inequality).

5. Now add a number (e.g., 7) to both of the original numbers.

6. Show the number 7 being added in the number line, seven units to the right of –8 **(–1)** and seven units to the right of 5 **(+12)**. Ask the students whether the sum of –8 and 7 is still less than the sum of 5 and 7. **(Yes, –8 + 7 < x < 5 + 7)**

7. Ask the students if the two sums (–1 and 12) are still the same distance apart. **(Yes, 13 units.)**

8. Discuss whether this result would happen with any two numbers.

9. Pick two new numbers to place on the number line, for example, 3 and 7.

```
←+─+─+─+─+─+─+─+─+─+─●─+─+─●─→
 –7 –6 –5 –4 –3 –2 –1  0  1  2  3  4  5  6  7
```

10. Now choose a negative number to add to both numbers, for example, –6.

```
          (3 – 6)        (7 – 6)
←+─+─+─+─●─+─+─+─●─+─+─+─+─+─→
 –7 –6 –5 –4 –3 –2 –1  0  1  2  3  4  5  6  7
```

11. Repeat the process of steps 6 through 8.

12. Ask the students to summarize this experiment. **(You can add or subtract the same numbers and it doesn't change the inequality.)**

Teacher's Tip:

Using the overhead to project the number line on the board works very well. You can then write on the board and erase the writing to start a new problem without having to redraw the number line.

13. Ask the students to decide if the following are true or false:

   a. If x > 3, then x − 3 > 3 − 3, or x − 3 > 0. **(True)**

   b. If x < 10, then x + 2 < 10 + 2, or x + 2 < 12. **(True)**

   c. If x − 3 < 4, then x − 3 + 3 < 4 + 3, or x < 7. **(True)**

   d. If x + 6 < 9, then x + 6 − 6 < 9 − 6, or x < 3. **(True)**

   e. If x + 2 ≤ 7, then x + 2 − 2 ≤ 7 − 7, or x < 0. **(False)**

14. Discuss that inequalities are like equations in that you can add (or subtract) the same quantity to both sides without changing the inequality. Use the number line to show that the inequality stays true if you add or subtract any quantity.

15. Discuss solving an inequality such as x − 4 > 6 → x > 10.
$$x - 4 > 6$$
$$x - 4 + 4 > 6 + 4$$
$$x > 10$$

16. Have the students solve the following inequalities. Discuss the addition or subtraction property used to solve each problem.

   a. x + 7 > 3   b. x − 3 ≤ 2

   c. x + 9 ≤ 2   d. 7 ≥ x + 2

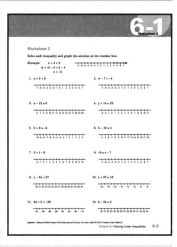
Balance Scale

Directions:

1. Divide the students into groups of four or five. Put nine weights in each paper bag. Give each group a closed paper bag containing weights, a balance scale, and extra weights.

2. Instruct the students not to open the bags or try to feel the number of weights. Have the students in the groups put the paper bag on one side of the scale and three weights on the other side. Explain that the paper bag has weights in it. Ask the class which is heavier. **(The paper bag)**

3. Ask the class, "If we let the paper bag be 'x,' can we write an inequality to represent the balance?" Solicit answers to get x > 3.

Materials:

▶ Elementary balance scale for each group of four or five students

▶ Weights for the balance (cubes, chips, paper clips— uniform weight)

▶ Small paper bag

Teacher's Tip:

Worksheet 3 for this objective, **page 6-4**, supports this activity with practice exercises.

This can be interpreted that there are more than three weights in the paper bag.

4. Have the groups add two more weights to each side of the balance. Ask, "What happened?" **(Nothing)** Ask, "How can we write an inequality to model what we did?" **(x + 2 > 3 + 2)** Explain that because they added the same amount to each side, the inequality stayed the same.

5. Ask, "What if we add 10 weights to each side, 100 weights to each side?" Communicate that as long as you add the same amount to each side, the heavier side will remain heavier. Ask the class to summarize.

$$x > y \;\rightarrow\; x + b > y + b$$

6. Have the groups remove the items from the balance and then put the paper bag (containing weights) on one side and five weights on the other side. Have the groups write the inequality on their papers. **(x > 5)**

7. Ask a group, "What would happen if we removed two weights from each side?" $(x - 2 > 5 - 2)$ **(The side with the bag would still be heavier.)**

8. Ask, "If we removed the same amount from each side, what would happen?" **(Heavier side would remain heavier)** Ask a group to summarize using inequalities.

$$\text{If } x > y \;\rightarrow\; x - b > y - b$$

9. Be sure students understand that this means you can add or subtract the same amount from an inequality and the inequality remains true.

10. Have the groups put the paper bag and three weights on one side $(x + 3)$ and seven weights on the other.

11. Ask a group to write the inequality modeled on the balance. **(x + 3 > 7)** Write the sentence on the board.

12. Ask, "How can I solve this inequality for x?" **(Take three away from each side.)** Write the inequality under the original problem.

$$x + 3 - 3 > 7 - 3 \;\rightarrow\; x > 4$$

Ask how this can be interpreted on the balance scale.

13. Have the groups use the weights, bag, and scale to model solving the following equations. Discuss each model and have the students solve for x (paper bag starts with nine weights).

    a. $x + 2 < 15$ b. $x + 5 > 8$

    c. $x - 2 < 5$ d. $x - 3 \geq 2$

Practice Activities

Writing and Solving an Inequality

Directions:

Materials:

▶ Blank cards

1. Give two cards to each student.

2. Instruct each student to write an inequality with addition on the first card, for example, $x + 9 \geq 3$.

3. Instruct each student to write an inequality with subtraction on the second card, for example, $x - 4 < 7$.

4. On the back of each card, have the students copy the inequality from the front of the card and then solve it and graph the solution set.

   Example: $x + 9 \geq 3$

   $$x + 9 - 9 \geq 3 - 9$$

   $$x \geq -6$$

5. Form groups of four or five students.

6. Have the students within each group exchange cards. The students should then solve the inequality on the front of the cards they receive and graph the solution set on a separate sheet of paper.

7. When the students have finished the problems, they should check their answers with the answers on the back of the cards.

8. Have the students exchange cards with someone else in their group and repeat steps 6 and 7 until each student has solved the problems of every other student in the group.

9. Ask students to compare solutions in the group and agree on the correct solutions and graphs.

10. Have the students exchange the cards between the groups and continue.

Inequality Bingo

Directions:

1. Distribute a copy of a 4 × 4 bingo card to each student.

2. Read the 16 solutions from the solution list (below) and have the students write them in the squares of the bingo card in a random fashion.

3. Now select a problem at random from the problem list below and write it on the board or overhead. Each student should solve the problem and then use a marker to cover the square on the bingo card that corresponds to that answer.

4. Repeat step 3 until a student has four markers in a row horizontally, vertically, or diagonally. When a student has four markers in a row, he or she should shout "Bingo!"

5. Check to see if the student has the correct solutions covered.

6. If the solutions are correct, declare that student the winner, have all of the students clear their cards, and begin play again. Be sure to pick the problems from the problem list in a random fashion.

7. This game can be repeated as long as you like.

Solution List	Problem List
1. $x < 4$	1. $x + 5 < 9$
2. $x > 4$	2. $x - 3 > 1$
3. $x \geq -3$	3. $x + 7 \geq 4$
4. $x \leq -3$	4. $5 + x \leq 2$
5. $x > 2$	5. $7 + x > 9$
6. $x < 2$	6. $x - 8 < -6$
7. $x \leq 0$	7. $x - 9 \leq -9$
8. $x > 0$	8. $x + 46 > 46$
9. $x < 1$	9. $x - 9 < -8$
10. $x < -1$	10. $x - 3 < -4$
11. $x \geq 7$	11. $x + 6 \geq 13$
12. $x < 7$	12. $x - 4 < 3$
13. $x = 6$	13. $x + 2 = 8$
14. $x > 10$	14. $x + 20 > 30$
15. $x = 2$	15. $x + 6 = 8$
16. $x < 10$	16. $14 > x + 4$

Problem-Solving Activity

Infor Inequalities Questions

Directions:

Give each student a copy of the blackline master **Inequalities Questions**. Have the students work individually to solve the problems, which are reprinted below, and discuss as a class.

1. Write an inequality if the graph of the solution set has a filled-in dot at 3 and an arrow to the right.

2. Write an inequality if the graph of the solution set has an open dot at 6 and an arrow to the left.

3. Write an inequality if the graph of the solution set has an open dot at −5 and an arrow to the right.

4. Write an inequality if the graph of the solution set has a filled-in dot at −8 and an arrow to the left.

5. Write an inequality with addition in it that has a solution of $n > 4$.

6. Write an unequality with subtraction in it that has a solution of $n \le -3$.

7. a. The record for home runs in a season is 73, set in 2001 by Barry Bonds. This year, Bonds hit 31 home runs by June 15. Write an inequality that shows how many home runs Bonds would need to hit to break his own record.

   b. Todd Helton hit 24 home runs by June 15. Write an inequality that shows how many home runs Helton would need to hit to break the record of 73 home runs in a season.

8. Write an inequality whose graph looks like

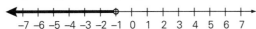

9. Write another inequality that would have the same graph as in problem 8.

10. Write an inequality whose graph looks like

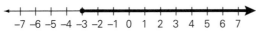

6-2 *Objective:* **Solve and graph the solution set of inequalities with multiplication and division.**

Sample Test: Solve each inequality and graph the solution on the number line provided.

1. $3a < -6$

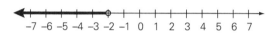

 Solution: a < –2

2. $-4y > -20$

 Solution: y < 5

3. $-5h \leq 15$

 Solution: h ≥ –3

4. $\frac{g}{2} \geq 3$

 Solution: g ≥ 6

Materials:

▶ Blackline master
Map the Products on the Number Line is located in the *Teacher's Resource Manual,* **page 79.**

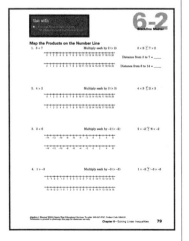

Concept Development Activities

Multiplication and the Number Line

Directions:

1. Give one copy of the blackline master **Map the Products on the Number Line** to each student.

2. Ask a student to read the first inequality (3 < 7). Point out the 3 and 7 plotted on the top number line. Ask a student to multiply 3 by 2 and 7 by 2. **(3 × 2 = 6, 7 × 2 = 14)**

3. Have the students map the numbers to their products: 3 → 6 and 7 → 14. Ask, "What is the relation between 6 and 14?" **(6 < 14)** Write on the board or overhead:

$$3 < 7$$
$$3 \times 2 < 7 \times 2$$
$$6 < 14$$

4. Now discuss the distance from 3 to 7 **(4)** and the distance from 6 to 14 **(8)**. Ask, "What is the relation between the distances?" **(twice as much)** Explain that if you take two numbers in an inequality (such as 3 < 7) and multiply by 2 on each side, the numbers in the resulting inequality (6 < 14) will be twice as far apart.

5. Repeat steps 2–4 for problem 2 on the blackline master **(4 > 2, multiply by 3, 12 > 6)**.

6. Ask a student to read problem 3 (2 < 6). Ask, "What do we get when each number is multiplied by –2?" **[2 × (–2) = –4, 6 × (–2) = –12]** Ask, "What is the relation between –4 and –12?" **(–4 > –12)**

7. Have the students map the 2 → –4 and the 6 → –12. Be sure they see that –12 is smaller than –4. Write on the board or overhead:

$$2 < 6$$
$$2 \times (-2) > 6 \times (-2)$$
$$-4 > -12$$

Note on the mapping how the *lines cross*. The relationship is reversed. When you multiply by a negative number, you reverse the relation. The larger number multiplied by a negative number becomes smaller than the smaller number multiplied by the same negative number.

8. Investigate with the students the outcome of problem 4. **(1 > –3, 1 × –3 < –3 × –3, –3 < 9)** Help the studens see that the relation is reversed.

9. Ask the students to write a generalization about inequalities and multiplication. For example, if a < b and c > 0, then ac < bc, and if a < b and c < 0, then ac > bc.

Practice With Numbers

Directions:

1. Give one copy of the blackline master **Inequalities With Multiplication** to each student. Have the students work independently to complete the activity. Then discuss it as follows.

2. Start by calling on one student. Ask whether the first number in the replacement set for a in problem 1 would make problem 1 true. Call on a second student and ask about the second number

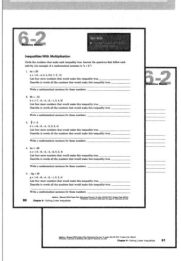

in the replacement set for a. Repeat until all numbers in the replacement set for problem 1 have been discussed.

3. Explain that in problem 1, all numbers less than 7 will work. **(a < 7)** Write on the board: 4a < 28, a < 7. Ask, "How do we get from 4a < 28 to a < 7?" **(Divide by +4, or multiply by +$\frac{1}{4}$.)**

4. Discuss problems 2 to 4 in a similar fashion.

5. Ask a student which numbers he or she circled in problem 5. **(–2, –1, 0, 2, 4)** Ask the student to describe the numbers that will work. **(g > –4)**

6. Discuss that to get from –5g < 20 to g > –4, you must divide both sides by –5, or multiply by –$\frac{1}{5}$, and then reverse the relation: $-\frac{1}{5}(-5g) < -\frac{1}{5}(20) \rightarrow g > -4$.

7. Discuss problems 6 to 8 in a similar fashion.

8. Ask the students to write a generalization for multiplying or dividing inequalities. For example, if a < b and c > 0, then ac < bc or $\frac{a}{c} < \frac{b}{c}$ and if a > b and c < 0, then ac < bc or $\frac{a}{c} < \frac{b}{c}$.

Practice Activities

Inequality Bingo

Directions:

1. Give a copy of a blank bingo card to each student. Read the 16 solutions from the solution list below, and have the students randomly write one solution in each square on their cards. They may write the solutions in any of the squares.

2. Now select a problem at random from the problem list and write it on the board or overhead. Each student should solve the problem and use a marker to cover the square on the bingo card with the corresponding answer. The students should work the problems on their own paper.

3. Write another problem (chosen at random) on the board, and so on, until someone has four markers in a row, horizontally, vertically, or diagonally.

4. Instead of shouting "Bingo!" the student could shout the name of the school mascot, or even just raise a hand.

5. Check to see if the student has the correct solutions covered. If the solutions are correct, declare that person the winner. You may then have the students clear their cards and play again.

6. Repeat the game as long as you like. You may alter problems by multiplying the same positive number to both sides of the inequalities.

<u>Solution List</u>

1. $x > 4$
2. $x < 4$
3. $x \le -3$
4. $x \ge -3$
5. $x < 2$
6. $x > 2$
7. $x > 0$
8. $x < 0$
9. $x < 1$
10. $x > 3$
11. $x < -1$
12. $x < 1$
13. $x > -2$
14. $x < -2$
15. $x \ge 5$
16. $x \le 5$

<u>Problem List</u>

1. $3x > 12$
2. $-5x > -20$
3. $4x \le -12$
4. $-3x \le 9$
5. $7x < 14$
6. $18 < 9x$
7. $7x > 0$
8. $-5x > 0$
9. $-27x > -27$
10. $3x > 9$
11. $5x < -5$
12. $-2x > -2$
13. $7x > -14$
14. $\frac{1}{2}x < -1$
15. $-2x \le -10$
16. $2x \le 10$

Switch It

Directions:

1. Distribute five cards to each student.

2. Instruct the students to write an inequality on each card, adhering to the following guidelines:

   a. At least two of the inequalities should involve multiplication and at least two should involve division.

   b. In at least one of the inequalities, the solution should involve a switch of inequality sign for each operation, and in at least

Materials:
▶ Blank cards

one of the inequalities, the solution should not involve a switch of inequality sign for each operation.

3. Place the students in groups of four.

4. Have the students in each group check all of the cards in that group to see that they follow the instructions in #2.

5. Have each group exchange cards with another group.

6. Each group should shuffle the cards it receives and place them equation-side down.

7. The first player should turn over a card quickly so that everyone in the group can see it. The object is to be the first one to recognize an inequality for which the solution involves switching the inequality sign. When such an inequality is spotted, the student should say "Switch it!" In turn, each of the players turns over a card.

8. The first player to say "Switch it!" gets all of the cards played in that round.

9. If a player says "Switch it!" incorrectly, he or she must put three cards from his or her own stack at the bottom of the deck.

10. The student with the most cards when the deck is gone is the winner.

11. A variation of this game is for the groups to exchange cards and solve the inequalities they receive. This exchange can continue among all of the groups.

Problem-Solving Activity

Equations and Inequalities

Directions:

1. Write the following equations and inequalities on the board. Ask the students to solve each equation and inequality.

   a. $5x = 35$ b. $5x < 35$ c. $5x > 35$ d. $5x \le 35$

2. Ask the students to describe the steps in solving the equation and the inequalities.

3. Ask, "Is there any difference in the inequality sign? If so, what is it?"

4. Repeat steps 1–3 for the following problems.

   a. $\frac{x}{3} = 4$ b. $\frac{x}{3} < 4$ c. $\frac{x}{3} \ge 4$ d. $\frac{x}{3} \le 4$

5. Repeat steps 1–3 for the following problems.

   a. $-4x = 16$ b. $-4x < 16$ c. $-4x > 16$ d. $-4x \ge 16$

6. Repeat steps 1–3 for the following problems.

   a. $\frac{x}{-2} = -8$ b. $\frac{x}{-2} < -8$ c. $\frac{x}{-2} \le -8$ d. $\frac{x}{-2} \ge -8$

7. Ask the students to finish this sentence: "The difference between solving the inequalities and the equation is _____."

Answer Key:
1 a. $x = 7$ b. $x < 7$
  c. $x > 7$ d. $x \le 7$
2. Steps: Divide both sides by 5.
3. No difference in sign.
4. a. $x = 12$ b. $x < 12$
   c. $x \ge 12$ d. $x \le 12$
   Steps: Multiply both sides by 3.
   No difference in sign.
5. a. $x = -4$ b. $x > -4$
   c. $x < -4$ d. $x \le -4$
   Steps: Divide both sides by -4 and switch the inequality sign in parts b, c, and d.
   The difference is that you must switch the inequality sign.
6. a. $x = 16$ b. $x > 16$
   c. $x \ge 16$ d. $x \le 16$
   Steps: Multiply both sides by -2 and switch the inequality sign in parts b, c, and d.
   The difference is that if you multiply or divide by a negative, you must switch the inequality sign.

6-3 *Objective:* **Solve and graph the solution set of inequalities using more than one operation.**

Sample Test: Solve each inequality and graph the solution on the number line provided.

1. $-3x + 9 < -6$

    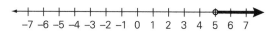

    Solution: x > 5

2. $4 - 8a > 20$

    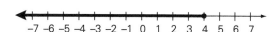

    Solution: a < –2

3. $-5 + 4h \leq 15 - h$

    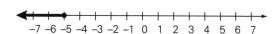

    Solution: h ≤ 4

4. $3g - 7 \geq 5g + 3$

    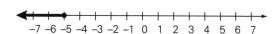

    Solution: g ≤ –5

Concept Development Activities

Inequalities and Equations

Directions:

1. Give a copy of the blackline master **Inequalities and Equations** to each student.

2. Have the students work in pairs. Ask each pair to solve problems 1, 2, and 3.

3. Compare the process of solving the problems as inequalities with the process of solving them as equalities. Substitute numbers if necessary. For example, say, "For 4x + 7 = 19, the solution is x = 3. Now, for 4x + 7 < 19, will x = 2 work? Will x = 3 work? What numbers work?"

4. Ask each pair of students to solve problems 4, 5, and 6. Again, discuss the relationship between the equation solution and the inequality solutions.

Materials:

▶ Blackline master **Inequalities and Equations** is located in the *Teacher's Resource Manual*, **page 82.**

5. Ask each pair of students to solve problems 7, 8, and 9. Discuss the solutions to these problems. Point out that in problems 1–6 the inequalities do not change, whereas in problems 7–9 the inequalities change due to division by a negative number.

6. Summarize and write on the board or overhead a good response to #10.

Solving Inequalities in More Than One Way

Directions:

1. Write the problem $2x + 3 < 7$ on the board or overhead. Ask the class what operations must be performed to solve this inequality. **[Divide by 2 (or multiply by $\frac{1}{2}$) and subtract 3, or reverse these operations.]**

2. Explain that the equations can be solved in two different ways: (a) divide and then subtract, or (b) subtract and then divide.

3. Ask the students to solve $2x + 3 < 7$ in each of the two ways:

    a. Divide each side by 2: $x + \frac{3}{2} < \frac{7}{2}$. Then subtract $\frac{3}{2}$: $x < \frac{4}{2}$, or $x < 2$.

    b. Subtract 3 from each side: $2x < 4$. Then divide by 2: $x < 2$.

4. Point out that the answers are the same. Explain that the order in which the operations are done makes no difference.

5. Try another problem with the class by solving it in two different ways. For example, use $3x - 7 > 5$.

    a. Divide each side by 3: $x - \frac{7}{3} > \frac{5}{3}$. Then add $\frac{7}{3}$: $x > \frac{12}{3}$, or $x > 4$.

    b. Add 7 to each side: $3x > 12$. Then divide by 3: $x > 4$.

6. Ask the class which process seemed easier, to divide and then add or to add and then divide. Add and then divide should be easier.

7. Give the class one more example: $5x - 9 \geq 6$.

    a. Divide and then add: $x - \frac{9}{5} \geq \frac{6}{5} \rightarrow x \geq \frac{15}{5}$, or $x \geq 3$.

    b. Add and then divide: $5x \geq 15 \rightarrow x \geq 3$.

    Ask, "Which method seemed easier?" Again, point out that the answers are the same regardless of which process is used.

Teacher's Tip:

Worksheet 1 for this objective, **page 6-11**, supports this activity with practice exercises.

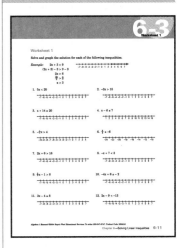

Teacher's Tip:

For students who need more developmental activities, refer to objective 3-3 on solving linear equations.

8. Ask the class to solve the problem 4x + 9 < −7. Ask a student to explain how he or she solved the problem. Show that the computation is easier if you subtract 9 first rather than divide by 4 first.

9. Ask the students to write a generalization about the process of solving any inequality of the form ax + b > c, where the > sign could also be <, ≥, or ≤. **(Do any addition or subtraction before any multiplication or division.)** The main concept is to undo the operations by principal operator first. Therefore, in ax + b > c, the principal operator is addition (ax + b), so undo the addition first by subtracting b: ax > c − b. Then the principal operator is multiplication (ax), so undo the multiplication by dividing by a: $x > \frac{c-b}{a}$. Note that "a" is a positive number here; if it is negative, the inequality sign would be reversed.

10. Ask students to solve the problem 3x − 4 > 14.

    a. **Undo the subtraction by adding 4: 3x − 4 + 4 > 14 + 4, or 3x > 18.**

    b. **Undo the multiplication by dividing by 3: $\frac{3x}{3} > \frac{18}{3}$, or x > 6.**

Practice Activities

Game of Solve and Graph, Beginning Level

Directions:

1. For this activity, each student will need at least one set of cards. A set contans one problem card and four solution cards. You can have the students make the cards.

2. To identify the problem cards, a large "P" or some more imaginative symbol should be written on the back of each problem card. An inequality problem, such as those shown below, should be written on each problem card. Each of the four steps needed to solve and graph that problem should be written on the four solution cards in that set, one step per card.

3. The steps used for solving problems in this game are as follows:

    a. Solution Card 1: Add to both sides of the inequality the opposite of the constant term on the side with variable.

Materials:

▶ Blank cards or 💿

b. Solution Card 2: Divide both sides of the inequality by the coefficient of the variable; if the coefficient is negative, reverse the inequality sign.

c. Solution Card 3: Write the solution.

d. Solution Card 4: Graph the solution set.

4. Sample problems and solutions for beginning-level students:

<u>Problem Cards</u>   <u>Solution Cards</u>

$2x + 3 < 5$ Card 1   Add –3 to both sides (or subtract 3 from both sides)

Card 2   Divide both sides by 2

Card 3 $x < 1$

Card 4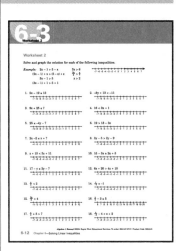

$5 – 3x > –4$ Card 1   Add –5 to both sides (or subtract 5 from both sides)

Card 2   Divide both sides by –3 and reverse the inequality

Card 3 $x < 3$

Card 4

$3x + 9 \geq 6$ Card 1   Add –9 to both sides (or subtract 9 from both sides)

Card 2   Divide both sides by 3

Card 3 $x \geq –1$

Card 4

$–4x – 7 \leq 9$ Card 1   Add 7 to both sides

Card 2   Divide both sides by –4 and reverse the inequality

Card 3 $x \geq –4$

Card 4

Teacher's Tip:

Worksheet 2 for this objective, **page 6-12**, supports this activity with practice exercises.

$4 + \frac{x}{2} > 3$

Card 1 Add –4 to both sides

Card 2 Multiply both sides by 2

Card 3 x > –2

Card 4

5. Directions for play:

  a. Divide the class into groups of four or five. Be sure each student has a pencil and paper to work the problems.

  b. Give each group a deck of cards with four or five problem cards and the matching solution cards. Be sure all the problems in each group are different, although different groups can have the same problem sets.

  c. Devise a method to determine who goes first in each group. One method would be to number the students in the group from 1 to 4 or 5 and to pick a random number by drawing a card or rolling a die.

  d. The person who is first shuffles all the solution cards and deals them all out, face down.

  e. The person to the left shuffles all the problem cards and deals them all out, face down.

  f. The person who is first starts the game by laying down his or her problem card. All of the students should work the problems on their paper.

  g. The person who has the solution card with the first step of the solution then plays it.

  h. Next, the person who has the next step of the solution plays that card.

  i. Then the person with the final solution plays that card.

  j. Then the person with the correct solution graph plays that card.

  k. The person who played the graph card begins the next round by playing his or her problem card. If he or she does not have a problem card, play continues with the next person in a clockwise direction who has a problem card.

  l. The winner is the first person to play all of his or her cards.

  m. Cards can be shuffled to play again.

Game of Solve and Graph, Experienced Version

Directions:

Materials:

▶ Blank cards or

1. For this activity, each student will need at least one set of cards. A set contans one problem card and five solution cards. You can have the students make the cards.

2. To identify the problem cards, a large "P" or some more imaginative symbol should be written on the back of each problem card. An inequality problem, such as those shown below, should be written on each problem card. Each of the five steps needed to solve and graph that problem should be written on the five solution cards in that set, one step per card.

3. The steps used for solving problems in this game are as follows:

   a. Solution Card 1: Add to both sides of the inequality the opposite of the variable term on one of the sides of the inequality.

   b. Solution Card 2: Add to both sides of the resulting inequality the opposite of the constant term on the side with variable.

   c. Solution Card 3: Divide both sides of the inequality by the coefficient of the variable; if the coefficient is negative, reverse the inequality sign.

   d. Solution Card 4: Write the solution.

   e. Solution Card 5: Graph the solution set.

4. Sample problems and solutions for the experienced-level students:

Problem Cards	Solution Cards	
$3x - 4 < x - 5$	Card 1	Add $-x$ to both sides (or subtract x from both sides)
	Card 2	Add 4 to both sides
	Card 3	Divide both sides by 2
	Card 4	$x < -\frac{1}{2}$
	Card 5	

Card 5 graph: a number line from -5 to 5 with an open circle between -1 and 0 and shading to the left.

$6 - 3x > 2x - 4$

Card 1 Add –2x to both sides (or subtract 2x from both sides)

Card 2 Add –6 to both sides (or subtract 6 from both sides)

Card 3 Divide both sides by –5 and reverse the inequality

Card 4 $x < 2$

Card 5

$4x + 7 \geq 6x + 15$

Card 1 Add –6x to both sides (or subtract 6x from both sides)

Card 2 Add –7 to both sides (or subtract 7 from both sides)

Card 3 Divide both sides by –2 and reverse the inequality

Card 4 $x \leq -4$

Card 5

$3x + 4 > 7x - 32$

Card 1 Add –3x to both sides (or subtract 3x from both sides)

Card 2 Add 32 to both sides

Card 3 Divide both sides by 4

Card 4 $x < 9$

Card 5

$x - 7 \leq 8 - 2x$

Card 1 Add 2x to both sides

Card 2 Add 7 to both sides

Card 3 Divide both sides by 3

Card 4 $x \leq 5$

Card 5

Teacher's Tip:

Worksheet 3 for this objective, **page 6-13**, supports this activity with practice exercises.

5. Directions for play:

a. Divide the class into groups of four or five. Be sure each student has a pencil and paper to work the problems.

b. Give each group a deck of cards with four or five problem cards and the matching solution cards. Be sure all the problems in each group are different, although different groups can have the same problem sets.

c. Devise a method to determine who goes first in each group. One method would be to number the students in the group from 1 to 4 or 5 and to pick a random number by drawing a card or rolling a die.

d. The person who is first shuffles all the solution cards and deals them all out, face down.

e. The person to the left shuffles all the problem cards and deals them all out, face down.

f. The person who is first starts the game by laying down his or her problem card. All of the students should work the problem on their paper.

g. The person who has the solution card with the first step of the solution then plays it.

h. Next, the person who has the next step of the solution plays that card, and play continues until the final solution card is played.

i. Then the person with the correct solution graph plays that card.

j. The person who played the graph card begins the next round by playing his or her problem card. If he or she does not have a problem card, play continues with the next person in a clockwise direction who has a problem card.

k. The winner is the first person to play all of his or her cards.

l. Cards can be shuffled to play again.

6-3
Problem-Solving

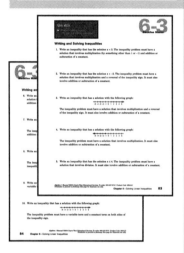

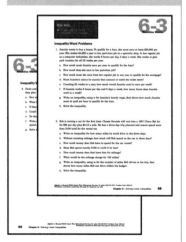

Problem-Solving Activities

Writing and Solving Inequalities

Directions:

1. Give one copy of the blackline master **Writing and Solving Inequalities** to each student. Students should work individually. Be sure each student has pencil and paper.

2. To provide an example for the class, have the students read problem 1 and come up with answers. On the board or overhead, write several of the inequalities that the students volunteer. Point out that there are many different possible answers. Have the class solve several of the student-created problems to check that the solution is x < 3.

3. Let the students work on the remaining problems independently and monitor their progress. After most students have completed problem 3, stop them and discuss some of the answers. Have the class solve several of the student-created problems.

4. When the students have completed all of the problems on the blackline master, ask them to exchange papers and check to see if the answers are correct solutions to the problems presented.

Inequality Word Problems

Directions:

Give each student a copy of the blackline master **Inequality Word Problems**. Have the students work individually to solve the problems, which are reprinted below.

1. Juanita wants to buy a house. To qualify for a loan, she must earn at least $30,000 per year. She makes $4,000 a year in her part-time job at a specialty shop. In her regular job as a computer technician, she works 8 hours per day, 5 days a week. She works or gets paid vacation for all 52 weeks per year.

   a. How much must Juanita earn per year to qualify for the loan?

   b. How much does she earn in her part-time job?

c. How much must she earn from her regular job in one year to qualify for the mortgage?

d. Must Juanita's salary be exactly that amount or could she make more?

e. Counting 52 weeks in a year, how much would Juanita need to earn per week?

f. If Juanita works 8 hours per day and 5 days a week, how many hours does Juanita work in a week?

g. Write an inequality, using w for Juanita's hourly wage, that shows how much Juanita must be paid per hour to qualify for the loan.

h. Solve the inequality.

2. Bob is renting a car for the first time. Classic Rentals will rent him a 1957 Chevy Bel Air for $20 per day plus $0.12 a mile. He has a three-day trip planned and cannot spend more than $180 total for the rental car.

a. Write an inequality for how many miles he could drive in the three days.

b. Without counting mileage, how much will Bob spend on the car in three days?

c. How much money does Bob have to spend for the car rental?

d. Must Bob spend exactly $180 or could it be less?

e. How much money does that leave him for mileage?

f. What would be the mileage charge for 100 miles?

g. Write an inequality, using m for the number of miles Bob drives on his trip, that shows how many miles Bob can drive within his budget.

h. Solve the inequality.

3. Paulo and Maria are going out to dinner. They have exactly $50, the tax rate is 5%, and they plan to tip the waiter 15% of the cost of the dinner.

a. How much do Paulo and Maria have to spend on dinner including tax and tip?

b. What is the total percent for tax and tip?

c. If they spent $45 on dinner, how much would tax and tip cost?

d. Could they spend $45 just for dinner and have enough for tax and tip?

e. Do they need to spend exactly $50? Can they spend more? Less?

f. Write an inequality, using d for the price of the food, that shows how much they can spend on dinner.

g. Solve the inequality.

6-4 *Objective:* Solve and graph the solution set of compound inequalities and inequalities involving absolute value.

Sample Test: Solve each compound inequality and graph the solution on the number line provided.

1. $x - 1 < 9$ or $4x - 23 \geq 37$

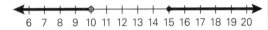

   Solution: x < 10 or x ≥ 15

2. $4y - 24 \leq 28$ and $6y \geq 54$

   Solution: y ≤ 13 and y ≥ 9

3. $|c| \leq 4$

   Solution: c ≥ –4 and c ≤ 4

4. $|a - 4| \geq 5$

   Solution: a ≥ 9 or a ≤ –1

Concept Development Activities

Introduction to Compound Inequalities

Directions:

1. Write "A number is less than 4 or greater than 10" on the board or overhead.

2. Ask, "Could the number be 11? 7? 3.8?" Solicit several numbers that work.

3. Discuss with the class that in mathematics, the word "or" means "if either or both are true, the whole statement is true."

4. Draw the graph of x < 4 or x > 10 on a number line on the board or overhead.

5. Present another example: n ≤ 6 or n ≥ 9. Solicit numbers that work for n and draw the graph on a number line on the board or overhead.

Teacher's Tip:

Worksheet 1 for this objective, **pages 6-16 and 6-17**, supports this activity with practice exercises.

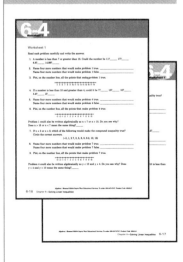

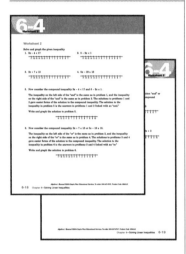

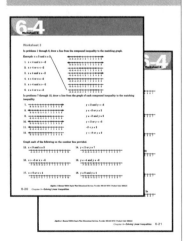

Teacher's Tip:

Worksheet 2 for this objective, **pages 6-18 and 6-19**, supports this activity with practice exercises.

Teacher's Tip:

Worksheets 3 and 4 for this objective, **pages 6-20 and 6-21**, support this activity with practice exercises.

6. Write the problem "x < 14 and x > 9" on the board or overhead.

7. Ask, "Can x be 7? 15? 10? 9.1? 13?" Solicit several numbers that work.

8. Discuss with the class that in mathematics, the word "and" means "all conditions must be true for the statement to be true."

9. Draw the graph of x < 14 and x > 9 on a number line on the board or overhead.

10. Present another example: x > –6 and x < 2. Solicit numbers that work for x and draw the graph on a number line on the board or overhead.

From Inequalities to Compound Inequalities

Directions:

1. Write the two inequalities "3x – 4 < 17" and "5 – 2x < 1" side by side on the board or overhead.

2. Ask students how to solve and graph each of the inequalities.

3. Then combine the inequalities into a compound inequality with the word "and": "3x – 4 < 17 and 5 – 2x < 1."

4. Ask the students, "What do you think is the solution to the inequalities connected with 'and'? Can you graph it on the number line?"

5. Then write the two inequalities "2x + 7 ≤ 13" and "5x – 19 ≥ 16" side by side on the board or overhead.

6. Solve and graph each inequality on the board.

7. Then have the students consider the compound inequality "2x + 7 ≤ 13 or 5x – 19 ≥ 16."

8. Ask the students, "What do you think is the solution to this compound inequality? Can you graph it on the number line?"

9. Explain that to solve a compound inequality, you need to solve each side of the conjunction "and" or "or." Then you must look at the conjunction and determine if it combines the solutions (or) or restricts them (and).

10. Solve and graph the following compound inequalities:

    x + 5 < 8 or −3x < −18

    4x − 3 < 17 and 2x + 9 > 13

    This can be done by the whole class in a discussion or by the
    students individually with the results then discussed as a class.

Introduction to Absolute Value

Directions:

1. Ask the students, "What is the absolute value of −7?" "What is the
   absolute value of 7?" (**Answer to both is 7; $|−7| = 7$ and $|7| = 7$**)
   Explain that the absolute value of a number is the distance from
   that number to 0 on the number line.

2. Ask, "How do we solve a problem such as $|x| = 4$?" Explain that x
   must be 4 units from 0. Graphically, this looks like:

   Ask the students for the solution. (**x = 4 or x = −4**)

3. Write "$|x| < 4$" on the board. Ask for some solution values.
   (**Answers will vary, for example, 3, −3, 2, 1, 0, −2**) Ask, "How can
   we graph this?" The solution for x must be all numbers less than
   4 units from 0 on the number line. Graphically, this looks like:

   Ask the students for the solution. (**x > −4 and x < 4**)

4. Now write "$|x| > 4$" on the board. Ask for some solution values.
   (**Answers will vary, for example, −5, −6, 5, 6, 7**) Ask, "How can we
   graph this?" The solution for x must be all numbers more than 4
   units from 0 on the number line. Graphically, this looks like:

   Ask the students for the solution. (**x > 4 or x < −4**)

5. Ask the students to write the compound inequality for $|x| > −2$.
   Discuss the solution and the graph. Solicit different explanations
   for how to arrive at the solution.

6. Repeat #5 with $|x| < 11$.

Concept Development

Absolute Value and Distance

► Blackline master **Absolute Value and Distance** is located in the *Teacher's Resource Manual*, **pages 87–92.**

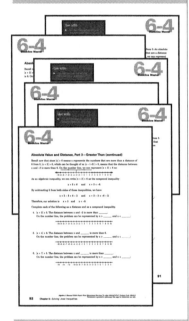

Teacher's Tip:

Worksheet 5 for this objective, **page 6-22**, supports this activity with practice exercises.

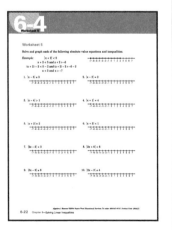

1. Give one copy of the blackline master **Absolute Value and Distance, Part 1—Equality** to each student.

2. Make an overlay to use with the overhead projector so the students can follow the explanation.

3. Discuss the definition of the absolute value of a number as the distance of the number from 0. Thus, $|7| = 7$ and $|-7| = 7$. Ask, "What does $|x - 4| = 5$ mean?" **(The distance from x – 4 to 0 is 5, or the distance from x to 4 on the number line is 5 units.)** Discuss the graph and solution from the blackline master.

4. Ask the students to work problems 1–3 on the blackline master. Discuss the solutions.

5. Ask, "What does $|x + 3| = 6$ mean?" **(The distance from x + 3 to 0 is 6, or the distance from x to –3 on the number line is 6 units.)** Discuss the graph and solution from the blackline master.

6. Ask the students to work problems 4–6 on the blackline master. Discuss the solutions.

7. Repeat steps 1 through 6 for the blackline master **Absolute Value and Distance, Part 2—Less Than**.

8. Repeat steps 1 through 6 for the blackline master **Absolute Value and Distance, Part 3—Greater Than**.

6-30   Chapter 6—Solving Linear Inequalities

Practice Activities

Pick Your Poison Card Game

Directions:

1. The goal of this game is to strengthen the students' skills with writing the solutions and graphs of compound inequalities.

2. Have the students work in groups of four or five.

3. Have the students make two decks of cards for each group. To do so, they should copy the inequalities and their graphs from the blackline master, one inequality plus graph to a card, for deck 1, and the words "AND" and "OR" as shown on the blackline master for deck 2 (five cards with "AND" and five cards with "OR").

4. Each group should then have two decks of cards:

   a. Deck 1 contains cards with an inequality and its graph.

   b. Deck 2 contains cards with either an "AND" or an "OR."

5. For the game, each student draws two cards from deck 1 and one card from deck 2, and combines them to form a compound inequality. He or she writes the compound inequality on a piece of paper.

6. Each student then writes the solution to the compound inequality and graphs it on his or her piece of paper.

7. After everyone in the group has finished, the students check one another's solutions to make sure they are all correct.

8. The students replace the cards in the appropriate decks and shuffle the decks.

9. Repeat steps 5 through 8 as long as time permits.

Materials:

▶ Blackline master **Pick Your Poison Card Game** is located in the *Teacher's Resource Manual,* **page 93.**

▶ Blank cards or

Materials:

▶ Blackline master **Absolute Value Rummy** is located in the *Teacher's Resource Manual*, **page 94.**

▶ Blank cards or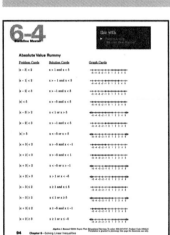

Absolute Value Rummy

Directions:

1. The goal of this game is to strengthen the students' skills in recognizing the solutions and graphs of absolute value equations and inequalities.

2. Have the students work in groups of four or five.

3. Have the students make a deck of cards for each group. To do so, they should copy the problems, solutions, and graphs from the blackline master, one to a card. Each group should then have a deck of 45 cards.

4. Directions for play:

   a. Devise a method to determine who will be the first dealer in each group. One method would be to number the students in the group from 1 to 4 or 5 and to pick a random number by drawing a card or rolling a die.

   b. The dealer shuffles the deck of cards and deals them, face down, one at a time, until each player has 6 cards.

   c. The dealer places the remaining cards face down in the center and turns over the top card and places it next to the remaining deck.

   d. The person to the left of the dealer begins. Play goes clockwise. The player may pick the top card from the deck or the top exposed card. If he or she can make a match, (matching problem, solution, and graph), the player puts the three cards face up in front of himself or herself. Whether or not a match is made, the player then discards one card face up on the exposed card pile to end his or her turn.

   e. As each match is made, the other players check to see if it is correct. If it is not correct, that player must replace the cards in his or her hand and continue play by discarding a card.

   f. The first player to get rid of all of his or her cards is the winner.

   g. If the deck runs out, the discard pile is shuffled and placed face down so that play can continue.

   h. When a game has been completed, the winner becomes the new dealer and play starts over as long as time permits.

Make It and Share

Directions:

1. Ask all students to write an inequality in the following form:
   ax + b > c *and* dx + e < f
   where a, b, c, d, e, and f are any integers ≠ 0.

2. Ask the students to write another inequality of the form
   ax + b < c *or* dx + e > f
   where a, b, c, d, e, and f are integers ≠ 0.
   Example: 5x + 9 < 54 or x + 6 > −5

3. Ask the students to write a third sentence of the form
   $|ax + b| < c$
   Example: $|2x + 6| < 14$

4. Finally, ask the students to write a fourth sentence of the form
   $|ax + b| > c$
   Example: $|3x + 4| > 19$

5. Form groups of four students. Have each group check all of the group members' written inequalities to see if they are in the forms described. The students should help one another fix any incorrectly written inequalities. These inequalities become the problems for the group.

6. The papers on which the inequalities are written are rotated in the group until everyone has worked all the problems. Students should write and do their work on their own paper, not on the problem sheets.

7. After each student has worked all of the problems in the group, have the students compare their solutions. If there is disagreement on a solution, the group should work the problem together and agree on the solution.

8. Each person in a group should have a set of problems and solutions to turn in at the end of the activity.

9. If time allows, have the groups exchange problems and repeat steps 6–8.

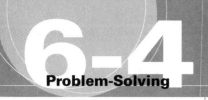

Problem-Solving Activities

Compound Inequalities

Directions:

1. Sketch each of the following graphs on the board or overhead and ask the students to name a compound inequality for each.

   a. 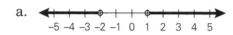   b.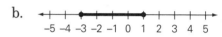

   c. 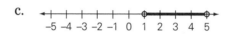   d.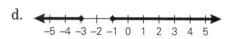

   e. 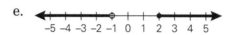   f.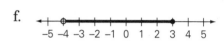

2. Sketch each of the following graphs on the board or overhead and ask the students to name an absolute value inequality for each.

   a. 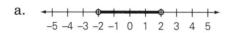   b.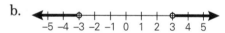

   c.    d.

   e.    f.

3. Ask the students to come up with a compound inequality with an "and" that has a solution of:

   a. x > 3   b. an empty set   c. x ≤ −4

4. Ask the students to come up with a compound inequality with an "or" that has a solution of:

   a. x < 2   b. all real numbers   c. x ≥ −1

Investigations With Inequalities

Directions:

Give each student a copy of the blackline master **Investigations With Inequalities**. Have the students work individually to solve the problems, which are reprinted below.

Materials:

▶ Blackline master **Investigations With Inequalities** is located in the *Teacher's Resource Manual,* **page 95.**

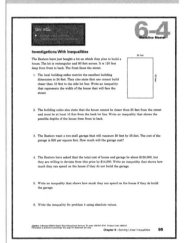

The Baxters have just bought a lot on which they plan to build a house. The lot is rectangular and 80 feet across. It is 120 feet deep from front to back. The front faces the street.

80 feet

120 feet

1. The local building codes restrict the smallest building dimension to 24 feet. They also state that one cannot build closer than 10 feet to the side lot line. Write an inequality that represents the width of the house that will face the street.

2. The building codes also state that the house cannot be closer than 25 feet from the street and must be at least 15 feet from the back lot line. Write an inequality that shows the possible depths of the house from front to back.

3. The Baxters want a two-stall garage that will measure 20 feet by 25 feet. The cost of the garage is $20 per square foot. How much will the garage cost?

4. The Baxters have asked the total cost of house and garage to be about $150,000, but they are willing to deviate from this price by $14,000. Write an inequality that shows how much they can spend on the house if they do not build the garage.

5. Write an inequality that shows how much they can spend on the house if they do build the garage.

6. Write the inequality for problem 4 using absolute values.

6-5 *Objective:* **Graph inequalities in the coordinate plane.**

Sample Test: Graph each of the following inequalities on the graph provided.

1. $y < 2x - 3$
   Solution:

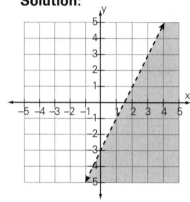

2. $3x + 2y \geq 4$
   Solution:

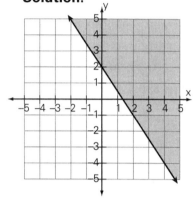

3. $y < x + 3$
   Solution:

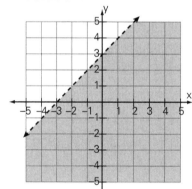

4. $y \leq 5$
   Solution:

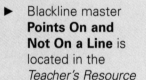

Materials:

► Blackline master
  **Points On and
  Not On a Line** is
  located in the
  *Teacher's Resource
  Manual,* **pages
  96 and 97.**

► Overhead graph
  paper transparency

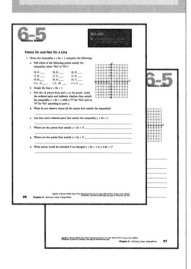

Concept Development Activities

Points On and Not On a Line

Directions:

1. Give one copy of the blackline master **Points On and Not On a Line** to each student. Students may work in pairs.

2. Ask the students to do problem 1.

3. After the students have completed problem 1, turn on the overhead projector and shine the coordinate plane on the board.

4. Ask a student to graph the line y = 2x + 1 on the board while the other students draw this graph at their seats.

5. Ask a second student to graph the first three points of problem 1 on the coordinate plane on the board. Ask a third student to graph the next three points on the coordinate plane, and a fourth student to graph the next three points on the coordinate plane, and a fifth student to graph the last three points on the coordinate plane. These students should label each point with "Y" if it is a solution to y < 2x + 1 or "N" if it is not.

6. Discuss the conjectures the students can make. Be careful not to correct conjectures about above and below the line for all points. Ask questions such as, "Do you think that might be true?" or "Do the rest of you agree or disagree?"

7. Ask whether the second point (2, 5) is part of the graph for y < 2x + 1.

8. Repeat this process for problem 2.

9. After problems 1 and 2 have been discussed, ask if the students were surprised about which side of the line for problem 2 had the "Y" points after their conjecture about problem 1.

Conjectures That Need To Be Made

Directions:

1. After completing the activity **Points On and Not On a Line**, you should lead the students into a method for graphing linear inequalities, as follows.

2. Compare a line on a plane to a point on a number line. Discussion ideas follow:

   a. A point on the number line divides the line into three parts: the point, all the points on one side of the point, and all the points on the other side.

   b. The solution to an equation with one variable is represented by just the point. The solution to an inequality with a less

> **Teacher's Tip:**
>
> Using the overhead to project the coordinate plane on the board works very well. You can then write on the board and erase the writing to start a new problem without having to redraw the coordinate plane.

> **Materials:**
>
> ▶ Blackline master for **graph paper** is in the Appendix.
>
> ▶ Overhead graph paper transparency

Concept Development

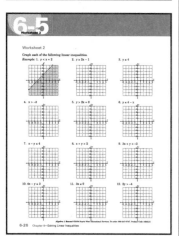

than sign is all the points on one side of the point. The solution to an inequality with a greater than sign is all the points on the other side of the point.

c. Similarly, a line divides the plane into three parts: the line, all the points on one side of the line, and all the points on the other side of the line.

d. The solution to an equation with two variables is represented by a line on a plane. The solution to an inequality with two variables is all the points on one side or the other side of the line.

3. Explain that to solve an inequality with two variables (or a horizontal or vertical line), the steps are as follows:

a. Graph the equation of the line with the inequality replaced by an equal sign.

b. Test a point on one side of the line to see if it satisfies the inequality. If it does, then all points on that side of the line satisfy the inequality, so shade that side of the line. If the point does not satisfy the inequality, shade the opposite side of the line.

c. For example, for the inequality $y < 3x + 1$, graph the line $y = 3x + 1$. Check the point $(2, 2)$ by substituting it in the inequality. Find the point on the graph. Because $(2, 2)$ satisfies the inequality, shade the side of the line that contains that point.

4. Present another comparison between points and lines to the class. On the number line, if an endpoint is included in the inequality (greater than or equal to, less than or equal to), it is filled in; if it is not included (greater than, less than), it is represented as an open dot. On a coordinate graph, if the line is not included (greater than, less than), we could use a series of open dots to represent the line, but that would take too much time, so we use a dashed or dotted line for a line that is not included, and we use a solid line for a line that is included (greater than or equal to, less than or equal to) and shade in the correct side of the graph.

5. Provide examples by graphing several inequalities with the class, such as $y > x - 2$; $y \leq 3 - x$; $y > 4$; and $x + y \leq 6$.

Practice Activities

Match the Graph

Directions:

1. Students will work in pairs. Have each pair of students make two decks of 10 cards each, including the inequalities in the blackline master **Match the Graph**, one inequality per card, and the second deck including the graphs from the blackline master, one graph taped to each card.

2. Working together, each pair of students should match each problem with the correct graph. The important concept is understanding whether the line should be solid or dashed and which side of the line should be shaded.

3. **Variation without cards:** Give each student a copy of the blackline master and have the students, working independently, write the correct inequality on each graph.

Share It

Directions:

1. Students will work in groups of five. Ask the students to write on their papers two inequalities of the form ax + by ___ c, where the blank can be any inequality ($<$, $>$, $\leq$, or $\geq$) and a, b, and c are nonzero numbers. Students should use different inequality symbols for each problem.

2. Ask the students to draw the graphs for their two inequalities on graph paper and label the graphs with the equation being graphed.

3. Now ask the students to exchange their inequalities (*not* the graph paper) with other members of their group and to graph the other students' inequalities. They should be sure to label their graphs with the equations being graphed. The students should continue exchanging problems until each student has graphed all ten inequalities.

4. Have the students compare their graphs and agree on the correct graphs for the problems.

Materials:

▶ Blackline master **Match the Graph** is located in the *Teacher's Resource Manual*, **page 98.**

▶ Blank cards or 💿

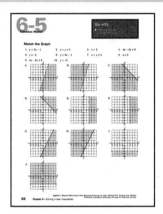

Materials:

▶ Blackline master for **graph paper** is in the Appendix.

Teacher's Tip:

Worksheet 3 for this objective, **page 6-27**, supports this activity with practice exercises.

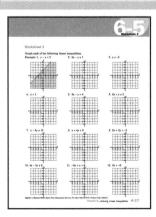

Materials:

▶ Blackline master **Graphing Situations** is located in the *Teacher's Resource Manual,* **page 99.**

▶ Blackline master for **graph paper** is in the Appendix.

Problem-Solving Activity

Graphing Situations 💡

Directions:

1. Read each problem presented below (and on the blackline master) to the class, writing relevant points on the board.

2. Ask the students to write the inequality for each problem and then graph the result, choosing an appropriate scale. Discuss what each graph should look like and have a student sketch it on the board.

3. Ask the students to suggest interpretations for the graph of each problem. The interpretations should be given in complete sentences.

4. The problems are as follows:

   a. The ski club is going on a ski trip to Gold Mountain Resort. The lift tickets for students under the age of 17 cost $30; for people age 17 and older, the cost is $40. The ski club has at most $900 to spend on lift tickets. Write an inequality for the possible cost of the lift tickets in which x represents the number of lift tickets for those under age 17 and y represents the number of lift tickets for those age 17 and older.

   b. The jazz band wants to attend the Ray Charles concert. Tickets cost $40 for general admission and $60 for reserved seating. The jazz band can spend at most $1,000 on the concert. Write an inequality for the possible cost of the tickets in which x represents the number of general admission tickets and y the number of reserved seat tickets.

Chapter 7

Solving Systems of Linear Equations and Inequalities

7-1 Solve systems of equations by graphing.

7-2 Determine whether a system of equations has one solution, no solutions, or infinitely many solutions.

7-3 Solve systems of equations by using the substitution method.

7-4 Solve systems of equations by eliminating one variable.

7-5 Solve systems of inequalities by graphing.

7-1 *Objective:* **Solve systems of equations by graphing.**

Sample Test: Solve the following system of equations graphically:

$x + y = 2$
$x - y = 8$

Solution:

(5, −3)

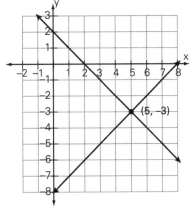

Concept Development Activities

Pick a Pair

Directions:

1. Have the students work in pairs. Each pair of students should decide who will be partner 1 and who will be partner 2.

2. Write the following equations on the board or overhead: x + y = 14; x − y = 6.

3. Each student should construct a table like the one shown below:

First Number (x)	Second Number (y)

4. In each group, the partners should fill in their own tables with combinations of numbers according to the following rules:

    Partner 1: Use integers from −5 to 10 to find six pairs of integers whose sum is 14.

    Partner 2: Use integers from −5 to 10 to find six pairs of integers whose difference is 6.

5. In each group, the students should now plot their individual solutions on a common standard x, y coordinate plane. Remind the students that a combination of integers that satisfies their situation is referred to as an ordered pair and that ordered pairs can be plotted on the coordinate plane.

6. The students should notice that each of their sets of points forms a straight line. Have each them connect their points using a ruler.

7. Review the slope-intercept form of an equation: y = mx + b. Write the two equations used in this exercise in the slope-intercept form and discuss the y-intercept and the slope of the line.
    $$x + y = 14 \ \rightarrow \ y = -x + 14 \qquad\qquad x - y = 6 \ \rightarrow \ y = x - 6$$

Materials:

▶ Blackline master for **graph paper** is in the Appendix.

▶ Overhead graph paper transparency

▶ Rulers

8. Ask for volunteers to discuss what they think the graph shows them about the combinations of integers whose sum is 14 and the combinations of integers whose difference is 6.

9. Point out that *exactly one* set of numbers makes both given situations true. **(10, 4)** Begin referring to the two situations as a "system of equations" and the point that both situations have in common as the "solution" to the system of equations. Have the students compare their tables to see if they have that set of numbers in common.

10. Have the students repeat this exercise with two more systems:

    a. two integers whose sum is 8 and two integers whose difference is 10

    b. $x - y = 7$ and $x + y = 3$

Materials:

▶ Blackline master for **graph paper** is in the Appendix.

▶ Overhead graph paper transparency

▶ Rulers

Which Lines Intersect?

Directions:

1. On the board or an overhead, draw an in/out (x/y) machine as shown to the right. Ask the students to make an in/out table for each of the following equations. For each equation, they should use the values −5, −4, −3, −2, −1, 0, 1, 2, 3, 4, 5 for their "in" (x) values.

   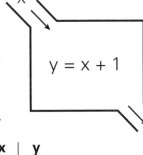

   $y = x + 1$

   a. $y = x + 1$

   b. $y = -1x + 3$

   c. $y = 0x - 4$

   Sample table:

x	y
−5	
−4	
−3	
.	
.	

Teacher's Tip:

Worksheet 1 for this objective, **pages 7-2 and 7-3**, supports this activity with practice exercises.

2. Ask the students, working individually, to graph their ordered pairs for $y = x + 1$ and draw the straight line connecting them. Ask one student to do this on the overhead projector graph. Do the same for $y = -1x + 3$ and $y = 0x - 4$, plotting each line on the same coordinate plane. Have the students determine the points where the graphs cross. The graph will look like the one to the right.

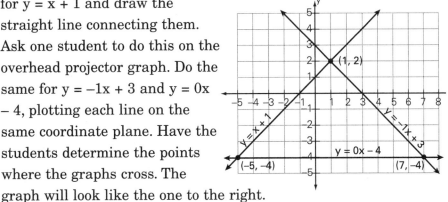

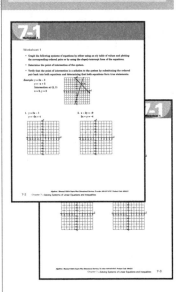

Materials:

► Blackline master for **graph paper** is in the Appendix.

► Overhead graph paper transparency

Teacher's Tip:

Worksheet 2 for this objective, **pages 7-4 and 7-5**, supports this activity with practice exercises.

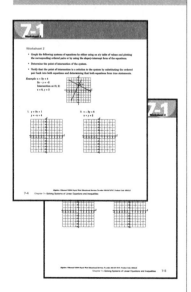

3. Ask the students what conclusion they can make about the points at which any two of the lines intersect. Take this opportunity to reinforce the idea that the point of intersection is also known as the solution to the system of two equations. In other words, any point where two lines intersect is a solution to both equations and thus is a solution to the system of equations. Discuss that this method is called *solving a system of equations by graphing.*

4. Have the students pick one of the points of intersection and substitute the x and y values into each of the two equations represented by the intersecting lines. Have them determine that these x and y values allow both equations to be true. Discuss with the students that those specific points of intersection are the *only* values that make both equations true statements and that only *one* pair will satisfy both equations.

Intersection Using the Slope/y-Intercept Form

Directions:

1. Write the equation y = x + 4 on the board or overhead.

2. Ask the students how they would construct the graph of this equation.

3. If the students suggest using the slope (1) and the y-intercept (0, 4), construct the graph from that information. If the students do not suggest the slope/y-intercept information, have them name at least three points and draw the graph. Ask, "What is the slope of this graph? What is the y-intercept of this graph? Are these numbers part of the original equation?"

4. Review that when an equation is written in the y = mx + b form, the slope is m and the y-intercept is b.

5. Have the students sketch graphs of y = 2x − 1 and y = $\frac{1}{2}$x + 2 on the same coordinate plane by using the slope/y-intercept information.

6. Ask, "Do the graphs of the equations intersect?" **(Yes)** Ask, "At what point?" **(2, 3)**

7. Have the students check to see whether the ordered pair (2, 3) satisfies both equations. Discuss that this is the only ordered pair

that works for both equations (refer to the graphs). Thus, this is the *solution* to the set of equations. Explain that the solution set is the set of ordered pairs that satisfy all conditions (in this case, the conditions are the two equations).

8. Have the students practice graphing equations by using the slope/y-intercept form and have them check their results. Example sets of equations are:

a. $y = -x + 2$ b. $y = x + 6$ c. $x + y = 3$
     $y = 2x - 1$ $y = x + 4$ $y - 2x = 9$

Calculator Solution

Directions:

Materials:

► Graphing calculators

1. Have the students form pairs. Each pair should have at least one graphing calculator.

2. Ask the students, working with their partner, to construct a graph of the equation $x + y = 5$ on their calculators. Review the steps for entering the equation and displaying the graph. Usually, it is necessary to enter the equation in a special form as required by the calculator input.

3. Have each pair students construct the graph of $y = x + 1$ on the same coordinate plane as the previous equation.

4. Ask the following questions and discuss the answers:
   a. Do the graphs intersect? **(Yes)**
   b. At how many points? **(One)**
   c. Can you find the coordinates of the point of intersection? **(2, 3)**
   d. What is unique about the point (2, 3)? **(It satisfies *both* equations)**

5. Substitute the values $x = 2$ and $y = 3$ into both equations to check that they do satisfy both equations. By doing this check, the students can be confident that they have found the point of intersection. This point is the *solution* to the simultaneous equations.

6. Repeat the process for other equations, such as:

a. $x + 2y = 6$ b. $x - y = -3$
     $y = 2x - 2$ $2x + y = 0$

Practice Activities

Which Lines Have Common Points of Intersection?

Materials:

▶ Blackline master for **graph paper** is in the Appendix.

▶ Rulers

Directions:

1. Have the students form groups of three. Then have each student in each group pick a letter, a, b, or c.

2. Assign the students the following equations, according to their letters:

   a. $y = 2x + 4$ b. $x + y = -2$ c. $2x + y = 4$

3. Ask each student to make an in/out or x/y table to determine the coordinate points for his or her equation and then graph the equation, *or* to solve each equation for y and use the slope/y-intercept form to graph the line more quickly. Instruct the students within each group to use the same scale for their coordinate planes when graphing their equations.

4. Ask the students in each group to find the three points of intersection by placing all of the graphs in a stack and holding them to the light.

5. Have the students then check their solutions by substituting the x and y values of the points of intersection into the equations of each of the two intersecting lines. If the solution causes both equations to be true, then the students know the solution is correct. The solution to this activity appears at right.

6. If time permits, assign three more equations.

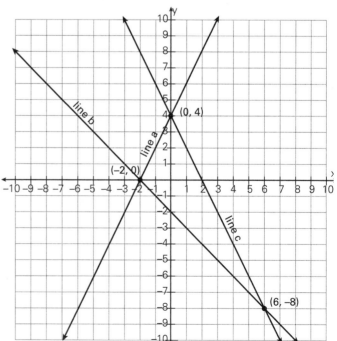

Chapter 7—Solving Systems of Linear Equations and Inequalities

Solve the System

Directions:

1. Have each student in the class write an equation in the form $y = mx + b$, where m and b are integers between -10 and $+10$. For example, $y = 4x + (-6)$.

2. Ask each student to construct the graph of their equation. Students may use graphing calculators and transfer the graph to graph paper.

3. Have the students form pairs to solve the system of equations determined by their two equations. *Note:* Check to see that the two equations have different slopes. If the equations have the same slope, one of the partners will need to create a new equation.

4. Next, have each student sketch the graph of his or her partner's equation on his or her own graph. The partners need to agree on the point of intersection (the solution to the system of equations). The students will need to estimate the intersection point because most will not be integer values.

5. Have the students substitute the values of the point of intersection into their equations to see if the values are correct.

6. If the values were estimated (not integers), have the students adjust the values to see if they can find the exact values that work for both equations.

7. Continue this activity by forming different pairs of students and repeating steps 3 through 6.

Materials:

► Blackline master **Comparing Earnings** is located in the *Teacher's Resource Manual*, **page 100.**

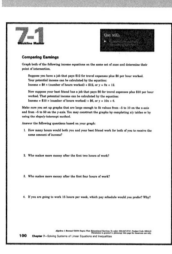

Problem-Solving Activities

Comparing Earnings

Directions:

1. Give each student a copy of the blackline master **Comparing Earnings**. Have the students graph both of the following income equations on the same set of axes and determine their point of intersection. Instruct them to set up graphs that are large enough to fit values from –5 to 10 on the x-axis and from –5 to 50 on the y-axis. The students may construct the graphs by completing x/y tables or by using the slope/y-intercept method.

   Suppose you have a job that pays $12 for travel expenses plus $8 per hour worked. Your potential income can be calculated by the equation:
   Income = $8 × (number of hours worked) + $12, or $y = 8x + 12$.

   Now suppose your best friend has a job that pays $6 for travel expenses plus $10 per hour worked. That potential income can be calculated by the equation:
   Income = $10 × (number of hours worked) + $6, or $y = 10x + 6$.

2. Ask the students to answer the following questions based on their graphs:

   a. How many hours would both you and your best friend work for both of you to receive the same amount of income?

   b. Who makes more money after the first two hours of work?

   c. Who makes more money after the first four hours of work?

   d. If you are going to work 15 hours per week, which pay schedule would you prefer? Why?

Find the Equation

Directions:

1. Have the students form pairs.

2. Write the equation $y = 3x - 1$ on the board or overhead. Have each student graph the equation individually.

3. Now have the pairs of students construct another equation that they think will intersect the given equation at the point $(0, -1)$.

4. Let the students decide the strategy they think will work and proceed with the solution. *Note:* Some students may draw a line and try to find the equation. Others may try to name an equation and make the graph, etc.

5. The solution is not complicated because the intersection point $(0, -1)$ is the y-intercept. Any equation of the form $y = mx + b$ where $m \neq 3$ and $b = -1$ will work (for example, $y = -2x - 1$). There are infinite possibilities.

6. Graph the equation $y = 3x - 1$ on an overhead graph. Ask for volunteers to name their equation and graph it on the overhead. Have several different pairs with different solutions make their graphs.

7. Ask, "Why are there so many correct solutions?"

8. Ask the students to explain the concepts and how they found their equation.

9. Ask for an equation whose graph would intersect $y = -x + 3$ at the point $(0, 3)$.

Concept Development

7-2 *Objective:* Determine whether a system of equations has one solution, no solutions, or infinitely many solutions.

Sample Test: Determine whether the following system of equations has one solution, no solutions, or infinitely many solutions. A coordinate graph has been provided for you, but you are not required to use it.

$$4x + 2y = 12$$
$$x - y = 9$$

Solution using slope/y-intercept:

**4x + 2y = 12 is equivalent to
y = –2x + 6; slope is –2,
y-intercept is +6**

**x – y = 9 is equivalent to y = x – 9;
slope is +1, y-intercept is –9**

**Since the slopes are different,
there is one solution, (5, –4).**

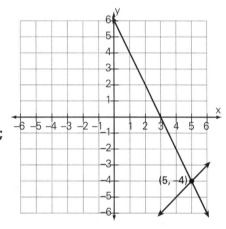

**The answer could also be determined
by graphing, as shown on the graph to the right.**

Concept Development Activities

How Many Times Do the Lines Intersect? 💡

Directions:

<table>
<tr><td>

1. Have the students work in pairs.

2. Assign each pair of students one of the following equations, and have them complete a table of values like the one at the right for their particular equation. Have the students use x values that are integers ranging from –5 to 5. Depending on the size of the class, you may have to assign more than one equation to a pair of students.

</td><td>

equation (y = mx + b)

x	y

</td></tr>
</table>

Materials:

► Blackline master for **graph paper** is in the Appendix.

► Overhead graph paper transparency

► Rulers

a.

$y = x + 1$	$y = -x + 1$
$y = 2x + 1$	$y = -2x + 1$
$-2x + 2y = 2$	$2x + 2y = 2$
$-4x + 2y = 2$	$4x + 2y = 2$

b.

$y = x + 3$	$y = -x + 3$
$y = 2x + 3$	$y = -2x + 3$
$-2x + 2y = 6$	$2x + 2y = 6$
$-4x + 2y = 6$	$4x + 2y = 6$

3. Have one of the students from each pair that has an equation in group "a" go to the overhead projector and write their given equation and their completed table, and then sketch a graph of that equation on an overhead graph paper transparency, using values from their completed table. Make sure that all students can observe all of the problems at once so they can make visual comparisons. All of the graphs should be drawn using the same scale for the coordinate plane.

4. Begin a discussion with the class to determine if the students see any graphs that would intersect or appear as if they would intersect. Have them look at the tables of values for those equations and see if they have a point in common. Remind the students of what they know about lines that share a common point. **(This point is where they will intersect.)**

5. Continue the discussion by asking the class if any of the lines look like they would *never* intersect. After they determine which ones they think won't intersect, have them look at the corresponding tables of ordered pairs. Point out that they have no points in common, and ask the students why they do not intersect. Be sure to point out that these lines are parallel. Next, discuss what the equations have in common. If needed, point out to the students that their *slopes* are the same.

6. Next, ask the students if they see any tables that have more than one point in common. If needed, point out that not only do these particular equations have more than one point in common, but also in fact they have all of their points in common. Have the students look at the graphs of these particular equations and ask them what they notice about them. If needed, point out that they appear to be the same line. Put these equations in slope/y-intercept form to show they are the same equation.

7. Have the students write all the equations in "a" in the slope/y-intercept form. Discuss which equations have the same slope or

different slope. Discuss that lines with different slopes will intersect. Lines with the same slope will not intersect if they have a different y-intercept.

8. Repeat steps 3 through 7 on a new graph transparency for the equations in group "b."

9. Conclude the discussion with a question. Ask the class if they can draw two different straight lines that intersect at more than one point. This may allow for another productive discussion to reinforce the fact that there are just three possibilities when graphing two different lines: lines that cross only once, lines that never cross, and lines that lie on top of each other and share every point in common.

How Many Times Do the Lines Intersect?

Part A: Parallel Lines

Directions:

1. Have the students work in groups of four.

2. Instruct the students that they will be drawing a graph on the top half of their sheet of graph paper and then they will be completing tables and writing equations on the bottom half of the paper.

3. Ask each student to write an equation in the form $y = mx + b$, with m and b being any integer from −3 to +3. Each student in the group should write a different equation.

4. Have each student complete a table of values for his or her equation. The x values should range from −5 to +5.

5. Have each student graph his or her equation on a coordinate plane and label the axes accurately. The students should then draw the line connecting their points.

6. Ask the students to pass their graphs to another student in their group.

7. Now have the students draw a line on the graph they just received that is parallel to the original line. On the bottom half of the

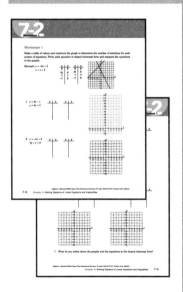

paper, have them complete a table of values for the points that appear on their new line.

8. Have the students then write on the bottom half of the paper an equation for the new line they drew in the form y = mx + b. They should circle the new equation.

9. Repeat steps 6 through 8 two more times until each student has the graph he or she originally designed.

10. Begin a discussion by asking the students if they see any similarities among all of the circled equations at the bottom of their papers. They should notice that the slopes are all the same. If the students do not see this, point it out to them. Also, ask the students what they notice about the tables of values. They should notice that their tables have no points in common. Reinforce the fact that if any two of the equations on their papers were in the form of a system of equations, there *would not be a solution* to the system because the lines have no points in common.

Part B: Intersecting Lines

Directions:

1. Repeat steps 1 through 6 of Part A, with the students using a different sheet of graph paper from that used for Part A.

2. On the sheet of paper the students have received, have them draw a line that is not parallel to the original line but instead intersects it. Have the students complete a table of values on the bottom half of the paper for the points that appear on their new line.

3. Have the students write an equation on the bottom half of the paper for the new line they drew in the form y = mx + b. Ask them to circle their new equation.

4. Have the students pass the papers back to their owners.

5. Begin a discussion by asking about the slope of the two intersecting lines. Ask the students how many points the two tables of values have in common. If needed, point out that when two straight lines intersect, they do so at exactly one point. Ask the students to conjecture about what this would mean if the two equations were a system of equations. Ask them how many

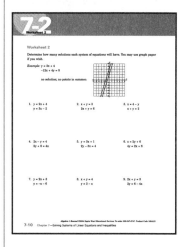

solutions they think the system would have. Again, if needed, point out that there would be exactly *one solution* to the system— the point that the lines have in common.

6. Reinforce the fact that if two lines intersect, their slopes are different.

Part C: Same Line

Directions:

1. Ask the students to make a table of values for each equation in the following system of equations: $y = 2x + 3$, $4x - 2y = -6$.

2. Have them draw the graphs of these two equations on the same axes.

3. The students will likely be asking how to do this because the two equations have the *same points*. Discuss that they do have the same table of values. Ask the students why they think this is so.

4. Put both equations in the $y = mx + b$ form. Show that the equations are the same: $y = 2x + 3$. Thus, the solution to this system of equations is all (*infinitely many*) points on the line because both equations are the same.

Practice Activities

What About These Lines?

Directions:

1. Have the students form groups of four. Distribute one copy of the blackline master **Line Graphs** and 15 blank cards to each group of students.

2. Have each group write the following line combinations on the blank cards:

line 1 and line 2	line 1 and line 3	line 1 and line 4
line 1 and line 5	line 2 and line 3	line 2 and line 4
line 2 and line 5	line 3 and line 4	line 3 and line 5
line 4 and line 5	line 3 and line 1	line 2 and line 2
line 4 and line 4	line 5 and line 1	line 5 and line 5

Materials:

▶ Blackline master **Line Graphs** is located in the *Teacher's Resource Manual*, **page 101.**

▶ Blank cards or 💿

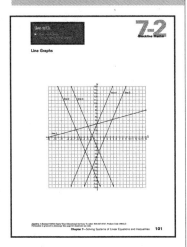

Chapter 7—Solving Systems of Linear Equations and Inequalities

3. One student in each group should shuffle the cards and place the deck face down on the table (or desk). Play begins with the student to the right of the shuffler. That student draws a card, reads what it says, looks at the lines on the blackline master, and makes a statement about those lines. For example, if the card reads, "line 2 and line 4," the student could say, "Line 2 and line 4 intersect at one point in Quadrant 3." *Optional:* The students could be instructed to name the point if the lines intersect.

4. The other students in the group should then confirm or dispute the answer.

5. Continue until all the cards have been used. Groups can shuffle and start again.

6. Circulate among the groups to answer any questions.

"One, None, or Many" Jeopardy

Directions:

1. Make an overhead transparency of the blackline master **Game Board**. The grid has six columns and five rows. Each row, successively, as you go down the page, contains more difficult systems of equations to solve graphically (i.e., more algebraic steps are needed before they fit the form y = mx + b). Systems in the top row are worth 100 points, systems in row 2 are worth 200 points, and so on, with systems in the bottom row being worth 500 points. Place rectangular pieces of paper over each of the boxes on the grid so that the problems are not visible to the students prior to being selected. Sticky notes work well for this.

2. Divide the class into two or three teams with an equal number of players. Determine a fair way to choose which student will go first and how the order of subsequent students will be selected. This may depend on the seating arrangement in your classroom. Explain that the students will be asked to determine if the graphs of two equations will intersect (one point), will be parallel (no points), or will be the same line (all points). Also explain that the problems get more difficult as you go down the grid.

3. Alternate turns between the teams. After a team member finishes a system of equations, whether he or she gets it right or wrong,

Materials:

▶ Blackline master **Game Board** is located in the *Teacher's Resource Manual*, **page 102.**

▶ Blackline master for **graph paper** is in the Appendix.

▶ Rulers

▶ Rectangular pieces of paper

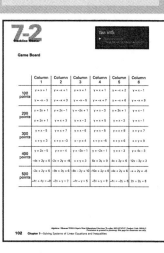

the next player on the other team selects the next system of equations to be solved.

4. To keep score in this activity, keep a running total for each team of the point values of each system that is answered correctly.

Problem-Solving Activities

Solving Problems by Using Systems of Equations ☀

Directions:

Give each student a copy of the blackline master **Solving Problems by Using Systems of Equations**. Have the students work individually to solve the problems, which are reprinted below.

For each problem, determine the pairs of integers that satisfy both of the conditions. Graph the solutions to determine if there is one solution, infinite solutions, or no solutions. Then answer question 4.

1. a. The sum of 4 times the first number, x, and 2 times the second number, y, is 12.

   b. When 3 times the second number, y, is subtracted from 6 times the first number, x, the result is 12.

2. a. The sum of 8 times the first number, x, and 2 times the second number, y, is 16.

   b. When the second number, y, is added to 4 times the first number, x, the result is 8.

3. a. The sum of 6 times the first number, x, and 3 times the second number, y, is 18.

   b. When the second number, y, is added to 2 times the first number, x, the result is 4.

4. How can you tell the number of solutions without constructing a graph? _____

_____

Materials:

► Blackline master **Solving Problems by Using Systems of Equations** is located in the *Teacher's Resource Manual,* **page 103.**

Sailing Ships 💡

Directions:

Give each student a copy of the blackline master **Sailing Ships**. Have the students work individually to solve the problem, which is reprinted below.

Solve the following problem by using a system of equations and graph the solutions:

Two ships are sailing in the same area. Ship A is following a course given by the equation $y = x + 8$. Ship B is following a course given by the equation $y = 2x - 2$. The danger spot for these two ships is where their courses would intersect. Both ships are heading northeast. Ship B will arrive at the danger point first, but to be safe, it makes a 90° turn (right angle) counterclockwise at the point of intersection. Ship B travels for a short period of time on this new course before it returns to its original path along the course $y = 2x - 2$. Find an equation that represents the course for Ship B during the time it is forced to change direction.

Materials:

▶ Blackline master **Sailing Ships** is located in the *Teacher's Resource Manual*, **page 104**.

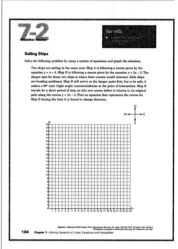

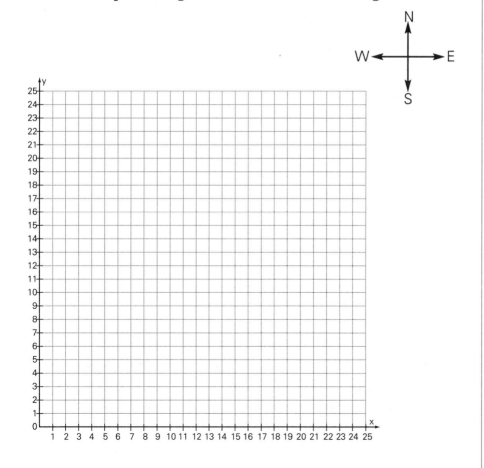

Concept Development Activities

Combination, Combination, Who's Got My Combination?

Directions:

1. Write the equation $5 + 3 = 8$ on the board (you can also use an overhead transparency).

2. Have the students work in pairs, with the partners using the same sheet of paper. On the paper, have them draw a table like the one to the right.

$5 + 3$	$=$	8

3. Ask the students to make a list of at least six pairs of integers other than 5 and 3 that combine to equal 8, and enter these into their tables.

4. Draw the table shown in step 2 on the board, and ask one student from each pair to come to the board and enter one of the pair's combinations that equals 8. Make sure there are no duplicates.

5. Have the class choose any two of the combinations, and set them equal to each other, causing a true equation (for example, $5 + 3 = 4 + 4$). Discuss how the value of 8 can be written in infinitely many ways, and that what they are doing is choosing different combinations to substitute for 8 that allow them to continue to

write true mathematical statements.

6. Repeat step 5 a few times, allowing different students to select different combinations for 8 and setting them equal to each other.

7. Conclude the activity by asking each pair of students to choose any integer and to complete a table of five combinations that add or subtract to be that integer. Have them write out at least three equations obtained by setting any two of their combinations equal to each other.

8. Discuss that any quantities that are equal can be *substituted* for each other. For example, if 6 + 4 = x and x = –3 + 13, then 6 + 4 = –3 + 13. When each side is evaluated, it can be shown that 10 = 10.

9. Use other variables and give some numerical examples.

The Algebra Alphabet ☀

Directions:

1. Write the following equations on the board (you may also use an overhead transparency):

A = 1 + 4	B = 2 + 7	C = –3 + 4	D = –1 + 6
E = 4 – (–3)	F = 10 – 7	G = 9 – 1	H = 4 + 2
I = 6 + 8	J = –6 + (–4)	K = (–1) · (–5)	L = $\frac{16}{2}$
M = 2 · 7	N = $\frac{18}{3}$	O = 5 · (–2)	P = (–1) · (–7)
Q = 3 · 3	R = $\frac{12}{12}$	S = $\frac{27}{3}$	

2. Have the students complete the following steps a through c for each situation (1) through (4):

    (1) Given: A = B   (2) Given: D = A

    (3) Given: E = P   (4) Given: G = R

  a. Substitute the numerical values into the equation and write the equation in numerical form. (For example, given Q = S, the student would write 3 · 3 = $\frac{27}{3}$.)

  b. Simplify both sides of the equation.

  c. Determine if each situation (1) through (4) is true or false.

3. Have the students make up four similar comparisons using the list of equations in step 1, creating two comparisons that are true

Teacher's Tip:

Worksheet 1 for this objective, **page 7-13**, supports this activity with practice exercises.

Answer Key for #2c:
(1) false
(2) true
(3) true
(4) false

and two comparisons that are false. Have them prove their answers by completing steps 2a through 2c.

4. Ask for volunteers (four or so) who would be willing to share their comparisons on the board. Ideally, two would show true comparisons and two would show false comparisons.

5. Next, write the following two equations on the board, one under the other.

$$5 = 2 + 3$$
$$5 = 1 + 4$$

Ask the students if the 5 has the same value in both equations and if it would be correct to write 5 = 5. In other words, is it correct to say that the left side of the top equation is equal to the left side of the bottom equation? Then, discuss whether the right sides of these same two equations are also equal. (That is, does 2 + 3 = 1 + 4?)

6. Discuss that wherever a "5" appears in these equations, anything that has a value of 5 can be substituted in its place.

7. Next, write the equation y = x + 4 on the board. Ask the class, "What does y equal?" This should provide you with the opportunity for a good class discussion about how the value of y depends upon the value of x, and that you don't have enough information to determine what y equals, other than x + 4.

8. After the discussion, write the equation y = 2x + 1 directly below the equation in step 7. *Example:* y = x + 4
$$y = 2x + 1$$

Remind the students that in an algebra problem, the value of a variable must remain the same throughout the entire problem. If the variable (letter) appears more than once in a problem, it has to have the same value each time it appears.

9. Ask the students to compare the problem in step 8 with the problem in step 5. Ask, "If the left sides of each equation are the same, shouldn't the right sides be equal as well?" Discuss that for the equations in step 8, since y = y, then x + 4 = 2x + 1.

10. Point out that the equation x + 4 = 2x + 1 has just one variable, x. Solve for x by the following method, writing the steps on the board or overhead:

$$\begin{array}{rcl}
x + 4 & = & 2x + 1 \\
-\,4 & & -\,4 \\
\hline
x & = & 2x - 3 \\
-2x & & -\,2x \\
\hline
-1x & = & -3
\end{array} \qquad \text{or } x = 3$$

11. Show that by now plugging in 3 wherever x appears in either of the original equations, the value of y can be determined:

$$\begin{array}{ccc}
y = x + 4 & \quad\text{or}\quad & y = 2x + 1 \\
y = 3 + 4 & & y = 2(3) + 1 \\
y = 7 & & y = 7
\end{array}$$

So the solution to the system of equations y = x + 4 and y = 2x + 1 is (3, 7). This is the point of intersection of the graphs of the equations.

12. Explain to the students that in the example in step 8, the value of y from the first equation was actually substituted in place of y in the second equation. Explain that they can substitute in this way with any system of equations. Use one of the equations to determine what one variable is in terms of the other variable, and then substitute that expression into the second equation. As an example, write this system of equations on the board:

$$\begin{array}{c}
y = 3 + x \\
x + 2y = 9
\end{array}$$

Show the students that the value of y in the top equation (in terms of x) can be substituted into the bottom equation:

$$x + 2(3 + x) = 9$$

and this new equation can be solved for x:

$$\begin{array}{c}
x + 6 + 2x = 9 \\
3x = 3 \\
x = 1
\end{array}$$

Show that by substituting x = 1 into either of the original equations, they can determine the value of y:

$$\begin{array}{ccc}
y = 3 + 1 & \quad & 1 + 2y = 9 \\
y = 4 & \text{or} & 2y = 8 \\
 & & y = 4
\end{array}$$

So the solution to this system of equations is (1, 4).

Teacher's Tip:

Worksheet 2 for this objective, **page 7-14**, supports this activity with practice exercises.

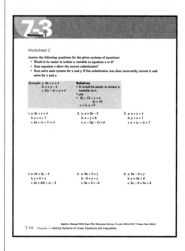

13. Have the students work in pairs to solve the system $y = x - 4$ and $y = 4x - 1$ by using the substitution method. Ask if any pair wants to present their work, and give them an opportunity to do so. You may want to do this with three or four pairs of students, which gives the class the opportunity to correct their own work. Sketch the graphs of the equations to show the intersection at $(-1, -5)$. Explain that substitution is another method for solving a system of equations without making graphs.

One, None, or Lots of Solutions ☀

Directions:

1. Divide the students into groups of four.

2. Ask the groups to write three pairs of equations, one in which the graphs will intersect, one in which they will be parallel, and one in which they will be the same line. Allow time for the groups to discuss how to create the equations and to write them. Tell the class that you will answer questions they have only with the responses of "yes" or "no."

3. Ask the groups to raise their hands when they have written the three pairs of equations. Check to see that each group:

   a. has a pair of equations with different slopes.

   b. has a pair of equations with the same slope and different y-intercepts.

   c. has two equations that are algebraically the same.

4. Ask the groups to:

   a. solve each pair of equations by substitution.

   b. discuss in the groups what happened when they solved each pair of equations.

   c. make a generalization on how you can identify equations that intersect, are parallel, or are the same line when solving by substitution.

5. Discuss the generalizations from different groups and summarize their generalizations. *Example:* (a) If you solve a system of equations by substitution and you get an ordered pair for the

answer, the graphs of the equations intersect at one point. (b) If you solve a system of equations by substitution and you get an *inconsistent* answer like 3 = 0, the graphs of the equations are parallel. (c) If you solve a system of equations by substitution and you get a consistent answer like 0 = 0, the equations are the same line.

Practice Activities

Substitution Rummy

Directions:

Materials:

▶ Blank cards or

1. Have the students make decks of cards with the equations listed below (one per card). Have the students put the letter E on the equation cards and the letter S on the substituted equation cards. There will be 48 cards per deck. The students should make enough decks for one deck for every four students.

Answers to "Substitution Rummy" Cards
a. (1, 4)   b. (−7, −5)
c. (−1, 7) d. (11, 16)
e. (3, 2)   f. (−1, 4)
g. ($\frac{1}{2}$, 6) h. (−16, −11)
i. (−5, −10) j. (1, 2)
k. (13, 19) l. (3, 0)
m. (−7, −10) n. (−8, −10)
o. (1, 2)   p. (−9, 14)

	Equation Card 1	Equation Card 2	Substituted Equation
a.	$x + y = 5$	$y = x + 3$	$x + (x + 3) = 5$
b.	$x = y - 2$	$x - 2y = 3$	$(y - 2) - 2y = 3$
c.	$2x + y = 5$	$y = 6 - x$	$2x + (6 - x) = 5$
d.	$y = x + 5$	$2x - y = 6$	$2x - (x + 5) = 6$
e.	$x = 2y - 1$	$3x - y = 7$	$3(2y - 1) - y = 7$
f.	$-x - y = -3$	$y = 2 - 2x$	$-x - (2 - 2x) = -3$
g.	$y = 5 + 2x$	$2x + y = 7$	$2x + (5 + 2x) = 7$
h.	$x - 2y = 6$	$x = y - 5$	$(y - 5) - 2y = 6$
i.	$x - y = 5$	$y = 2x$	$x - 2x = 5$
j.	$y = 3 - x$	$x + 2y = 5$	$x + 2(3 - x) = 5$
k.	$6 + x = y$	$2x - y = 7$	$2x - (6 + x) = 7$
l.	$2x - y = 6$	$x = 2y + 3$	$2(2y + 3) - y = 6$
m.	$x - 3 = y$	$2x + 4 = y$	$2x + 4 = x - 3$
n.	$x = 2 + y$	$y - 2x = 6$	$y - 2(2 + y) = 6$
o	$x = 2y - 3$	$x = y - 1$	$2y - 3 = y - 1$
p.	$y = 5 - x$	$2x + y = -4$	$2x + (5 - x) = -4$

2. Have the students form groups of four. One student in the group should shuffle a deck of cards and deal six cards to each of the students in the group. The remainder of the deck should be placed face down in the middle of the group.

Teacher's Tip:

Worksheet 3 for this objective, **page 7-15**, supports this activity with practice exercises.

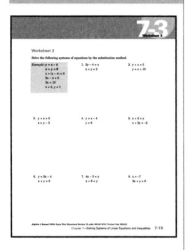

3. The object of the game is for the students to make books of three cards each. A book should contain two equation cards and one matching substitution equation card. This activity uses substitution of one expression into another equation.

4. The person to the left of the dealer begins. He or she turns over the top card of the deck. The player can take this card and discard a card from his or her hand face up, or he or she can ask if anyone else wants the first card. If another player takes the card, he or she then discards a card from his or her hand face up, and the original player can take this card or ask if anyone wants that card, repeating the above procedure. If no one wants an offered card, then the original player must take the next card in the deck (no matter what it is) and discard one card face up from his or her hand, and the play goes to the left with a new player.

5. Whenever a player has a book, he or she may lay it down. The first person to get two books is the winner. That player will lay down all of his or her cards so the other players can check them.

6. A variation of this activity involves having the students who did not lay down all their cards search the remaining cards in the deck to make two books.

7. Have the students solve the systems of equations for their books.

Make It and Share

Directions:

1. Tell the students that in this activity they will be making up a system of two equations that others in the class will solve. Ask them, "How can we make up equations?" Explain that although there are different ways to make up equations, the simplest way is to start with the answer (ordered pair) and write equations that satisfy this solution. For example, for the solution $(4, -2)$, two possible equations are $y = x - 6$ and $x + y = 2$.

2. Ask the students to write their two equations, one in the form $ax + by = c$ and the other in the form $y = dx + e$ or $x = fy + g$, where a, b, c, d, e, f, and g are values they choose. Urge the students to make the equations as difficult as they wish.

3. Have the students write the solution to their system of equations and to check it by substituting those values into the original equations. Have the students keep the paper on which they do this work.

4. On a new sheet of paper, have each student write his or her name and the system of two equations (no solutions). Call this the "equation sheet."

5. Have the students form groups of four or five. Have them exchange the equation sheets and solve the other student's system of equations on their worksheet. Each person should work all of the problems created by members of the group. Then, as a group, they should check the solutions by comparing them with the original students' solutions.

6. Repeat with new groups as time allows.

Individual Match

Directions:

1. Use one or two decks of cards that were prepared in the activity **Substitution Rummy**, depending on the size of the class. Each deck will serve 16 students.

2. Place all of the cards face up on a table or desk. Have the students come up in pairs, and have each student select three matching cards that make a book: the two equation cards and the substitution equation card. After all cards have been matched, have the students solve the system of equations for the cards they selected.

3. Discuss that the solution is an ordered pair that works for both equations.

4. Have the students check their answers by substituting the numbers back into the original equations.

Materials:

▶ Blank cards or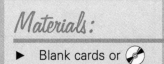

Teacher's Tip:

Worksheet 4 for this objective, **page 7-16**, supports this activity with practice exercises.

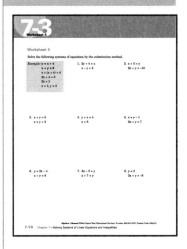

Materials:

▶ Blackline master
Matching Equations is located in the *Teacher's Resource Manual*, **page 105.**

Problem-Solving Activities

Matching Equations

Directions:

Give each student a copy of the blackline master **Matching Equations**. Have the students work individually to solve the problems, which are reprinted below.

1. Given equations A through D,

   A. $y = -3x + 4$ B. $y = 2x + 3$ C. $y = -3x + 2$ D. $-2x + y = 3$

   use the process of substitution to determine:

   a. Which two equations form a system with exactly one solution? What is the solution?

   b. Which two equations form a system that has no solution?

   c. Which two equations form a system that has infinite solutions?

2. Explain how you made decisions for 1a, 1b, and 1c.

Comparing Earnings

Directions:

Give each student a copy of the blackline master **Comparing Earnings**. Have the students work individually to solve the problems, which are reprinted below.

Solve the following problems by using a system of equations:

> Carrie and Cooper are working at the same store selling sporting goods. They have options on earning their salaries. Carrie chose to get paid by straight commission, which is 25% of all of her sales per month. The amount (A) that she earns is therefore .25 of sales (s), or A = .25s.
>
> Cooper decided to get paid by having a salary of $600 per month plus 10% of his sales. The amount (A) that he earns is $600 plus .10 of sales (s), or A = 600 + .10s.

1. If each of them had $3,000 in sales for one month, who will earn more that month? How much would each earn?

2. If each person had $6,000 in sales for one month, who will earn more that month? How much would each earn?

3. Solve the system of equations by substitution. What does this solution represent?

7-4 *Objective:* Solve systems of equations by eliminating one variable.

Sample Test: Solve the following systems of equations by eliminating one variable.

1. $2x - y = 7$
    $x + y = 2$

    Solution: (3, –1)

2. $2x + y = 8$
    $x - 3y = -10$

    Solution: (2, 4)

Concept Development Activities

Elimination Makes the Problems Easier, Part I

Directions:

1. Write the simple, true equation $3 + 4 = 7$ on the board and ask the students if it is a true statement.

2. Write another simple, true equation, $3 + 2 = 5$, on the board just below the original equation, so they look like this:

    $$3 + 4 = 7$$
    $$3 + 2 = 5$$

    Refer to these equations as a "system of equations with no variables."

3. Ask the students to add the columns together and write their answer as another equation, so it looks like this:

    $$3 + 4 = 7$$
    $$\underline{3 + 2 = 5}$$
    $$6 + 6 = 12$$

    Discuss with the students how the new equation is also a true statement.

4. Next, ask the students to rewrite the second equation by changing the sign of every number in it. (Multiply both sides by –1.) Have them verify that the new equation, $-3 - 2 = -5$, is still a true statement.

5. Repeat step 3, this time using the original first equation and the new second one (with the signs changed). Explain that adding the equation with the signs changed is the same as subtracting the equation.

$$\begin{array}{r} 3 + 4 = 7 \\ -3 - 2 = -5 \\ \hline 0 + 2 = 2 \\ \hline \text{or} \ \ 2 = 2 \end{array}$$

6. Discuss that the new equation (2 = 2) is still a true statement, but now it is even easier to read because one of the numbers, the 3's, have been eliminated (opposites), leaving a simpler equation of just 2 = 2. This is a good time to discuss the idea that being able to rewrite mathematical equations in a simpler way often makes it easier to solve difficult problems.

7. Have the students work in groups of four. Pass out one overhead transparency and one marker to each group.

8. Instruct the students to divide the sheet into four rectangles so that each student has a workspace on the sheet. Have each student write an original equation of his or her choice, similar to the original simple equation, 3 + 4 = 7, in his or her particular workspace.

9. Have each group exchange its transparencies with another group. Then, have each member of the group choose a different true equation on the new transparency and, under that equation, write a second equation that begins with the *same first number.* This is similar to step 2 above.

10. Have each student "add" his or her "system of equations" together, column by column. The student should come up with an "answer equation" that is also a true statement, as in step 3 above.

11. Next, have each student perform steps 4 and 5 on his or her system of equations. In other words, the students should multiply each side of the second equation by (−1) and add the equations. The result of adding these equations will also be a true equation in which the first number was eliminated, making the answer an even simpler equation.

12. As the students work, circulate through the classroom to see which groups have at least one problem done correctly. Ask them

to present their findings on the overhead for the rest of the class to see.

13. At the conclusion of the presentation, reinforce through discussion the idea of how eliminating a variable in a system can make the problem much easier to solve.

Elimination Makes the Problems Easier, Part II

Directions:

1. Write the simple, true equation, $1 + 2 = 3$, on the board. Ask the students if it is a true statement.

2. Write another simple, true equation, $1 + 4 = 5$, on the board just below the original equation, so they look like this:

$$1 + 2 = 3$$
$$1 + 4 = 5$$

Continue referring to these equations as a "system of equations with no variables," just like in the previous activity (Part I).

3. Ask the students to substitute the variables x and y for the numbers 1 and 2 in the original equation. That is, $1 + 2 = 3$ becomes $x + y = 3$.

4. Ask the students if any numbers in the second equation were the same as those in the first equation. If needed, point out that both equations began with a "1." Remind the students that whenever a variable is used in a system of equations, it must retain the same value throughout the problem. Therefore, "x" can be substituted for "1" in the second equation. That is, $1 + 4 = 5$ becomes $x + 4 = 5$.

5. Now ask the students if they see any relationship between the second numbers in the two equations. If needed, point out that the "4" in the second equation is twice as large as the "2" in the first equation. We substituted "y" for the "2" in the first equation, so we can substitute "2y" for "4" in the second equation. That is, $x + 4 = 5$ becomes $x + 2y = 5$.

Materials:

▶ Overhead transparencies

▶ Overhead markers

Teacher's Tip:

Worksheet 1 for this objective, **page 7-19**, supports this activity with practice exercises.

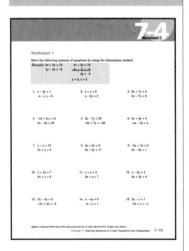

6. Now write the system of equations using the two equations that
    use x and y as variables:

$$x + y = 3$$
$$x + 2y = 5$$

Add the two equations, column by column, to get
$$2x + 3y = 8$$

7. Point out that this equation is not easily solved because it still
    contains two variables. Ask the students if they remember
    anything from the previous activity (Part I) that might help them
    make this equation easier to solve. If needed, remind the students
    about changing the signs of all the terms in one of the equations
    (multiply by –1) before adding the equations column by column.
    Remind them also that this yielded a much easier equation to
    solve. Ask for a volunteer to help you rewrite the second equation
    by multiplying each side by –1.

8. Finish the example by writing the system as follows:

$$x + y = 3$$
$$-x - 2y = -5$$

9. Have the students add this system together, column by column,
    and point out that one of the variables, x, is eliminated. Reaffirm
    how this makes the resulting equation one that can be solved
    more easily.

$$x + y = 3$$
$$-x - 2y = -5$$
$$\underline{0 - y = -2}$$
$$-y = -2, \text{ or } y = 2$$

10. Now is a good time to emphasize the idea of substitution. Ask for
    volunteers who think they know how to find x once they know
    what y equals. If needed, remind the students about how to use
    substitution to plug the value they found for y back into either of
    the original equations and finish solving for the other unknown
    variable, x.

$$x + y = 3$$
$$x + 2 = 3$$
$$x = 1$$

11. This may seem repetitive to your students, but be sure to
    emphasize to them that the purpose of this example was to show
    them a method for solving two equations with two variables by
    first eliminating one of the variables from the problem.

12. Write the following system of equations on the board. Have the students form groups of two. Give each group a blank overhead transparency and a transparency marker, and have the group members write the system on the transparency.

$$x + y = -4$$
$$x - 3y = -8$$

13. Ask the students, "Which variable do you think is the easiest to eliminate when adding the two equations column by column? Why? What makes it seem so?" Have them complete the following steps on their transparency:

   a. Rewrite the second equation by multiplying both sides by –1.

   b. Add the equations together, column by column.

   c. Come up with a resulting equation that contains only a single variable.

   d. Solve this equation for the remaining variable.

   e. Substitute this answer back into either of the original equations to solve for the other variable.

14. Select a pair of students who feel confident in their work to present it on the overhead for the rest of the class to use for comparison. If needed, have additional pairs present their work until a correct solution is presented.

15. Write another system of equations on the board to be solved. For example:

$$x + y = 1$$
$$2x + 3y = -1$$

Let the students decide how to eliminate one of the variables. Discuss how different groups solved the system.

16. Discuss the following problems where, as in #15, the elimination of a variable requires something different from multiplying by –1.

   a. $2x + y = 7$
   $3x - 2y = 14$

   b. $x + 3y = 16$
   $4x + 7 = -2$

   c. $2x + 4y = 14$
   $3x + 2y = 17$

Elimination Makes the Problems Easier, Part III

Directions:

1. Review the overall concept of **Elimination Makes the Problems Easier**, both parts I and II, with the students. Emphasize how eliminating a variable makes a system of equations much easier to solve.

2. Write the following two systems on the board for the students to copy:

   a. $x + 3y = 5$
      $-x + y = 3$

   b. $x + 2y = 4$
      $-x - 2y = -1$

3. Have the students practice the process of eliminating a variable by solving the first system, "a," through elimination. Question them and check for their understanding.

4. Ask for a volunteer to attempt to solve system b on the board for others to observe. Make sure the student uses the elimination method. The students should see that both variables are eliminated in this case, leaving them with nothing on the left side of the system. Substitute zero in for the "nothing."

$$
\begin{array}{r}
x + 2y = 4 \\
-x - 2y = -1 \\
\hline
0 + 0 = 3 \\
\hline
0 = 3
\end{array}
$$

5. Take this opportunity to ask the following question: "Is this result always true or never true?" Someone should respond with "never true." Inform the class that if a system is found to be "never true" using elimination, then the system has no solution and the two lines have no points of intersection. The following word association can be used as a reminder:

   never true = no intersection

   Have the students find the slope of the two lines $\left(-\frac{1}{2}\right)$. Reinforce that the graphs will be parallel with no intersection.

6. Now, put a new system on the board and have the students attempt to solve it by the elimination method.

$$x + 4y = 5$$
$$-3x - 12y = -15$$

7. After multiplying the top equation by 3, the students should come up with a slightly different result than for the previous problem.

$$3(x + 4y) = 3(5)$$
$$\underline{-3x - 12y = -15}$$

$$3x + 12y = 15$$
$$\underline{-3x - 12y = -15}$$
$$0 + 0 = 0$$
$$0 = 0$$

8. Repeat step 5, asking the students the following question: "Is this result always true or never true?" Someone should say "always true." Inform the class that if a system is found to be "always true" using elimination, then there are infinitely many solutions to the system because the two lines share all the same points. As before, word association can be used as a reminder:

always true = all points in common (infinitely many solutions)

Simplify the equations and show that these are the same equation ($x + y = 5$).

9. Have the students solve the following systems to reinforce the concepts of systems with no solutions and systems with infinitely many solutions.

   a. $2x - 8y = 4$
      $x - 4y = 2$

   b. $-3x + y = 5$
      $3x - y = 2$

   c. $2x - 4y = 5$
      $-6x + 12y = -15$

   d. $5x - y = 4$
      $10x - 2y = 1$

Practice Activities

Matching

Directions:

1. Give one copy of the blackline master **Matching** to each student.

2. Write two systems of equations on the board, one that can be added directly to eliminate a variable, and one that needs modification first to eliminate one variable. Examples are:

$$x + 3y = 4 \qquad\qquad x - y = 12$$
$$2x - 3y = 8 \qquad\qquad 2x + 2y = 8$$

3. Discuss with the class which system of equations can be solved easily with no manipulation necessary. This system will be solved by adding the equations to eliminate one of the variables.

4. Have the students determine which equations on the blackline master can be easily solved by adding the equations together to get the resulting equation. Then have them match those systems to the proper resulting equations.

5. Discuss the matches. As a group, *solve* the one-variable resulting equation and discuss how to substitute to find the other variable.

6. An extension of this activity would be to have the students solve the remaining equations on the blackline master by multiplying both sides of one equation by an integer and continuing as above.

Materials:

► Blackline master **Matching** is located in the *Teacher's Resource Manual*, **page 107.**

Teacher's Tip:

Worksheet 2 for this objective, **page 7-20**, supports this activity with practice exercises.

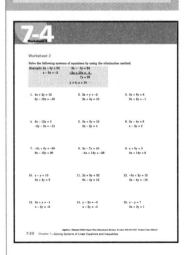

Which Pairs Work Nicely?

Directions:

1. Write the following equations on the board. Ask the class which ones they think would pair up nicely so that they could use the elimination method to solve them quickly if they were a system of equations.

   a. $x - 3y = 9$ b. $2x + 5y = 20$ c. $-x + y = 3$

   d. $3x + 4y = 24$ e. $-2x - y = 4$ f. $4x + 6y = 48$

   g. $-x - 4y = -16$ h. $5x + 7y = 26$ i. $-5x - y = -8$

2. Have the students write three of the pairs of equations they selected in step 1 and solve them using the elimination method.

3. Discuss how to solve "b" and "d," or a system in which both equations need to be multiplied by a different factor.

Answer Key:

A and C $(-9, -6)$
A and G $(1, 12)$
B and E $(-5, 6)$
C and E $\left(-2\frac{1}{3}, \frac{2}{3}\right)$
C and I $\left(\frac{5}{6}, 3\frac{5}{6}\right)$
D and G $(4, 3)$
H and I $(1, 3)$

Tic-Tac-Toe

Directions:

1. Have the students work in pairs. Give one copy of the blackline master **Tic-Tac-Toe** to each pair of students.

2. Have the students choose who will be "X" (one colored marker) and who will be "O" (another colored marker). Have them flip a coin to determine who will go first.

3. Each student, when it is his or her turn, selects a "square" to work on. The student must use the elimination method to determine if the system of equations has one solution (and, if so, what it is), no solutions, or infinitely many solutions. After completing the problem, that student must prove to the other student that the solution works, indicating which variable was eliminated in the solution. It is the other student's responsibility to check and make sure that the elimination method was used and the answers check in the equations.

4. If the student is correct, he or she covers the square with his or her colored marker. If the student is incorrect, the other student gets to cover the square with his or her colored marker.

Materials:

▶ Blackline master **Tic-Tac-Toe** is located in the *Teacher's Resource Manual,* **page 108.**

▶ Two colors of markers (beans, chips, etc.)

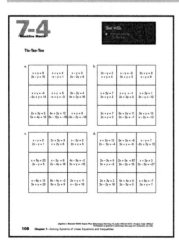

5. The first student to get three markers in a row—vertically, horizontally, or diagonally—or to get five covered squares (5 out of 9) wins.

6. Remind the students that systems of equations can have one solution, no solution, or infinitely many solutions.

7. **Variation:** Continue play until a student gets five squares covered will provide students with more practice.

Problem-Solving Activities

Eliminating a Variable

Directions:

Ask the students to use elimination of a variable to determine whether there is an ordered pair of integers that satisfies each of the following conditions, whether there is no solution, or whether there are infinitely many solutions.

1. a. The sum of the first number, x, and 2 times the second number, y, is 12.
   b. When 2 times the second number, y, is subtracted from 3 times the first number, x, the result is 12.

2. a. The sum of 8 times the first number, x, and 2 times the second number, y, is 28.
   b. When the second number, y, is subtracted from 4 times the first number, x, the result is 10.

3. a. The sum of the first number, x, and 3 times the second number, y, is 3.
   b. When 3 times the second number, y, is subtracted from 5 times the first number, x, the result is 15.

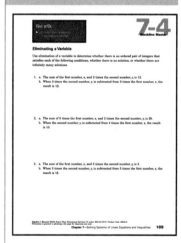

Materials:

▶ Blackline master **How Many Men and How Many Women?** is located in the *Teacher's Resource Manual,* **page 110.**

How Many Men and How Many Women?

Directions:

1. Give each student a copy of the blackline master **How Many Men and How Many Women?**

2. Have the students, working individually, write a system of equations from the information given in the situation below. One of the equations should be based on the number of employees, and the other equation should be based on the cost of the food. Remind the students that items with similar labels (e.g., cost) probably belong together in a single equation.

   Situation: During the past quarter, a manufacturing company earned more profit than the company owner expected. To thank the employees for their hard work, he planned a barbeque. The owner determined that he had around \$320 to spend on food, and according to the catering company, the average cost per person would be around \$8 per male and \$4 per female. The party would be given for all 50 employees of the company. Determine the number of male and female employees.

3. Have the students solve the problem presented by eliminating a variable in the system of equations and then determining how many employees are male and how many are female.

7-5 *Objective:* Solve systems of inequalities by graphing.

Sample Test: Solve the following two systems of inequalities graphically.

1. −2x + y < −4 and
   x + y ≥ −5

2. y > x − 1 and
   −4x + 2y ≤ 10

Solution:

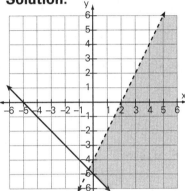

Solution:

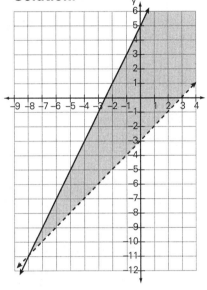

Concept Development Activities

Are You in My Region?

Directions:

1. Have the students work in pairs. Give one copy of the blackline master **Graph Inequalities** to each pair of students. Make an overhead transparency of the blackline master so the students can check their work as you discuss the points being plotted.

2. Have the students determine if the first point on the blackline master (0, 3) satisfies both inequalities by substituting the values for x and y in the inequalities. **(Yes)**

3. On the overhead, plot the point by putting a Y for "yes" on the point (0, 3).

4. Have the student pairs determine if the ordered pairs B through P on the blackline master satisfy the inequalities. Call on

Materials:

► Blackline master **Graph Inequalities** is located in the *Teacher's Resource Manual*, **page 111.**

► Overhead transparency of blackline master

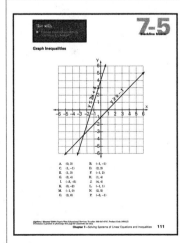

individual students to come to the overhead and plot a point on the transparency until all the points are plotted. Have them place a Y on the point if it satisfies the system of inequalities and an N on the point if it does not.

5. Discuss where all of the "Y" points lie. Ask questions such as, "Which region is the solution? Could there be more than one region? What about the lines?"

6. Discuss how to shade the region and how to determine if the lines should be dashes or solid lines.

Plot Some Solutions

Directions:

1. Have the students work in groups of four.

2. On their own sheets of graph paper, have the students create a system of inequalities in the form y ___ mx + b, where the blank is to be replaced by $<, >, \leq,$ or $\geq$. They should write one "less than" and one "greater than" inequality.

3. Suggest that the students choose numbers between –5 and +5 for m and b in their inequalities.

4. Have the students graph their inequalities as if they were equations (that is, replace the inequality sign by an equal sign).

5. Have the students pass their graphs to another student in their group.

6. Each student should now choose four coordinate points (ordered pairs), one in each quadrant. The students should limit the values to between –10 and +10.

7. The students should determine if each of these four points is a solution to the system of inequalities by substituting the values into each of the inequalities and seeing if true statements are formed.

8. Have the students plot all four of their test points directly on the graph. Any point that is a solution (satisfies *both* inequalities) should be designated with a Y, and any point that *is not* a solution (does not satisfy *both* inequalities) should be designated with an N.

Materials:

▶ Blackline master for **graph paper** is in the Appendix.

Teacher's Tip:

Worksheet 1 for this objective, **page 7-23**, supports this activity with practice exercises.

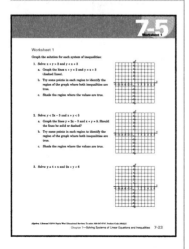

9. Have the students pass the papers to another student in the group. Then repeat steps 6 through 8. Continue until each student has his or her original graph.

10. Discuss that all of the points that make their individual systems true (the Y's) are limited to one of the regions formed by the two intersecting lines. Explain the concept of infinite solutions within a region on a graph if the students do not come up with this themselves during the discussion.

Intersection of the Shaded Regions

Directions:

1. Write the inequality $y > -x + 3$ on the board or overhead. Review the following steps for graphing this inequality:

   a. Graph the line $y = -x + 3$.

   b. Make the line dashed because the inequality does not include the line (it is > rather than ≥).

   c. Select some coordinate points and shade the side in which the points satisfy the inequality.

2. Call on a student to describe how to graph $y = -x + 3$. Construct the graph on the overhead as the student describes the process (use a dotted line).

3. Ask another student to determine where the points are that satisfy the inequality $y > -x + 3$ [for example, (0, 0) doesn't work, but (5, 5) works]. Shade the half plane in which the coordinates satisfy the equation $y > -x + 3$.

4. Repeat steps 2 and 3 for the equation $y < 2x - 1$, for which, for example, (0, 0) doesn't work, but (3, 0) works. Shade this region in a different pattern than the shading for the previous inequality. The graph should look like the one at the right.

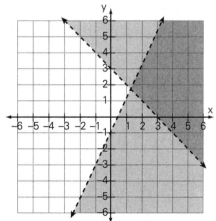

Materials:

▶ Blackline master for **graph paper** is in the Appendix.

▶ Overhead graph paper transparency

Teacher's Tip:

Worksheet 2 for this objective, **page 7-24**, supports this activity with practice exercises.

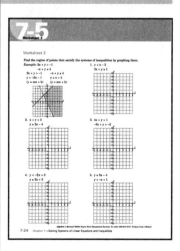

5. Ask the class, "Which points do you think will work for both equations?" **(Double-shaded region)** Explain that the double-shaded region is the intersection of the two sets of points. Only those points in the double-shaded region will work for both inequalities.

6. Discuss that the points on the dashed lines will not work for both inequalities. Select points such as (2, 1) and (1, 1) to show that they lie on the lines but don't satisfy *both* inequalities.

7. Explain that the solution to the system of inequalities $y > -x + 3$ *and* $y < 2x - 1$ is represented by the double-shaded region on the graph, and the word "and" means the solution satisfies both inequalities.

8. Have the students find the solution to the system of inequalities $x + y > 3$ and $y \geq x - 2$ on their graph papers. Circulate through the classroom and select a student to show his or her solution on an overhead graph.

Practice Activities

Which Points, Which Graph?

Directions:

1. Give one copy of the blackline master **Graphs** to each student.

2. Tell the students that you are going to name three points, and they need to identify the graph on the blackline master that contains all three points in the solution region.

3. Review the idea that the shaded portion of the graph contains all the points in that region that satisfies a system of inequalities.

4. Ask the students the following questions: Which graphs contain the following points in the solution region?

   a. (2, 4)

   b. (3, –1)

   c. (5, 2)

   d. Which graphs contain all three points in the solution region?

Materials:

▶ Blackline master **Graphs** is located in the *Teacher's Resource Manual*, **page 112.**

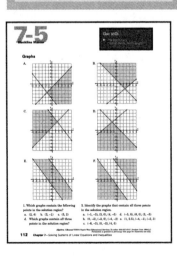

5. Continue this process, naming three points and having the students identify the graphs that contain all three points in the solution region.

   a. (−1, −3), (3, 0), (4, −5)

   b. (0, −3), (−3, 0), (−4, −2)

   c. (−6, −3), (0, −2), (4, 6)

   d. (−5, 6), (0, 0), (3, −3)

   e. (1, 2.5), (−4, −1), (−2, 3)

Teacher's Tip:

Worksheet 3 for this objective, **page 7-25**, supports this activity with practice exercises.

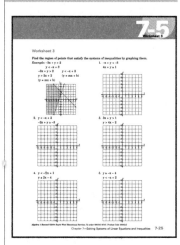

Share the Graphs

Directions:

1. Have each student write two inequalities of the form y ___ mx + b, where the blank in one of the inequalities is to be replaced by < and the blank in the other inequality by >. The values for m and b should not be 0.

Materials:

▶ Blackline master for **graph paper** is in the Appendix.

2. Have the students solve this system of inequalities on graph paper and shade the region. Discuss using a dashed line because the inequalities are < and >, not ≤ and ≥. Have the students write their system of inequalities at the top of four blank sheets of graph paper.

3. Have the students form groups of five and give their graph papers (the ones without the graph on them) to the other members of the group. The other members should then graph the systems of inequalities created by all of the other students in the group.

4. Have the groups compare the graphs for each system of inequalities. If differences exist, the group should decide which graphs, if any, are correct by using substitution.

Problem-Solving Activities

Satisfying Combinations

Directions:

1. Present the following problem to the students:

   The system of inequalities $y \geq \frac{1}{2}x + 6$ and $y \geq 2x$ is based on the scenario of a street vendor who sells ice cream cones. The first inequality is for his expenses, or costs of doing business, and the second inequality represents the income from sales for each cone. In each case, x represents the number of cones sold.

2. Ask, "Can x ever be negative?" **(No, it is the number of cones.)** Have the students fill in the following tables:

   "Cost": $y \geq \frac{1}{2}x + 6$ "Income from Sales": $y \geq 2x$

x	$\frac{1}{2}x + 6$
0	
2	
4	
6	
8	

x	2x
0	
2	
4	
6	
8	

3. Have the students graph the first inequality for costs and shade the region it represents. Then have them repeat the process for the second inequality for profits on the same graph.

4. Ask, "What do you think the point where the two lines cross represents?"

5. Ask, "What do you think the region where the two shaded regions overlap represents?"

6. Have the students try different values for x and determine which satisfy *both* inequalities. Have the students them on the graph to see where they are. Ask what they notice about these points.

Answer Key:

2.

x	$\frac{1}{2}x + 6$
0	6
2	7
4	8
6	9
8	10

x	2x
0	0
2	4
4	8
6	12
8	16

3.

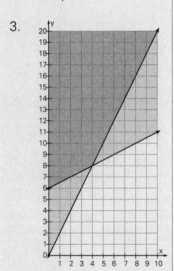

4. The break-even point.
5. All points that satisfy *both* equations.
6. They appear in the same region of the graph.

Chapter 7—Solving Systems of Linear Equations and Inequalities

Bean Bag Darts 🔅

Directions:

1. Have the students form groups of four. Give each group a piece of butcher paper (approximately 3 feet by 3 feet), a yardstick, and three different colored markers.

2. Have each group write at the top of the paper two linear equations in the form $y = mx + b$, where $m \neq 0$ and $b \neq 0$. Then they should draw a large coordinate plane centered on the rest of the butcher paper.

3. Each group should then graph the first equation in a different color than they used for the coordinate plane. They should write the equation in small print along this line. Then they should do the same for the second equation, using a different colored marker.

4. Have them lay the paper down on the floor or on the desk. Then have one person from the group toss the beanbag so it lands completely within one of the four regions formed by the two lines crossing on the coordinate plane. The student should mark the location with an X.

5. The other three members of the group must then come up with a system of inequalities based on the two equations such that point X is a solution to the system. They should then write this system of equations on the paper next to point X.

6. Steps 4 and 5 should be repeated for each member of the group. Mention that it would be a good idea for each student to toss the beanbag into a different region formed by the two lines.

7. As you observe the activity, choose a group that appears to be having success and ask if they would present their "dartboard" to the class. They should hold up their paper and explain how they came up with the inequalities for each location marked by an X.

8. This type of presentation offers great opportunities for class discussions, questions, explanations, and to hear about different problem-solving strategies. It also gives the students a chance to show what they know.

9. Have all the students solve the inequalities for each region of their graphs.

Teacher's Tip:

Whenever students produce "posters" such as these, they should be posted on the classroom walls for future reference. This is a great way to "decorate" a mathematics classroom, and the students can use the posters for assistance on later problems, if needed.

Exploring Polynomials

8-1 Multiply and divide monomials and simplify expressions.

8-2 Write numbers in scientific notation and find products and quotients of these numbers.

8-3 Add and subtract polynomials and express the answer so the powers of the terms are in descending order.

8-4 Multiply a polynomial by a monomial and arrange the power of the terms in descending order.

8-5 Multiply two binomials and simplify the expressions, including special products of $(a + b)(a + b)$ and $(a + b)(a - b)$.

8-1 *Objective:* **Multiply and divide monomials and simplify expressions.**

Sample Test:

Simplify:

1. $(2x)(3x^3)$

2. $\frac{9y^2}{12y}$, $y \neq 0$.

    Solution: $6x^4$

    Solution: $\frac{3}{4}y$

Teacher's Tip:

It is assumed that when dividing polynomials, no denominator is zero. Restrictions for denominators should be discussed briefly.

Concept Development Activities

Multiplying and Simplifying Monomials

Directions:

1. Give a copy of the blackline master **Powers** to each student.

2. Discuss problems 1–4 on the blackline master with the class and explain why $5^3 \cdot 5^2 = (5 \cdot 5 \cdot 5) \cdot (5 \cdot 5) = 3{,}125$. Have the students compute the answers by using calculators.

3. Next, have the students answer problems 5–8. Check for understanding of how to get the final exponent (total).

4. Have the students complete problem 9. Discuss problem 10. Make sure the students understand the relationship between the chart in problem 9 and the number of factors from problems 5–8.

5. Let the students work in pairs to answer problems 11–17. Discuss the answers.

6. As a class, work through problems 18–20. Help the students to verbalize how to simplify products of monomials.

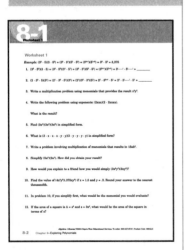

Calculator Experiment

Directions:

Materials:

▶ Scientific calculators

1. Discuss with the students the idea that for thousands of years
    algebra has been considered a tool, much like a shovel or a
    hammer is a tool. People have used algebra to make calculations
    easier to do. It is especially useful in helping us decide which
    results would be best or if relationships exist between events
    when values of numbers vary. Using algebra, you can decide, for
    example, which credit offer is best or find relationships that exist
    between such events as speed and braking distance.

2. Present the idea that we simplify algebraic expressions to make
    our calculations easier to do.

3. Give the students the example $(2x^2)(5x^3y)$. Write on the board:
    "If $x = 3$ and $y = 4$, how could we calculate the result of this
    example?" Have students explain how they would do it by using
    their calculators. For example, have students use the definition of
    exponents for the calculation:

    and then by using the power key y^x:

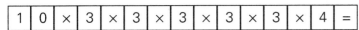

5. Show the students that they can simplify $(2x^2)(5x^3y)$ to get
    $2 \times 5 \times x^2 \times x^3 \times y = 10x^5y$, and then compute this expression by
    using the simplified result. Have them use the definition of
    exponents for the calculation:

    | 1 | 0 | × | 3 | × | 3 | × | 3 | × | 3 | × | 3 | × | 4 | = |

    Then have them use the y^x key:

6. Ask the students the results they received for the calculation.
    (9,720)

7. Ask the students, "If you were to choose the method you liked
    best, which one it would be and why?"

8. Ask the students which method they would prefer to use if $x = 23$
    and $y = 75$ or if $x = 1.975$ and $y = .325$.

Concept/Practice

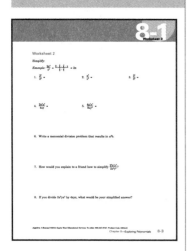
9. Help the students to summarize that simplifying first does make calculations more simple.

Dividing and Simplifying Monomials

Directions:

1. Give a copy of the blackline master **Dividing Monomials** to each student.

2. Show the students how to write problems 1–4 from the blackline master in expanded notation. Using the identity $\frac{2}{2} = 1$, have them find the answers.

3. Ask the students how they will fill in the table for problem 6, part a. Have them complete the rest of the table.

4. Have the students complete problem 7. Ask them to verbalize the rule they developed for problem 7. Discuss why and if these rules are true.

5. Use problems 8–11 to confirm that the students understand they should subtract the power of the denominator from the power of the numerator.

6. Have students simplify problems 12–16. Tell them to watch for the correct signs in their computations, and remind them that if a number or variable is raised to the power of zero, it is always equal to 1. For example: $\frac{x^3}{x^3} = x^{3-3} = x^0 = 1\,(x \neq 0)$. Remind the students that it is not possible to divide by a denominator that equals 0.

Practice Activities

Exchange Problems for Multiplying and Simplifying Monomials 💡

Directions:

1. Write the example $(5x^2y^3)(10x^2y)$ on the board. Ask the students to simplify the expression. **($50x^4y^4$)**

2. Have the students write an algebraic expression for the multiplication of two monomials, each with a coefficient and up to

three variables having exponents from 1 to 10. *Example:* $(7x^2y^4)(-2x^5y^7)$.

3. Divide the students into groups of five. Have them exchange papers and work each other's problems. Each student should work all of the problems that the group members created.

4. Then ask them to check the other students' work for the problem they created.

5. Have the students discuss any differences in the answers and come to agreement on the correct answer.

Exchange Problems for Dividing and Simplifying Monomials

Directions:

1. Give the students the example $\frac{6x^4y^2}{2x^5y}$. Have them simplify the expression. ($\frac{3y}{x}$)

2. Ask them if the result is a monomial. Why or why not? (**No, a monomial is a number, variable, or the product of a number and one or more variables and does not include having a variable in the denominator.**)

3. Have the students write an algebraic expression for the division of two monomials, each with a coefficient and up to three variables, and each having exponents from 1 to 10. For example, $\frac{24x^4y^6z^2}{6x^3y}$.

4. Have the students form groups of five. Ask a student in each group to shuffle the papers on which the students wrote their expressions. Have each student draw a paper and then simplify the expression.

5. Have the students check the other group members' work in simplifying the expressions they created.

6. Have the students resolve any questions concerning the simplification.

7. Ask some of the students to show their expressions to the class. Determine which expressions are monomials and which are not. Discuss why.

Materials:

▶ Blackline master **Monomial Rummy** is located in the *Teacher's Resource Manual*, **page 115.**

▶ Blank cards or 💿

Teacher's Tip:

Worksheets 3 and 4 for this objective, **pages 8-4 and 8-5**, support this activity with practice exercises.

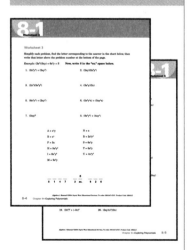

Monomial Rummy

Directions:

1. Have the students form groups of two. Give a copy of the blackline master **Monomial Rummy** to each pair.

2. If you are using index cards, ask each student to fold six cards in half and cut the cards on the fold. If you are using $8\frac{1}{2}'' \times 11''$ cardstock, give each student one sheet to fold into fourths the long way and thirds the short way, and cut on the folds. It may be quicker for you to make blank cards by using a large paper cutter.

3. Each student should end up with 12 cards. Ask each student to copy 12 of the problems from the blackline master **Monomial Rummy** onto their 12 cards so that each pair ends up with 24 different cards to make a deck. For example, one student could copy the odd problems and the other the even problems. There should be one deck of 24 cards for every pair of students.

4. Have the students sit across from each other. Ask one of the students in each pair to shuffle the deck.

5. Have the students play Monomial Rummy by using the usual rules for rummy. Six cards are dealt to each player. Students are to make matches of three cards that have the same solution. (There are actually four cards that have the same answer in the deck.) Students take turns either picking up a discard or drawing a card and then discarding a card face up until one of them gets two matches. That student then puts the matches down in front of himself or herself, and the other student checks to see if these are indeed matches before declaring a winner.

Problem-Solving Activities

How Many Ways 🔅

Directions:

1. Write the expression $12x^4y^6$ on the board. Ask the students to write as many monomial multiplication or division problems as they can that are equivalent to this expression. Have the students write their problems individually or in groups.

2. Compare the students' results. Discuss who had the most problems and who had the "best" problem.

3. Have students describe how they went about finding the results. Ask whether they developed a pattern. Have them share their patterns.

Best Buy 🔅

Directions:

1. Have the students work individually.

2. Discuss with the students the formulas for finding the area of a circle. Include the formula using the diameter $\left(A = \pi r^2 = \dfrac{\pi d^2}{4}\right)$. Remind the students that $\pi \approx 3.14$ and that they should use 3.14 for the value of π.

3. Have the students bring in ads for at least two pizza restaurants that show the prices and diameters of their different sizes of pizzas, or have the students call at least two restaurants and obtain the data for pizzas having the same ingredients.

4. Discuss that "large" is an ambiguous term. To one restaurant, it might be 14 inches and to another it might be 16 inches.

5. Have the students calculate the cost per square inch of the various pizzas and determine which pizza is the best buy.

6. Discuss other factors that might be considered in determining the "best buy," such as real cheese, taste, etc.

Materials:
▶ Telephone directory
▶ Pizza restaurant ads

Areas and Perimeters of Squares

Directions:

1. Review with the students the meanings of perimeter and area. Write or develop the formulas for the perimeter and area of a square ($P = 4s$ and $A = s^2$).

2. Have the students suggest ways to construct a table that shows areas and perimeters of squares. Ask what columns are required. Copy the table to the right on the board and ask the students to fill it in.

s	A	P
1 in.		
2 in.		
3 in.		
4 in.		
5 in.		
6 in.		

3. Ask the students to verbalize what they discovered about the numerical values of the perimeters and areas of the various squares. Ask them, "When is the numerical value of the perimeter equal to the numerical value of the area? When is it larger? When is it smaller?"

4. Now have the students use decimal values for s, such as s = 2.5 inches or s = 7.95 inches, and repeat the problem.

Answer Key for #3:
The numerical value is the same when s = 4. P is greater when s < 4, and less when s > 4.

8-2 *Objective:* Write numbers in scientific notation and find products and quotients of these numbers.

Sample Test: Express each number in scientific notation:

1. 8,450,000

2. .000845

Solution: 8.45×10^6

Solution: 8.45×10^{-4}

Express each number in standard notation:

3. 4.37×10^{-5}

4. 4.37×10^5

Solution: .0000437

Solution: 437,000

Concept Development Activities

Experiment for Large Numbers 💡

Directions:

1. Discuss with the students that they are already familiar with different ways to write numbers. For example, Y2K is used for the year 2000. The number K is used to indicate thousands. A house that costs $259K costs $259,000. In a similar way, we can write 259,000 in scientific notation (just another shortcut way) as 2.59×10^5. (Scientific notation consists of a base number that is less than 10 but greater than or equal to one times 10 to a power.)

2. Have the students write the number 2.59×10^5 in standard notation. Remind them that the decimal moves to the right five places. Discuss whether this is a large number.

3. Draw a number line from −5 to 5 on the board. Ask the students why they think the decimal moves to the right in #2. How does this correspond to the number line on the board?

4. Ask the students to write 2.59×10^{-5} in standard notation. Remind them that in this case the decimal moves to the left. (10^{-5} means $\frac{1}{10^5}$, or .00001.)

5. Ask the students why they think the decimal moves to the left in

Materials:

▶ Blackline master **Calculator Experiment for Large Numbers** is located in the *Teacher's Resource Manual*, **page 116.**

▶ Scientific calculators

#4. How does this correspond to the number line on the board? Discuss whether this is a large number.

6. Ask the students to write their ages in scientific notation.

7. Ask the students to write the age of a 6-month-old baby in scientific notation. Remind them they need to change months to years first. **(5 × 10⁻¹ years)**

8. Give a copy of the blackline master **Calculator Experiment for Large Numbers** to each student. Ask the students to do problems 1 through 4.

9. Have students discuss their answers to problems 1 through 4.

10. Review with the students place values for hundreds, thousands, millions, and trillions, such as

$$000{,}000{,}000{,}000{,}000$$

trillions billions millions thousands hundreds

11. Distribute scientific calculators to the students. Have them work on problems 5 through 9.

12. Ask the students what they think the calculated answer means in problem 5. Have them compare the calculator result with their answer to problem 7. Ask them why they think the calculator does not write 10 but leaves a space? Show them how to change the calculator display to standard notation in problem 9. **(3,250,000,000,000)**

13. Have the students write 6 billion on their calculators. **(6. 09)**

14. Ask the students, "If the calculator display reads 5. 03, what does that mean? **(5,000)**

15. Have the students work on problems 10 through 13.

16. Ask the students to verbalize how they used the calculator to answer problems 11 through 13. Students should share that they put the number into scientific notation and used the powers key.

17. Remind the students that in problem 12 they should write the result using the 10, even if the calculator does not.

Experiment for Small Numbers 🔅

Directions:

1. Copy the blackline master **Calculator Experiment for Small Numbers** and distribute the copies and scientific calculators to the students.

2. As the students work on problem 1 on the blackline master, help them write .0035 in scientific notation. Remind them that to get back to standard notation, they need to move the decimal to the left when the exponent of 10 is negative. Review with the students place values for tenths, hundredths, etc., such as

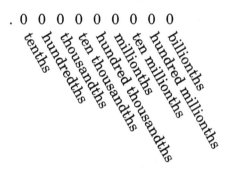

3. Continue with problem 2 on the blackline master. Help the students determine a calculator entry program to write 3.5×10^{-3} on their calculators. For example:

| 3 | . | 5 | × | 1 | 0 | y^x | 3 | +/− | = |

Help the students to see that the calculator moves the decimal to the left three places.

4. Have the students confirm that the standard notation (calculator display) has moved the decimal to the left. Then, have the students complete problems 3 and 4 on the blackline master. Discuss answers.

5. Ask the students to do the multiplication in problem 5 on the blackline master by using the "long" method. Then have them complete problem 6.

6. Talk with the students about how short the "answer" is in scientific notation compared to their result in problem 5.

7. Have the students work on problem 7. Have them compare the result of problem 7 with the result of problem 6.

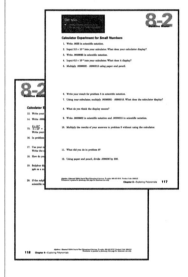

8. Discuss problem 8. Encourage the students to verbalize that the calculator does not write the 10 and that it is "just understood" to be there.

9. Have the students complete problems 9 and 10. In problem 10, they should notice that the exponents, even though they are negative, are added.

10. Discuss problem 11. Encourage the students to verbalize the rule for multiplying monomials (add the exponents when multiplying).

11. Ask students to use the "long" method of division for problem 12. They should move the decimal and fill in the zeros. Next, have them complete problem 13, where they change the answer into scientific notation.

12. Have the students work problem 14. The problem requires them to move the decimal to the left and also to the right. Check to see that the students use the correct signs.

13. Problem 15 sets up the division problem they did in problem 12. Remind the students to use fractional notation to show division. Remind them to subtract exponents when dividing monomials.

14. Use problem 16 to help the students verbalize rules for subtracting signed numbers.

15. Have the students complete problem 17. Ask them to interpret the calculator display. Then discuss problem 18, in which students are asked to compare the result for problem 17 with that for problem 15.

16. Discuss with the students that most numbers used in daily life do not require scientific notation. Ask them where they might see numbers in scientific notation. One example they might have heard of is *parts per million or billion,* as in testing car exhaust gases or pollution.

17. Ask the students to work on problems 19 and 20.

18. Discuss with the students why 5 ppb × 2 = 10 ppb (ppb = parts per billion) and that in scientific notation the decimal must go between the 1 and the 0. Therefore, because the exponent is negative 8, the decimal was already moved one place to the left to get it into scientific notation.

Numbers in Scientific Notation

Directions:

1. Remind the students of the definition of a number in scientific notation: It is a number between 1 and 10 times a power of 10. Usually we use only two decimal places. Write 3.25×10^3, 3.25×10^{-3}, 53×10^2, and $.214 \times 10^4$ on the board. Discuss with the students which are in scientific notation and which are not.

2. Students already know how to multiply monomials. Write $x^3 \cdot x^2$ on the board. Have the students come up with the result $x^3 \cdot x^2 = x^5$. Write $10^3 \times 10^2 = 10^5$ on the board and ask them if this is correct. Ask the students what $10^3 \times 10^{-5}$ would be.

3. Write a few problems on the board, such as $6(1.1 \times 10^3)$, $(2.1 \times 10^2)(1.1 \times 10^5)$, and $(3.1 \times 10^7)(2.1 \times 10^{-3})$. Ask the students to work on these problems. Discuss their answers.

4. Ask the students to compute $(3.5 \times 10^5)(4.1 \times 10^4)$. Usually they will give the answer as 14.35×10^9. Ask the students if this is a number in scientific notation. Discuss with the students the definition of numbers in scientific notation. Write 14.35 as $(1.435 \times 10^1) \times 10^9 = 1.435 \times 10^{10}$. Review round off rules as required, and write 1.435 as 1.44 because scientific notation usually has only two decimal places.

5. Write $(4.7 \times 10^3)(3.6 \times 10^5)$ on the board. Have the students discuss why 1.69×10^9 is the correct response.

6. Remind the students that in monomial division, $\frac{x^5}{x^3} = x^2$. Review the rules for dividing monomials with the students. Write $\frac{10^5}{10^3}$ on the board and ask the students for the result. Ask them what $\frac{6x^5}{2x^3}$ would be. Then ask, "How about $\frac{6 \times 10^5}{6 \times 10^3}$?"

7. Write $\frac{4.2 \times 10^8}{2 \times 10^5}$ on the board. Ask the students for the results of the division.

8. Ask the students to compute the following problems:

   a. $(2 \times 10^3)(4 \times 10^7)$ b. $(1.8 \times 10^5)(2 \times 10^4)$

   c. $(2 \times 10^{-3})(4 \times 10^{-7})$ d. $(2 \times 10^{-2})(4 \times 10^{-6})$

Teacher's Tip:

Worksheets 1 and 2 for this objective, **pages 8-8 and 8-9**, support this activity with practice exercises.

8-2
Worksheet 1

Worksheet 1
Write the following standard notation numbers in scientific notation form.
Example: 200 = 2 × 10²
1. 400 = _____   2. 5,000 = _____

3. .0004 = _____   4. .000015 = _____

5. 3,400,000 = _____   6. .0000556 = _____

7. 456,000 = _____   8. 206,451 = _____

Write these scientific notation numbers in standard notation form.
Example: 3 × 10² = 300
9. 2 × 10³ = _____   10. 2 × 10⁻⁴ = _____

11. 4.3 × 10⁵ = _____   12. 6.2 × 10⁻⁴ = _____

13. 4.5 × 10⁶ = _____   14. 3.54 × 10⁻⁴ = _____

8-8   Chapter 8—Exploring Polynomials

8-2
Worksheet 2

Worksheet 2
Multiply, and then write the result in scientific notation.
Example: (2 × 10³)(3 × 10³) = 6 × 10⁷
1. (3 × 10⁴)(2 × 10⁵)   2. (1.1 × 10⁴)(3 × 10⁵)

3. (2.8 × 10⁻⁴)(3 × 10⁻⁵)   4. (7 × 10⁸)(2 × 10⁶)

5. (1.4 × 10⁴)(5 × 10⁻⁷)

Divide, and then write the result in scientific notation.
Example: $\frac{6 \times 10^5}{2 \times 10^3} = 3 \times 10^2$
6. $\frac{8 \times 10^6}{2 \times 10^3}$ 7. $\frac{9 \times 10^5}{3 \times 10^2}$

8. $\frac{6 \times 10^8}{3 \times 10^3}$ 9. $\frac{2.8 \times 10^6}{7 \times 10^2}$

10. (8 × 10⁶) ÷ (4 × 10⁻⁵)

Multiply or divide as indicated, and then write the result in standard notation.
Example: (2 × 10⁴)(3 × 10⁴) = 6 × 10⁸ = 600,000,000
11. (4 × 10⁴)(2 × 10⁴)   12. (4 × 10⁵) ÷ (2 × 10⁴)

13. (5 × 10⁴) ÷ (4 × 10⁴)   14. (6 × 10⁴) ÷ (2 × 10⁴)

15. 7(2.6 × 10⁵)   16. $\frac{4.2 \times 10^6}{7 \times 10^3}$

Chapter 8—Exploring Polynomials   8-9

Answer Key for #8:
a. 8×10^{10}
b. 3.6×10^9
c. 8×10^{-10}
d. 8×10^{-8}

Answer Key to #8:

e. 2×10^4

f. 1.4×10^6

g. 2.6×10^4

h. 9×10^3

e. $\dfrac{8 \times 10^6}{4 \times 10^2}$

f. $\dfrac{2.8 \times 10^4}{2 \times 10^{-2}}$

g. $\dfrac{5.2 \times 10^4}{2}$

h. $\dfrac{1.8 \times 10^4}{2}$

9. Review with the students problems 8f, g, and h for correct decimal placement and correct power.

Materials:

▶ Blackline master **Multiplying and Dividing Large and Small Numbers** is located in the *Teacher's Resource Manual*, **page 119.**

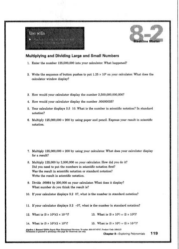

Teacher's Tip:

Worksheet 3 for this objective, **page 8-10**, supports this activity with practice exercises.

Practice Activities

Multiplying and Dividing Scientific Numbers

Directions:

1. Have the students work on their own or in pairs. Copy the blackline master **Multiplying and Dividing Large and Small Numbers** and distribute one copy and a scientific calculator to each student or student pair.

2. For problem 1, discuss with the students that calculators can display only eight characters, and when the calculator is "full," it simply quits registering inputs.

3. For problem 2, write on the board the sequence of button pushes to enter 1.25×10^8. Have the students input these numbers on their calculators. Discuss the calculator display.

4. Discuss whether it is possible to enter problem 3 into the calculator. Have the students try to input it. Then have the students write it in scientific notation and input it into the calculator.

5. Repeat step 4 using .00000035. Help the students to interpret the calculator display.

6. Have the students complete problems 6 and 7 on the blackline master. Compare the results of the problems with the students. Compare how they wrote 2.5×10^{10} and how the calculator expressed the result.

7. Have the students complete problems 8 and 9. Discuss with them to ensure they notice that the numbers can be put directly into the calculator but the result is in scientific notation. Be sure students interpret the negative exponent correctly.

8. Problems 10 and 11 reinforce the interpretation of the calculator displays. Discuss with the students how to convert the display to standard notation.

9. Problems 12 through 15 can be done mentally, with paper and pencil, or with a calculator. If the students use calculators, be certain they can use the parenthesis and sign-change buttons.

Standard and Scientific Notation

Directions:

1. Give a copy of the blackline master **Standard and Scientific Notation** to each student.

2. For problems 1 and 2, remind the students that the exponent tells them how far to move the decimal and which direction it needs to be moved.

3. Problems 3 and 4 are not written in standard notation. Remind the students that the number must be between 1 and 10 in scientific notation. Have the students write the numbers in scientific notation first, then in standard notation.

4. Help the students with the signs on the exponents for problems 5 through 8.

5. Review with the students the rules for multiplying and dividing monomials.

6. Review with the students that 14×10^5 is written as 1.4×10^6 in scientific notation.

7. Problem 14 yields $.5 \times 10^3$. In scientific notation, the students must change it to 5×10^2. Review with the students that although the two results are equivalent, they must be consistent in the application of the definition of scientific numbers.

8. Problems 15 through 20 reinforce how results in scientific notation can be converted to standard notation.

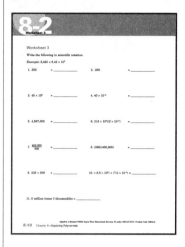

Materials:

▶ Blackline master **Standard and Scientific Notation** is located in the *Teacher's Resource Manual*, **page 120.**

Materials:

▶ Blackline master for a **3 × 3 bingo card** is in the Appendix.

▶ Game markers to cover squares

Teacher's Tip:

Review place value from billions to billionths with students.

Bingo

Directions:

1. Give a copy of a 3 × 3 bingo card to each student.

2. Instruct the students to randomly put the following numbers on their bingo card. Write the numbers on an overhead or on the board.

   a. 2.4×10^3 b. 2.5×10^6 c. 3.0×10^9

   d. 2.5×10^4 e. 3.0×10^{-4} f. 2.5×10^{-3}

   g. 2.5×10^{-5} h. 3.0×10^5 i. 2.5×10^7

3. The students should now have a number written in scientific notation in each of the nine squares on their bingo card.

4. Write one of the following numbers, at random, on the overhead or board in standard notation. Have the students use a marker to cover the equivalent number written in scientific notation on their bingo card.

   a. 25,000   b. 3,000,000,000   c. .0003

   d. 2,500,000   e. 2,400   f. .0025

   g. 25,000,000   h. .000025   i. 300,000

5. When a student has covered three numbers in a row, he or she should call out, "Bingo!" Check the numbers to be sure they are correct.

6. Have the students exchange cards and repeat as time allows.

Problem-Solving Activities

Magic Chessboard 🔆

Directions:

1. Have the students work in pairs. Give each pair a copy of the blackline master **Magic Chessboard**.

2. Ask the students to discuss their thoughts for problem 1.

3. Ask the students to fill out the table in problem 2. You might discuss with them that each square is the double of the square before it. Students might write the values of the squares as powers of 2. They could use paper and pencil or calculators. (When the students get to the eighth square, the answers are over $1.00.)

4. Ask the students whether recording the results, when they have reached day 17 or so, would be written easier in scientific notation. For example: $2^{16} = 65,536$ or 6.55×10^4, and so day 18 would be 1.31×10^5, and day 19 would be 2.62×10^5. Some students might want to know the exact amount of money. You might ask on day 17 how much money that is in dollars. **($655.36)**

5. Ask the students, "Is the amount of money for day 22 a million dollars?" **(No, it is one million cents.)**

6. Discuss with the students that on the 28th day, they would have a little more than a half million dollars.

7. You might suggest that the students find one million dollars in pennies as a scientific number. Have them do the same for one billion dollars.

8. Discuss that on the 64th day, they would receive 2^{63} pennies, which would be 9.22×10^{18} cents, or 9.22×10^{16} dollars. Ask them if you could have their magic chessboard for your retirement fund.

Materials:

▶ Blackline master **Magic Chessboard** is located in the *Teacher's Resource Manual*, **page 121.**

Answer Key:
5.33×10^9 or 5.35×10^9,
depending on how
students rounded off in
doing the calculations.

Bacteria Growth

Directions:

Present the following scenario to the students and discuss their
answers:

> A petri dish is 2.5 inches in diameter. In three days, a lab
> technician notices that a bacteria culture has grown and covers
> one-fourth of the area of the petri dish. If each bacterium takes
> up 2.3×10^{-10} square inches of this area, how many bacteria are
> in the dish?

8-3 *Objective:* Add and subtract polynomials and express the answer so the powers of the terms are in descending order.

Sample Test:

Add or subtract these polynomials and express your answer so the powers are in descending order.

1. $(2x^2 + 3x + 4) + (4x + 5x^2 + 3)$ **Solution: $7x^2 + 7x + 7$**

2. $(2x^2 + 3x + 4) - (x^2 - 2x + 3)$ **Solution: $x^2 + 5x + 1$**

Concept Development Activities

Ascending and Descending Order of Powers

Directions:

Teacher's Tip:

Worksheet 1 for this objective, **page 8-13**, supports this activity with practice exercises.

1. Draw two staircases on the board (see sketch at right). Explain to the class that to ascend means to start at the bottom and go up, and to descend means to start 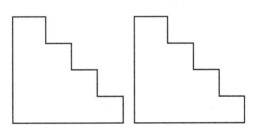 at the top and go down. Relate that the whole numbers {1, 2, 3, 4} ascend because they start at a lower end and become successively larger. Explain that the whole numbers {4, 3, 2, 1} descend because they start with the largest and become successively smaller.

2. Write 16, 12, 24, 18, 5, 3 on the board. Have the students write the numbers in descending order. Ask the students to exchange papers with their neighbors to see if the answers agree. If they do not, the students should have a discussion on which answer is correct. **(24, 18, 16, 12, 5, 3)**

3. Have the students arrange the same numbers in ascending order. Then, have them exchange papers to see if the answers agree.

4. Write several letters on the board, for example, r, m, s, t, v, z, d, l. Have the students write them in ascending and then descending order. **(ascending: d, l, m, r, s, t, v, z; descending: z, v, t, s, r, m, l, d)**

5. Write x^5, x^3, x, 3, x^2 on the board. Ask the students to name the powers for the x's. Write the powers, 5, 3, 1, 0, 2 on the board. Discuss that $3 = 3x^0$, so the power of x is 0. Have the students write the powers in descending order. Now have them write the terms in descending order using the x's. **(5, 3, 2, 1, 0; x^5, x^3, x^2, x, 3)**

6. Write $5x^2$ on the board. Ask the students, "What is the coefficient of $5x^2$?" Then ask, "What is the power of the x term?" Write $4x^5$ on the board. Ask, "What is the power of $4x^5$?" Write 3x on the board and ask, "What is the power of x?" Do the same thing for the number 5. Remind students that you are asking for the power of the variable, so it is 0. Ask what the powers are for $2x^5$, $3x^2$, 4x, −3. **(5, 2, 1, 0)**

7. Write a few terms on the board, such as 2x, $5x^2$, $3x^5$, $4x^7$, 6. Ask the students to write them in descending order. Remind the students that numbers are ordered by the powers of the variable, not the coefficients. Therefore, $4x^7$ is the first number and 6 is the last. **($4x^7$, $3x^5$, $5x^2$, 2x, 6)**

8. Write a^2, b^2, 2ab on the board. Ask the students how they would order these three terms. Discuss that when there is more than one variable, the variables are usually ordered in ascending alphabetical order, which would mean, in this case, that "a" is first and "b" is second. Then the terms are ordered using the powers. Ask the students what the powers of "a" are in a^2, b^2, 2ab. Put the powers of "a" in descending order, 2, 1, 0. Write a^2, 2ab, b^2 on the board and explain why this is the usual way of ordering expressions. Point out that the powers of "b" ascend: 0, 1, 2.

9. Write $6x^3$, $2xy^2$, $3x^2y$, $4y^3$ on the board. Ask the students to order the terms. **($6x^3$, $3x^2y$, $2xy^2$, $4y^3$)**

Like Terms in Ascending or Descending Order

Directions:

1. Define the expression "like terms" for the class. Then ask, "Is x like y?" Tell the students that if they know what "like" means, the question is easy. Point out that "like" terms mean that the variables are alike. Because they aren't, x is not like y.

2. Write $3x^2$ and $4x^2$ on the board. Discuss that they are like terms. Write $3x$ and $4x$ on the board and show why they are like terms. Write $3x^2$ and $3x$ on the board. Discuss whether they are like terms.

3. Ask the students to write $3x^2 + 4x$ on their papers. Ask them to evaluate the expression for $x = 3$. **(39)** Ask them to write $7x^2$, $7x^3$, and $7x$. Have them evaluate each of these terms when $x = 3$. **(63, 189, 21)** Ask, "When $x = 3$, does $3x^2 + 4x$ equal $7x^2$, or $7x^3$, or $7x$?" Point out that these expresions do not have the same values and that they do not have like terms. Remind them that $3x^2 + 4x$ is 39 when $x = 3$.

4. If possible, place an apple and an orange on the desk and ask if they are like. Point out that they are both fruit, but an apple is not an orange. Ask, "What would we get if we mixed them?" Discuss that you might get a fruit salad but that is changing the character of the apple and the orange. Place two different objects on the desk, such as a shoe and a notebook. Ask, "Are these 'like terms'?" Place two shoes and three notebooks on the desk in a scattered order. Then place the shoes on the right side and the notebooks on the left. Say, "We have two shoes plus three notebooks," and discuss the concept of "likeness" for the shoes and notebooks.

5. Ask the students to tear a scrap piece of paper into fourths. Have them write $4x^2$, $2x$, $3x^2$, and $3x$ on the pieces of paper, one term per piece of paper. Ask the students to group the papers into those that are like terms. Ask how many of each "like term" they have. Reinforce the example from above with the shoes and the notebooks and that, similarly, you could have x^2's and x's, and that the coefficients are added (or subtracted) but not the powers.

6. Write the two sums $5x^2 + 7x$ and $7x + 5x^2$ on the board. Ask the students which is in descending order. Discuss why they chose the one they did.

7. Write $2x$, $5x^2$, $3x^5$, $4x^7$, 6, 5, $3x$, $2x^7$, x^5 on the board. Ask the students to put the like terms together and then find the sum for each term. Have the students put the sums in descending order.

8. Ask the students to find the sum $(2x^2 + 3x + 4) + (5 + 2x + x^2)$. Ask them what they did first, second, and third. Did they reorder the second polynomial? Did they put like terms together?

Teacher's Tip:

Worksheet 2 for this objective, **page 8-14**, supports this activity with practice exercises.

Answer Key for #2:
No, they must be to the same power to be considered "like" terms.

Answer Key for #7:
$(4x^7 + 2x^7) + (3x^5 + x^5) +$ $(5x^2) + (2x + 3x) + (6 + 5)$ $= 6x^7 + 4x^5 + 5x^2 + 5x + 11$

9. Ask the students what they would do to subtract 2x from 5x. Write 5x – 2x to show that the order of subtraction is the same as if we have 5 of something and remove 2. Remind the students about subtracting being the same as adding additive inverses, for example: 5x – 2x = 5x + (–2x).

10. Ask the students to write (5x + 2) – (3x + 1) on their papers. Have them do the subtraction. Ask them to exchange papers with their neighbors to see if their results are the same. Ask, "Is the answer in descending order?"

11. Ask the students to write $(2x^2 + 3x + 4) - (x^2 + x - 1)$ on their papers. Have them do the subtraction. Check to see if they have written the correct additive inverse. Ask, "Is the result in descending order?"

12. Write b^2, 2ab, a^2 on the board. Ask the students to add the like terms. Discuss that there are no like terms. Ask, "How would you write the result of this addition?" Remind them that variables are written in ascending alphabetical order, so the "a's" would be the first variable considered, not the "b's." Remind them also that the lead variable is then written in descending order of powers, so the correct order is $a^2 + 2ab + b^2$.

13. Write several terms on the board, such as x^2, y^2, 2xy, –3, $2x^2$, $3y^2$, and 3xy. Ask the students to add the like terms and place the terms in descending order. **($3x^2$ + 5xy +$4y^2$ – 3)**

14. Discuss with the students that by combining like terms and writing the results in ascending alphabetical order and descending order of powers, everyone obtains the same "unique result."

Adding and Subtracting Polynomials

Directions:

1. Give a copy of the blackline master **Adding and Subtracting Polynomials** to each student.

2. Ask the students to work on problems 1a through 1d. Ask them why they wrote the results they did for these problems. Stress the definition of descending order. Ask, "Why did #1a start with "a" and go to "z"?" "Why was –1 placed last in problem 1b?"

Materials:

▶ Blackline master **Adding and Subtracting Polynomials** is located in the *Teacher's Resource Manual,* **page 122.**

3. Be certain the students know the difference between coefficient and power in problem 1c. Stress that when adding terms the coefficients but not the powers are added. Ask, "Why is x different from x^2?"

4. Discuss with the students that just as in problem 1a, problem 1d starts with x^2 because x comes before y in the alphabet, and no other "x term" has a higher power.

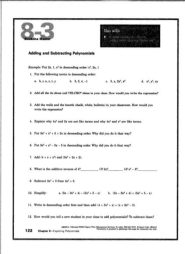

5. For problem 2, ask the students to count the number of tie shoes and the number of VELCRO® shoes. Ask them whether they want to count other shoes, such as sandals, and name them "others." Have them write the expression as "so many" tie shoes plus "so many" Velcro shoes. Ask which would come first in the expression. Help the students to see that "other" shoes would come first (if counted), then tie shoes, and then Velcro shoes because "o" comes before "t" and "t" comes before "v" in the alphabet.

6. For problem 3, emphasize that walls are different from boards. Discuss with the students that the combined total of walls plus boards (e.g., there are 7 walls and boards) does not tell how many of each. It would be more meaningful to say that there are 4 walls and 3 boards. **(3b + 7w for the example given)**

7. Have the students explain their answers to problem 4. This problem reviews again the definition of like terms.

8. For problems 5 and 6, reinforce the definitions of "like terms" and "descending order." Point out that although smaller coefficients start the answers, it is the powers that "rule." Point out that "sign" has nothing to do with order.

9. Ask the students how they did problem 7. Ask, "Did you put the polynomials in descending order first?" "Did you group like terms first?" Ask the students whether $6 + 3x + 4x^2$, $3x + 6 + 4x^2$, and $4x^2 + 3x + 6$ yield the same results. Have them evaluate each when x = 2 to show that the results are the same. Ask them why the results should be written in descending order. Point out that by writing in descending order everyone gets the same results to evaluate.

10. Use problem 8 to review the definition of additive inverse. Remind the students that all the terms of the polynomial must change signs.

11. Reinforce the use of additive inverse in problem 9. Discuss with the students which polynomial is being subtracted.

12. Problem 10 reinforces the idea of descending order and additive inverses.

13. Problem 11 shows that the "workload" is reduced when the terms are written in descending order. Students often will point out that they could add like terms together without writing them out first. Point out that they are correct but that writing the terms out helps prevent simple errors.

14. See whether the students can use expressions such as like terms, descending order, powers, and additive inverses in their algorithm for problem 12.

Practice Activities

Share Problems

Directions:

1. Have the students form groups of five. Have each student individually write two problems involving adding or subtracting polynomials. The first problem should have only one variable and powers no larger than 3. The second problem should have two variables and powers no larger than 3. Examples include: $(3x^2 - 4x + 6) - (x^2 + 9 - 4)$ and $(2a^2b + 3ab - 6) + (ab - 3a^2b + 9)$.

2. Have the students write the same problems on another sheet of paper and simplify each problem. This sheet of paper will be the answer sheet they use after sharing. Have the students exchange the problems without the solutions within their group. They should continue exchanging papers until they have worked all the problems produced by their group.

3. Have the students discuss their solutions. Correct solutions will have like terms combined and be organized in proper order. If there is disagreement, have the group consult another group. Have the groups exchange their sets of problems and continue.

Algebra Tiles

Directions:

1. Distribute algebra tiles to each student or pair of students. Ask the students to model a polynomial such as $x^2 + x + 1$ by using algebra tiles. Ask them to model an additive inverse. Be certain students change the signs of all the terms.

2. Review how to add two polynomials, such as $(2x + 1) + (x + 3)$.

3. Review how to subtract two polynomials such as $(2x + 1) - (x + 3)$. This is a great opportunity to review a zero pair, to demonstrate taking 3 from 1.

4. Ask the students to model $x + 3$ and then to model the inverse of $x + 3$. Ask them to now add the inverse of $x + 3$ to $2x + 1$ and compare the results with what they did in step 3.

5. Have the students model $x^2 + 2x + 1$ and $x^2 + x + 2$. Use algebra tiles to find $(x^2 + 2x + 1) + (x^2 + x + 2)$. Have the students write the resulting polynomial.

6. Now have the students use algebra tiles to find $(x^2 + 2x + 1) - (x^2 + x + 2)$. Have them use zero pairs to do the subtraction. Have the students write the resulting polynomial.

7. Now have the students model the additive inverse of $x^2 + x + 2$. Ask them to model and write the polynomial the tiles represent for $(x^2 + 2x + 1) + (-x^2 - x - 2)$, using the additive inverse.

8. Monitor the students as they work with the polynomials and the use of zero pairs. Discuss the results of steps 6 and 7 and why they are the same.

9. Model $2x^2 + 3x + 1$ and $3x^2 - 2x + 1$ with algebra tiles, and have the students find $(2x^2 + 3x + 1) - (3x^2 - 2x + 1)$. Ask the students how they obtained their results.

10. Discuss with the students which method they prefer: zero pairs or additive inverses. Validate the use of both methods.

Materials:
- ▶ Algebra tiles

Answer Key:
Note that the following solutions are suggested models only.

5. $\left(\blacksquare + \| + \blacksquare\right) +$

$\left(\blacksquare + | + \blacksquare + \blacksquare\right)$

$= \blacksquare \ \blacksquare + \|\|\| +$

$\blacksquare + \blacksquare + \blacksquare = 2x^2 + 3x + 3$

6. $\left(\blacksquare + \| + \blacksquare\right) -$

$\left(\blacksquare + | + \blacksquare + \blacksquare\right)$

$\left[\blacksquare + \| + \boxtimes\right] -$

$\left[\blacksquare + | + \boxtimes + \blacksquare\right]$

$= | - \blacksquare = | + \square = x - 1$

7. $\square + | + \square\,\square,$

$\blacksquare + \| + \blacksquare + \square + |$

$+ \square\,\square = \blacksquare + \| + \boxtimes + $

$\boxtimes + \boxtimes + \boxtimes\square = | + \square$

$= x - 1$

8. Subtracting is the same as adding the additive inverse.

9. Answers will vary. Some students use subtraction, and others add the additive inverse to obtain:

$\square + \|\|\|\| = -x^2 + 5x$

Chapter 8—Exploring Polynomials   **8-25**

Problem-Solving Activity

Problems for Answers 💡

Directions:

1. Tell the students you are thinking of an "answer" to a polynomial addition problem. Say, "The answer is $2x + 3$. What is the problem?" Students might say, for example, $(x + 1) + (x + 2)$ or $(3x + 2) + (1 - x)$. They may need an example to get started.

2. Tell the students the first polynomial in an addition problem is $(5x + 4)$. Ask, "What is the second when the solution is $2x + 3$?" If the students have difficulty, explain that if the answer is $2x + 3$, then for $5x$ to become $2x$, they need a $- 3x$, and for the 4 to become a 3 they need a $- 1$, so the second polynomial is $(-3x - 1)$. Ask the students to make up a similar problem.

3. Tell the students you are thinking of a polynomial subtraction problem. Say, "The answer is $2x + 3$ and the first polynomial is $(5x + 7)$. What is the second?" If the students have difficulty, explain that if the answer is $2x + 3$, then for $5x$ to become $2x$, they need to subtract $3x$, and from 7 they need to subtract 4 to get 3, so $5x + 7 - 3x - 4 = (5x + 7) - (3x + 4)$ works. Ask the students to help you find a similar problem.

4. Write $2x - 3$, $x^2 + x + 1$, $x^2 + 2xy + y^2$, and 7 on the board. Ask the students to form groups of two. Direct the groups to come up with two different addition problems for each of the above polynomial "answers."

5. Now ask the students to to write two different subtraction problems for each of the polynomial "answers" in step 4.

6. Have several students share their "problems" with the class.

7. Have each student in each group make up a polynomial answer and exchange it within the group. Direct students to write an addition and a subtraction problem for the "answer" they received.

8-4 *Objective:* **Multiply a polynomial by a monomial and arrange the power of the terms in descending order.**

Sample Test: Find each product:

1. $3x(2x^2 - 1)$ 2. $3xy^2(x^2 + 2y)$

   Solution: $6x^3 - 3x$ **Solution: $3x^3y^2 + 6xy^3$**

Concept Development Activities

Multiplying a Monomial by a Binomial

Directions:

1. Ask the students if they could write 23 as a binomial (two terms). Ask for some examples. Possibilities are 20 + 3, 17 + 6, etc. Ask whether 27 − 4 or 30 − 7 would also be examples.

2. Ask the students to multiply 3 by 23. Ask, "How did you do it?" Discuss several of the algorithms used by the students. Write

   $$\begin{array}{r} 23 \\ \times\,3 \\ \hline \end{array}$$

   on the board. Show the students the standard method of 3 times 3 and then 3 times 2 to get 69.

3. Ask the students to write 23 as the binomial 20 + 3. Say that you want to multiply the binomial by 3. Write the 3 below, as

   $$\begin{array}{r} 20 + 3 \\ \times\,3 \\ \hline \end{array}$$

   Multiply, asking questions about how you should do it. Usually students will say 3×3 and then 3×20.

   $$\begin{array}{r} 20 + 3 \\ \times\,3 \\ \hline 60 + 9 \end{array} \qquad = 69.$$

   Ask the students whether 3 is a monomial. Ask whether 20 + 3 is a binomial. Explain that they have been multiplying a binomial by a monomial for quite some time, they just write it differently.

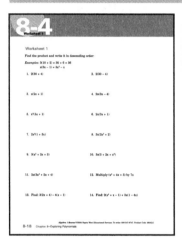

4. Write the following problems on the board. Ask the students to multiply them by forming a binomial times a monomial.

   a. $2 \cdot 43$ **(86)**   b. $7 \cdot 37$ **(259)**

5. Check to see what binomials the students used in the previous step. Usually, they use 40 + 3 and 30 + 7. This is a good opportunity to have the students practice mental arithmetic. Have the students multiply the 43 by 2 and 37 by 7 to confirm they obtain the same result.

6. Refer back to $3 \cdot 23 = 3(20 + 3)$. Ask the students, "What would happen if the 20 were an x?" Explain that in that case, the problem would be $3(x + 3)$, or

$$\begin{array}{r} x + 3 \\ \times\ 3 \\ \hline 3x + 9 \end{array}.$$

   Now say, "Let's go back, again, to $3(20 + 3)$. What if the 3 were an x?" Explain that in that case, the problem would be $x(20 + x)$, or $20x + x^2$. Ask, "Is the result in descending order? Is $x^2 + 20x$ the same?" If the students have questions, ask whether 20 + 3 is the same as 3 + 20.

7. Have the students work the following problems:

   a. $a(a^2 + 2)$ b. $2a(a^2 + 2)$ c. $3ab(a^2 + b)$

   Ask for the results, and have the students check for descending order.

8. Ask the students to recall that $23 = 20 + 3 = 30 - 7$. Write

$$3(30 - 7) = \qquad \begin{array}{r} 30 - 7 \\ \times\ 3 \\ \hline 90 - 21 \end{array} \qquad = 69.$$

   Ask them to determine what $2(20 + 3)$ is.

9. Write $y(y^2 - y)$ on the board. Have the students write

$$\begin{array}{r} y^2 - y \\ \times\ y \\ \hline \end{array}$$

   and work the problem to get $y^3 - y^2$. Have the students then do the problem by distributing the y over $y^2 - y$: $y(y^2 - y) = y^3 - y^2$.

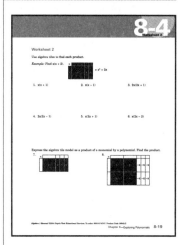

8-4

Worksheet 2

10. Write the following problems on the board. Give the students time to work them. Then ask for the results, and have the students check for descending order. Students may write the problems in vertical form or distribution form.

a. $4(2a^2b + 3ab^2)$

b. $4a(2a^2b + 3ab^2)$

c. $x(2x^3 - 3x^2)$

d. $3xy(2x^2 + 3xy)$

Algebra Tiles Model

Directions:

1. Have the students form groups of two. Distribute a set of algebra tiles to each group.

2. Ask the students to help make a model of $x(x + 3)$. Draw a table and mark off on the top a measure of x and then three 1s. On the side, mark off a length of x. Fill in the rectangle with $x^2 + 3x$. The table should look like this:

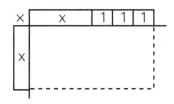

Fill in the rectangle:

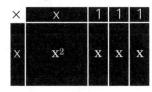

$= x^2 + 3x$

3. Have the students model $x(x - 3)$. Check to see that they have the correct rectangle.

$= x^2 - 3x$

Materials:

► Algebra tiles

Teacher's Tip:

Worksheet 2 for this objective, **page 8-19**, supports this activity with practice exercises.

4. Have the students model $2x(x + 3)$. Check to see that they have the correct rectangle.

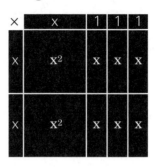

$$= 2x^2 + 6x$$

Continue with other problems such as $2x(x - 3)$, $-x(x + 1)$, and $x(2x + 1)$.

Multiplying a Monomial by a Polynomial

Directions:

1. Ask the students to give some examples of monomials. Write them on the board. Pick two that have the same variable, such as $3x$ and $4x^2$. Multiply these monomials by using the associative and commutative properties. Write the steps on the board, with the students' help. For example,

$$(3x)(4x^2) = (3)(4)(x)(x^2) = [(3)(4)][(x)(x^2)] = (12)(x^3) = 12x^3$$

2. Repeat this procedure with other groups of two monomials until the students feel comfortable with the process. Add difficulty with examples such as $(3x^2y^3)(4x^5y^4)$.

3. Ask the students to give examples of binomials. Write them on the board. Pick an example, such as $2x + 3$. Pick one of the monomial examples with the same variable, say $3x$, and ask the students what $3x(2x + 3)$ would be. Write out the steps by using the distributive, associative, and commutative properties. For example:

$$3x(2x + 3) = (3x)(2x) + (3x)(3) = 3 \cdot 2 \cdot (x)(x) + 3 \cdot 3 \cdot x = 6x^2 + 9x.$$

4. Show the students that 23 is a binomial when written as $(20 + 3)$. Pick an integer that is less than 10, such as 3. Multiply $3 \cdot (20 + 3)$

horizontally as $3(23) = 3(20 + 3) = 3(20) + 3(3) = 60 + 9 = 69$, and then multiply it vertically:

$$
\begin{array}{ccccc}
23 & & 20 + 3 & & 20 + 3 \\
\underline{\times\,3} & = & \underline{\quad\times\,3} & = & \underline{\qquad\qquad\times\,3} \\
& & & = & 3(20) + 3(3) \\
& & & = & 60 + 9 = 69
\end{array}
$$

5. If the students didn't give any examples with more than one variable, write some on the board—for example, $2xy$ and $5x^2y$. Then multiply these monomials together:
$(2xy)(5x^2y) = (2)(5)(x)(x^2)(y)(y) = 10x^3y^2$

6. Repeat the procedure by multiplying $(5x^2y)(3xy^2)$ to obtain $15x^3y^3$. Ask what $(3ab)(4cd)$ equals. Show that $3ab = 3abc^0d^0$ and that $4cd = 4a^0b^0cd$. So, multiplied together, they become $12abcd$.

7. Ask the students what $2x(3x + 4)$ equals. See if they distribute $2x$ over the $3x$ and the 4. Review adding like terms and that $6x^2 + 8x$ is the product because $6x^2$ and $8x$ are not like terms.

8. Ask the students to multiply 123 by 3. Discuss with the students that 123 could be written as a polynomial: $100 + 20 + 3$. Have the students multiply $3(100 + 20 + 3)$ vertically and then by distributing the 3 over $(100 + 20 + 3)$.

9. Ask the students to form groups of two and then to multiply $3x^2(2x^2 + x + 1)$ and agree on a result. Check the result and come to a consensus that the result is $6x^4 + 3x^3 + 3x^2$. Ask the students whether the result is in ascending or descending order.

10. Write $2xy^2(3x^2 + 2xy + 1)$ on the board. Discuss the distribution of $2xy^2$ over the trinomial. Write
$$2xy^2(3x^2) + 2xy^2(2xy) + 2xy^2(1)$$

on the board. Ask the students to do the monomial multiplication.

11. Ask the students to find the result of $2b^2(a^2b + 2b + 2a)$. They will probably give a result such as $2a^2b^3 + 2b^3 + 4b^2a$. Ask them whether it is in ascending or descending order. Point out that "a" comes first in the alphabet, so they should start with "a" to get $2a^2b^3 + 4ab^2 + 2b^3$. Ask the students, "Why do you think we do it that way?" Write several possible answers, such as $2a^2b^3 + 2b^3 + 4b^2a$ and $2b^3 + 4b^2a + 2a^2b^3$. Ask the students if these are the

same. **(They differ in order.)** Discuss, again, that the rules make checking easier because everyone has the same result.

12. Have the students make up at least four problems in which a monomial is multiplied by a polynomial (two that are easy and two that are difficult). Have them exchange papers and work each other's examples. Then have them check the results. Some problems could be shared with the class.

Practice Activities

Multiply to Win

Directions:

1. Have students form groups of two or three. Distribute a copy of the blackline master **Multiply to Win**, a die, and markers to each pair of students.

2. Ask the groups to roll the die to determine who goes first. The student with the highest number will go first.

3. At their turns, the students should roll the die and move on the board to the indicated square. They then should write the result to the problem on that square. If they are correct, they remain where they landed. If they are wrong, they return to the square they had been on and forfeit their turn. (You can resolve conflicts or a student can referee.) Be sure to remind students about descending order.

4. The student who gets to the finish line first could win a prize such as a bonus point or a piece of candy or could have his or her name written on the board as "winner."

Geometry

Directions:

1. Review the formulas for area with the students. Write on the board the formulas for areas of a triangle ($A = \frac{1}{2}bh$), rectangle ($A = l \cdot w$), parallelogram ($A = b \cdot h$), trapezoid [$A = \frac{1}{2}(b_1 + b_2) \cdot h$], and circle ($A = \pi r^2$).

Materials:

▶ Blackline master **Multiply to Win** is located in the *Teacher's Resource Manual,* **page 123.**

▶ Dice

▶ Game markers

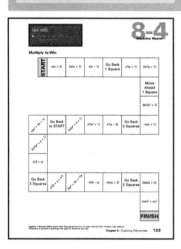

Materials:

▶ Blackline master **Geometry** is located in the *Teacher's Resource Manual,* **page 124.**

2. Distribute a copy of the blackline master **Geometry** to each student. Ask the students to work the problems individually. Check that they use b and h (and not s) in problem 3 and that students add the bases in problem 4.

3. Have the students use $\pi = 3.14$ in problem 5. Some students will convert the measurements first and then find the area, and some will do the polynomial algebra and then substitute. Discuss with the students the two methods of arriving at the answer.

4. Remind the students that an area can be divided into parts. Some students will divide the figure in problem 6 vertically and others will do it horizontally. Have the students find the dimensions each way to show that the results are the same.

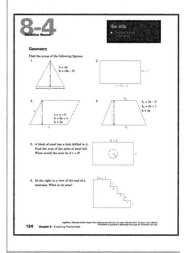

Problem-Solving Activity

Hungry Goat ☀

Directions:

1. Remind the students of the formulas for area (square, rectangle, circle).

2. Distribute a copy of the blackline master **Hungry Goat** to each student. Ask the students to look at problem 1. Ask them if they think grass would grow in the pen area. Check students' addition and subtraction of polynomials. Have them complete problem 2.

3. Have the students look at problem 3. Ask them how they would go about finding the area Ben must mow. Draw the figure on the board. Shade in the part to be mowed. Have the students point out the figures that are grazed. Butter can graze $\frac{3}{4}$ of the 4x radius circle, but the rope contacts the corner of the house and forms a new circle of radius x (help the students to discover this). Butter can graze only one quarter of this circle. Help the students discover the area of the yard, which has dimensions of (10x + 3) by 8x.

5. Have the students complete problem 4, reminding them to use 3.14 for π and to round off the results to the nearest hundredth.

Materials:

▶ Blackline master **Hungry Goat** is located in the *Teacher's Resource Manual*, **page 125**.

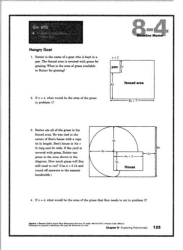

8-5 *Objective:* **Multiply two binomials and simplify the expressions, including special products of (a + b)(a + b) and (a + b)(a − b).**

Sample Test: Find each product:

1. (x + 2)(x − 2)   2. (x + 3)(x + 4)

    Solution: $x^2 − 4$ **Solution: $x^2 + 7x + 12$**

Concept Development Activities

Multiplying "Binomial Numbers"

Directions:

1. Write 25×12 on the board. Ask the students to do the multiplication. They will usually write

    $$\begin{array}{r} 25 \\ \times\,12 \end{array}$$

    Students then typcially start on the right side and work to the left side, such as 2 times 5, then 2 times 2.

    $$\begin{array}{r} 25 \\ \times\,12 \\ \hline 50 \end{array}$$

    Then they multiply by the one and indent to get

    $$\begin{array}{r} 25 \\ \times\,12 \\ \hline 50 \\ 25 \end{array}$$

    and then they sum the columns. Ask the students why they indent. Discuss with them that the "1" in 12 is really a 10. Help them to see that we just do not write the "0."

2. Ask the students to write 25 as a binomial, such as 20 + 5. Have them write 12 as a binomial, such as 10 + 2. Write

    $$\begin{array}{r} 20 + 5 \\ \times\,10 + 2 \end{array}$$

    on the board. Remind the students that when they multiplied 25×12 they started multiplying on the right side with the 2.

Write

$$20 + 5$$
$$\times\ 10 + 2$$
$$40 + 10.$$

Show them that

$$25$$
$$\times 12$$

gave a result of 50 on the first multiplication, and refer to the 40 + 10. Be sure the students see that the result is the same.

3. Now multiply (20 + 5) by 10. First multiply the 5 by the 10. Ask the students where you should write the result. Ask about the 10 times the 20. Where should you write it? Direct them to see if it would have two zeros so it might fit best in the next column to the left, and then sum the result:

$$20 + 5$$
$$\times\ 10 + 2$$
$$40 + 10$$
$$\underline{200 + 50}$$
$$200 + 90 + 10\ = 300$$

4. Point out to the students that the multiplication on the right is a short-cut way to show the work required to obtain the result.

$$25$$
$$\times 12$$
$$50$$
$$\underline{25}$$
$$300$$

5. Write 25 = 30 − 5 and 12 = 20 − 8 on the board. Have the students multiply

$$30 - 5$$
$$\times 20 - 8.$$

6. Check to see if they have

$$30 - 5$$
$$\times\ \ 20 - 8$$
$$-240 + 40$$
$$\underline{600 - 100}$$
$$600 - 340 + 40\ = 300$$

Point out that they are multiplying polynomials, in this case, a binomial by a binomial. Discuss that the results of (20 + 5)(10 + 2) = (30 − 5)(20 − 8). Ask the students what they think about the results.

7. Write 15×12 on the board. Have the students write the problem as a product of two binomials. Use the $15 = 10 + 5$ and $12 = 10 + 2$ combination.

$$
\begin{array}{r}
10 + 5 \\
\times\ 10 + 2 \\
\hline
20 + 10 \\
100 + 50 \quad\quad \\
\hline
100 + 70 + 10
\end{array}
$$

Leave the problem on the board.

8. Ask the students to let $10 = x$. Then $15 = 10 + 5 = x + 5$, and $12 = 10 + 2 = x + 2$. Start on the right side to parallel the above discussion to obtain

$$
\begin{array}{r}
x + 5 \\
\times\ x + 2 \\
\hline
2x + 10 \\
x^2 + 5x \quad\quad \\
\hline
\end{array}
$$

Be sure the students notice that the columns contain like terms. Sum the results to obtain $x^2 + 7x + 10$. Ask the students to remember that $x = 10$, and have them evaluate the result:

$$x^2 + 7x + 10 = (10)^2 + 7(10) + 10 = 100 + 70 + 10.$$

Refer the students to the example you left on the board so they can see that the results are the same.

9. Write $(x + 2)(x - 3)$ on the board. Have the students multiply the binomials to obtain $x^2 - x - 6$. Check for alignment of like terms.

10. Again, point out to the students that they already know how to multiply binomials. Reinforce the similarities in multiplying $(15)(12)$ and $(x + 5)(x + 2)$.

11. Write $(2x + 3)(x - 1)$ on the board. As you complete the multiplication on the board, have the students multiply the binomials. Check how they do the work. Leave the result of your work on the board. Show them how you distributed the $2x$ and then the 3 as an introduction to the next activity.

Distributive Property

Directions:

1. Review the distributive property of multiplication over addition. For example, $(a + b) \cdot c = ac + bc$.

2. Use numbers to verify for the students that this property works and is true for all numbers. For example:
    $$(2 + 8) \cdot 7 = 2 \cdot 7 + 8 \cdot 7$$
    $$10 \cdot 7 = 14 + 56$$
    $$70 = 70$$

3. Go over other examples, including negative numbers. For example, $(8 - 4) \cdot 3 = ?$

4. Write $(6 + 7)(8 + 2)$ on the board. Ask, "How can we use the distributive property to find the answer?" Let the students work in pairs to come up with a "possible" solution. One way to explain how to apply the distributive property is:

    Let $(6 + 7)$ be $(a + b)$, and let $(8 + 2)$ be c.

    Then $\qquad (6 + 7) \cdot (8 + 2) = 6 \cdot (8 + 2) + 7 \cdot (8 + 2)$

    or $\qquad (a + b) \cdot \quad c \quad = a \cdot \quad c \quad + b \cdot \quad c$

    Now substitute in the number values and apply the distributive property again:
    $$6 \cdot (8 + 2) + 7 \cdot (8 + 2) = 6 \cdot 8 + 6 \cdot 2 + 7 \cdot 8 + 7 \cdot 2$$
    $$= 48 + 12 + 56 + 14$$
    $$= 130$$

5. The key is that the distributive property is applied *twice*.

6. Now write
    $$(x + 3)(x + 5) =$$
    on the board. See if the pairs of students can figure out how to apply the distributive property to this algebra example:
    $$x(x + 5) + 3(x + 5) \text{ or } (x + 3)x + (x + 3)5$$
    $$x^2 + 5x + 3x + 15 \text{ or } x^2 + 3x + 5x + 15$$
    $$x^2 + 8x + 15 \text{ or } x^2 + 8x + 15$$

7. Provide several more problems for the students to try. For example:

    $(x - 2)(x + 5)$ $\qquad\qquad$ $(x + 3)(x - 4)$ $\qquad\qquad$ $(x - 5)(x - 1)$

Teacher's Tip:

Worksheet 1 for this objective, **page 8-23**, supports this activity with practice exercises.

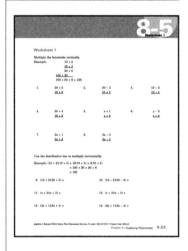

Generalize that $(a + b)(c + d) = ac + ad + bc + bd$. Many teachers use the word FOIL as a mnemonic device (first, outer, inner, last).

8. After the students have worked on several problems, discuss the terms that can be combined. They are always the middle two terms, ad and bc. See if the students can find the answer to a binomial multiplication problem by mentally combining the two middle terms. If the students have difficulty doing this mentally, let them write the terms and combine them on paper. With more practice, doing this mentally will become easier.

Multiplying Binomials

Directions:

1. Distribute a set of algebra tiles to each student.

2. Write $x(x + 2)$ on the board. Remind the students how to draw the product mat and place the required tiles on the mat. Write the product, $x^2 + 2x$.

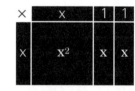

3. Ask the students how they would set up the product mat if they were going to multiply $(x + 1)(x + 2)$.

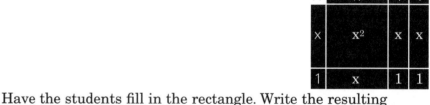

Have the students fill in the rectangle. Write the resulting polynomial, $x^2 + 3x + 2$. Have the students leave the tiles on the mat.

4. Write $(x + 1)(x + 2)$ on the board. Tell the students that they learned to multiply vertically a long time ago. Write the example vertically.

$$x + 1$$
$$\underline{x + 2}$$

Remind the students about multiplying by a monomial and "distribute the 2":

$$x + 1$$
$$\underline{x + 2}$$
$$2x + 2$$

Materials:

▶ Algebra tiles

Teacher's Tip:

Worksheet 2 for this objective, **pages 8-24 and 8-25**, supports this activity with practice exercises.

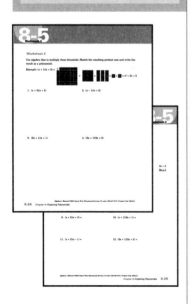

Point out that if they look at the tiles on the right of their mat, they have 2x + 2. Now, show the students how to "distribute" the x.

$$
\begin{array}{r}
x + 1 \\
\underline{x + 2} \\
2x + 2 \\
\underline{x^2 +\ \ x\ \ \ \ } \\
x^2 + 3x + 2
\end{array}
$$

Write the results in the proper columns and sum them. Point out that the left side of their tile mat has $x^2 + x$, just like the board example.

5. Discuss with the students why you "indented" the second product in the multiplication on the board. Remind them about the terms and how they were kept together by "indenting."

6. Ask the students to set up their product mat for $(x + 2)(x - 1)$. Have the students fill in the rectangle.

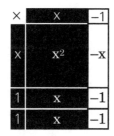

7. Take the results and rearrange the tiles to get:

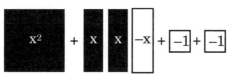

Write the resulting polynomial $x^2 + x - 2$ by using zero pairs.

8. Ask the students to multiply $(x + 2)(x - 1)$ vertically.

$$
\begin{array}{r}
x + 2 \\
\underline{\times x - 1}
\end{array}
$$

Draw out the similarities between the product and the tile model.

9. Ask the students to multiply $(2x + 1)(x + 1)$ with algebra tiles or by multiplying vertically. Have the students who multiplied by using the tiles check their results with those who multiplied "vertically."

10. Write $(2x + 1)(x + 3)$ on the board. Have the students find the result. Check to see that like terms are in the same columns.

11. Write $(2x + 1)(x + 3)$ on the board. This time, point out to the students that you multiplied two monomials, the x and the 3,

times the other polynomial in the previous example. Ask the students what they would obtain if they multiplied by the 2x and then the +1. They should get $2x^2 + 6x$ and $x + 3$. Combine like terms. Compare this result with the example in step 10.

12. Ask the students to try this method with $(2x - 1)(x + 3)$. See whether some students need to write all of the steps, $(2x - 1)(x + 3) = 2x(x + 3) - 1(x + 3) = 2x^2 + 6x - x - 3$, or whether they can write $2x^2 + 6x - x - 3$ directly. Be sure they combined like terms to obtain $2x^2 + 5x - 3$.

Multiplication of Binomials—Special Cases

Directions:

1. Distribute a set of algebra tiles to each of the students. Ask them to make a product mat.

2. Have the students find the product $(x + 1)(x - 1)$ by using the tiles. Ask them what kind of product they have. Lead them to note that the product is also a binomial, $x^2 - 1$.

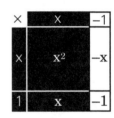

3. Have the students use the tiles to find $(x + 2)(x - 2)$ and $(x + 3)(x - 3)$. Discuss that each time the product has a zero pair, the result is that the x term drops out.

4. Ask the students to develop some problems such as $(2x + 1)(2x - 1)$ or $(2x + 2)(2x - 2)$. Students might notice that the result is the difference of two terms in each example. They might also notice that the terms in the result are squares. Develop the vocabulary of "a sum times a difference equals a difference of two squares" with the students.

5. Ask the students to test their conclusions with $(3x + 5)(3x - 5)$ and $(x + 8)(x - 8)$. Students can use tiles, vertical multiplication, or horizontal multiplication with these problems.

6. Ask the students for a few additional examples and have the class work the problems.

7. Use the tiles to model $(x + 1)^2 = (x + 1)(x + 1)$. Then model $(x + 2)^2$ and $(x + 3)^2$. Help the students see a developing pattern. The first

Materials:

▶ Algebra tiles

Teacher's Tip:

Worksheets 3 and 4 for this objective, **pages 8-26 and 8-27**, support this activity with practice exercises.

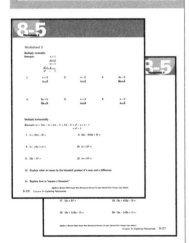

Chapter 8—Exploring Polynomials

term is squared, the second is the double of the first and second term in the multiplier, and the last term is the square of the second term. You may need to continue the pattern using $(x + 4)^2$, $(x + 5)^2$, and so forth, until the students see what is happening.

8. Ask the students to generalize what happens when $(a + b)$ and $(a - b)$ are multiplied. Then have the students generalize what happens when $(a + b)^2$ or $(a - b)^2$ is multiplied.

Practice Activities

Match and Keep

Directions:

Materials:

▶ Blank cards or

1. Place students in groups of two. Distribute 16 cards to each pair of students.

2. Write the following two columns vertically on the board. Have one student in each pair copy an item from the left column on each of eight cards. Have the other student copy an item from the right column on each of the other eight cards.

Left Column	Right Column
$(x - 3)(x + 3)$	$x^2 - 1$
$(x - 3)^2$	$x^2 - 6x + 9$
$(2x + 1)(2x - 1)$	$x^2 + 4x + 4$
$(2x + 1)^2$	$x^2 - 9$
$(x + 1)(x - 1)$	$2x^2 - x - 1$
$(x + 1)(x + 2)$	$x^2 + 3x + 2$
$(2x + 1)(x - 1)$	$4x^2 + 4x + 1$
$(x + 2)^2$	$4x^2 - 1$

3. Have the groups of students shuffle the 16 cards and form a 4-card by 4-card square in front of them, cards facing down.

4. Have the students do "scissors, paper, rock" or some other method to see who goes first. Each student, at his or her turn, should turn over two cards. If the problem matches the answer, the

student keeps the cards and it is the next student's turn. If the problem and answer do not match, the cards are turned face down again, and it is the next student's turn. (Students may use paper and pencil to simplify problems.)

5. The student who has the most cards when all the cards are "matched" wins. The game can be played several times if time permits.

Middle-Term Bingo

Directions:

1. Copy and distribute the 4×4 bingo card to each student.

2. On the board, write $-19x$. Have students choose a square at random and write $-19x$ in that square. Do the same for x, $3x$, $4x$, $6x$, 0, $5x$, $7x$, $8x$, $12x$, $-2x$, $-3x$, $-6x$, $-7x$, $-12x$, and $-25x$. Each square should have a different result in it.

3. Have the students exchange bingo cards.

4. Tell the students that you will write a problem on the board. The students are to find the middle term for that problem. For example, the middle term for $(x + 10)(x - 1)$ would be $9x$, so they would cover the $9x$ with a marker.

5. Select a problem from the list in #7 and write it on the board. Wait a reasonable amount of time (15 seconds), erase the problem, and write another problem. Continue this process until someone has covered four squares in a row, column, or diagonal, and calls out "Bingo!" Prizes could be awarded, at your discretion.

6. Have the students who win explain how they got the answers so quickly.

7. Have the students exchange cards and play again if time allows.

   Problems:

   $(x + 2)(x + 3)$ $(3x + 1)(x - 1)$

   $(x + 4)(x - 3)$ $(3x + 1)(x + 1)$

   $(2x + 1)(x + 1)$ $(x + 6)^2$

$(4x - 3)(3x - 4)$

$(2x - 1)(x - 1)$

$(3x + 4)(2x - 5)$

$(x - 2)(x + 2)$

$(x + 3)^2$

$(4x - 1)(x + 2)$

$(x + 2)(x + 6)$

$(3x - 2)^2$

$(x + 3)(x - 9)$

$(4x - 1)(3x - 4)$

Problem-Solving Activity

Multiplying Binomials 💡

Directions:

1. Write 8x on the board.

2. Ask the students how 8x could be the middle term of the result when two binomials are multiplied (use integers). Write
   $(\underline{})(\underline{}) = \underline{} + 8x + \underline{}$. Students might suggest:
   $(x + 2)(x + 6) = x^2 + 8x + 12$ $(x + 4)(x + 4) = x^2 + 8x + 16$
   $(x + 1)(x + 7) = x^2 + 8x + 7$ $(x + 9)(x - 1) = x^2 + 8x - 9$

3. Ask the students what could be put in the blanks in the following equation:
   $(2x + \underline{})(\underline{}) = \underline{} + 8x \underline{}$.

4. Ask the students, "In $(x + 2)(x - 3)$, if you add the results of the product of the inside terms and the outside terms, do you get the middle term of the result?" Have them try that with a few examples, such as $(2x + 1)(x - 4)$ or $(x + 6)(x - 4)$. Ask the students if they used this "discovery" to help in finding possible products in step 2.

5. Place the students in groups of two. Ask the groups to find some products with a middle term of 5x. Some possible solutions are $(x + 2)(x + 3)$, $(x + 7)(x - 2)$, $(2x - 1)(x + 3)$, or $(14x - 9)(x + 1)$.

6. Determine which group found the most answers, and which group had the most unusual answers.

Using Factoring

9-1 Find the greatest common factor through prime factorization for integers and sets of monomials.

9-2 Use the greatest common factor and the distributive property to factor polynomials with the grouping technique, and use these techniques to solve equations.

9-3 Factor quadratic trinomials of the form $ax^2 + bx + c$ and solve equations by factoring.

9-4 Factor quadratic polynomials that are perfect squares or differences of squares and solve equations by factoring.

9-5 Solve quadratic equations by completing the square.

9-1 *Objective:* **Find the greatest common factor through prime factorization for integers and sets of monomials.**

Sample Test: Find the greatest common factor (GCF) by using prime factorization.

1. 56 and 80

2. $12x^4y^3$ and $40x^3y^7$

   Solution: 8

   Solution: $4x^3y^3$

Concept Development

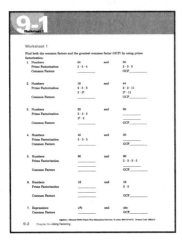

Teacher's Tip:

Worksheet 1 for this objective, **page 9-2**, supports this activity with practice exercises.

Concept Development Activities

Sets of Factors of Numbers

Directions:

1. Review the term "factor" with the students by asking a student to name the factors of 10. **(1, 2, 5, 10)**

2. Ask the class to define "factor of a number." **(an integer that divides evenly into the number)**

3. Ask a student, "What are the factors of 14?" **(1, 2, 7, 14)**

4. List the factors of 10 and 14 on the board. Ask, "What are the common factors?" **(1 and 2)** Ask, "Which factor is the largest?" **(2)** Let the students know that this is called the "greatest common factor," or GCF.

5. Repeat this process for the following pairs of numbers: 8 and 12; 6 and 9; 18 and 27; 20 and 30; 16 and 36. Ask individual students to list the factors and name the GCF for each pair.

6. Review with the class how to find the prime factors of the number 10, which are the prime numbers that when multiplied together yield 10. **(2 · 5)** Repeat with 14. **(2 · 7)** Discuss the factors that 10 and 14 have in common. **(2 · 5 and 2 · 7 have 2 in common)** Have the students compare this answer to the work on the board from step 4. Review the terms "prime," "composite," and "relatively prime."

7. Ask the students to try the numbers 8 and 12. They should first find the prime factors for each. **(2^3 and $2^2 \cdot 3$)** Then they should find the common factors. **(2^2)** Ask, "What is the GCF?" **($2^2 = 4$)** Have the students compare this answer to the work on the board for step 5.

8. Continue with prime factors for 6 and 9; 18 and 27; 20 and 30; and 16 and 36. Have the students compare the GCFs to the ones listed on the board from step 5.

Greatest Common Factor for Variables

Directions:

1. Review with the students how to find the GCF of a pair of numbers such as 18 and 24. Show that since $18 = 2 \cdot 3^2$ and $24 = 2^3 \cdot 3$, the common factors are 2 and 3, and the GCF is 6. Answer any questions about this process.

2. Introduce variables by letting 2 be "a" and 3 be "b." Explain that for $18 = 2 \cdot 3^2$, substituting a for 2 and b for 3 would yield $18 = a \cdot b^2$. Likewise, since $24 = 2^3 \cdot 3$, substituting a and b would yield $24 = a^3 \cdot b$. Discuss the common factors a and b, and the GCF $a \cdot b$. Show the students that $a \cdot b^2$ is the same as $a \cdot b \cdot b$ and $a^3 \cdot b$ is the same as $a \cdot a \cdot a \cdot b$. What they have in common is a and b. Therefore, the GCF is $a \cdot b$, or $2 \cdot 3 = 6$.

3. Present the students with the following expressions: ab^2c^2 and a^2b^3c. Ask "What is the GCF?" Students may need to write each expression in the complete factored form ($a \cdot b \cdot b \cdot c \cdot c$ and $a \cdot a \cdot b \cdot b \cdot b \cdot c$). Help them to see that what the expressions have in common is $a \cdot b \cdot b \cdot c$ and that the GCF is therefore ab^2c.

4. Repeat the process using the following pairs of expressions: abc and a^2b; ab^2c^3 and a^2bc^2; x^2y and xy^3; $x^2y^2z^2$ and x^2yz^3.

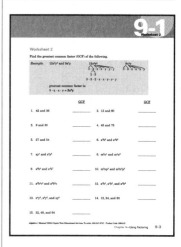
Numbers and Variables

Directions:

1. Review with the students how to find the GCF of numbers by asking them to find the GCF for 8 and 12. **(Since $8 = 2^3$, and $12 = 2^2 \cdot 3$, the GCF is 2^2, or 4.)**

2. Review finding the GCF for a^2b and ab^2. **(ab)**

3. Ask, "What is the GCF for $8a^2b$ and $12ab^2$?" Show that from steps 1 and 2, the answer is 4ab because the GCF for 8 and 24 is 4 and the GCF for a^2b and ab^2 is ab.

4. Review the complete factored form for each expression: $8a^2b = 2 \cdot 2 \cdot 2 \cdot a \cdot a \cdot b$ and $12ab^2 = 2 \cdot 2 \cdot 3 \cdot a \cdot b \cdot b$. Show that the two expressions have a common factor of $2 \cdot 2 \cdot a \cdot b$, or 4ab.

5. Give the students the expressions $16a^2b^3$ and $36a^2b^2$. Ask them to find the GCF for these expressions. Review the complete factored forms of each. Show that since $16a^2b^3 = 2 \cdot 2 \cdot 2 \cdot 2 \cdot a \cdot a \cdot b \cdot b \cdot b$ and $36a^2b^2 = 2 \cdot 2 \cdot 3 \cdot 3 \cdot a \cdot a \cdot b \cdot b$, the GCF is $2 \cdot 2 \cdot a \cdot a \cdot b \cdot b$, or $4a^2b^2$.

6. Ask the students to find the GCF for the following pairs on their own:

$6x^2y^3$ and $15xy^2$ $18ab^2c$ and $24a^2b^3$

Answer Key for #6:
$3xy^2$, $6ab^2$

Practice Activities

"Factors of 12"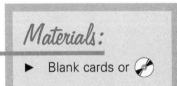

Directions:

1. Organize the class into groups of four.

2. Have each group number cards with the numbers 1 to 12 (one number per card). They should do this four times for a deck of 48 cards. Then have a member of each group "shuffle" the deck.

3. Each group should choose one student to deal five cards to each student in the group face down, as if playing "rummy," so each student has a "hand" of five cards. The dealer will also be the first player.

4. The remaining cards should be placed in a stack, face down, and the top card turned over and placed next to the deck as a discard pile.

5. Each player can either take the face-up card or draw one card from the top of the face-down deck. The object is to end up with a hand of five cards that are all factors of 12. After drawing a card, the player must discard one card from his or her hand and place it face up on the discard pile.

6. This process continues until a player can discard one card and have left in his or her hand five cards, all with numbers that are factors of 12. That student is the winner.

7. Repeat the game using 18 or 24 as the factor number. Discuss which number makes the game better, and why.

Materials:

▶ Blank cards or 💿

M&M® GCF

Directions:

Materials:

► A large bag of M&M's®

1. Randomly divide students into groups of five. Give each group an equal amount of M&M's® (at least 20 per group).

2. Have the students group their M&M's by color and have them determine how many of each color they have (for example: 5 red, 3 orange, 4 green, 4 yellow, and 5 blue).

3. Ask the students to write their data as, for example, 5r3o4g4y5b.

4. Ask one member of each group to write the group's combination on the board, one next to another. Place a "plus" symbol between each combination. Explain that the reason for the plus symbols is that the total will represent the total number of M&M's of the class.

5. Ask the groups to determine the "greatest common M&M combination" (the M&M GCF) for the combinations on the board.

6. Walk around the room to observe the groups. When a group appears to have an answer, ask the group to select a member to write the answer on the board.

7. Have the students discuss whether they agree with the M&M GCF that group found. If the students do not agree, have the class discuss what the correct M&M GCF is. Students should be able to prove their answers to the class.

8. When the class agrees on the GCF, ask the groups to remove that combination of M&M's from their M&M pile and to write a term that represents their group of leftover M&M's (how many from each color are still left).

9. Place an open parenthesis just to the right of the agreed-upon M&M GCF on the board. Then, once the groups have determined their "leftover combinations," ask another member of each group to write the group's new expression, one next to another, to the right of the parenthesis on the board. Have the students leave enough room to write a plus symbol between each expression. Explain to the class that again the plus symbols are needed so that the total represents the total number of M&M's.

10. Close the parentheses once all of the groups' new combinations are written in the expression on the board.

11. Discuss with the class that what they just did was factor out a GCF based on color for the entire set of M&M's for the class. Reaffirm with the students that this is really just the distributive property performed backward and that this process is called factoring out the GCF from a set of different given terms.

12. Let the students in each group divide their M&M's evenly among the members of the group and CONSUME!

13. As an extension of this activity, have the class graph the data according to colors. You may also review the probability of drawing one particular color from the bag.

Prime Factors

Directions:

1. Organize the class into groups of four. Give a copy of the blackline master **Number Chart** to each group.

2. Have each student in the group write a number from the **Number Chart** on his or her own paper and put a marker on that number on the blackline master so it can't be used again.

3. Then instruct the students to complete the prime factorization for the number they selected.

4. Next, have the students in each group write all of their completed prime factorizations on one piece of paper so that they may look at them all at once to make comparisons.

5. Have each group decide which numbers appear in all of the lists.

6. Each group should then write the new combination of numbers that all of the lists have in common.

7. Remind the students that if a number appears more than once in all of their lists, it should be included in their new list more than once also—one time for each time it appears in all of their lists.

8. Explain that the new list of numbers will be the factors of the GCF from all of their original lists.

Materials:

► Blackline master **Number Chart** is located in the *Teacher's Resource Manual*, **page 126.**

► Game markers to cover numbers

9-1

Blackline Master

Number Chart

12	24	18	52	36	30
10	40	9	22	15	30
48	20	38	51	21	26
32	14	27	4	55	8
56	54	6	34	45	42
44	60	16	58	28	50

126   Chapter 9—Using Factoring

9. Have the students in each group multiply the numbers in their new list. Remind them that the product is the GCF of the original four numbers they selected.

10. Each student should check to see if the group's GCF is correct by dividing his or her original number by the group's GCF. If the GCF divides into all of the group members' original numbers evenly, then the group has successfully found the GCF of all of the original numbers.

11. Have the groups repeat this activity with four new numbers from the **Number Chart** as often as time allows.

Student Factoring With Variables

Directions:

1. Organize the class into groups of three. Give one copy of the blackline master **Monomial Table** to each group. Also give each group a pair of dice (different colors may be helpful).

2. Have one student in each group roll the dice and form two ordered pairs from the numbers rolled. *Example:* If the roll is a 2 and a 4, the ordered pairs are (2, 4) and (4, 2). If the roll is a 3 and a 3, the ordered pairs are (3, 3) and (3, 3).

3. The student then writes on a sheet of paper the monomials that are in the squares on the blackline master that correspond to the roll. *Example:* The monomial for (2, 4) is $3a^3bc^3$; the monomial for (4, 2) is $6a^3b^2$. (The monomial table is read like a graph. The first component is read on the horizontal axis and the second component is read on the vertical axis. If two different colored dice are used, the different colors can be used for the labels of the axes.) The student would write "$3a^3bc^3$" and "$6a^3b^2$" on his or her paper.

4. The student should then write the GCF ($3a^3b$) next to the pair. The other two students in the group should check the work. If it is correct, the student gets a point.

5. The three students should take turns rolling the dice and naming the GCF for the pair of monomials. If a double is rolled (e.g., 3, 3) the ordered pairs are identical [e.g., (3, 3) and (3, 3)], and the

Materials:

▶ Blackline master **Monomial Table** is located in the *Teacher's Resource Manual*, **page 127**.

▶ Dice

monomials are identical ($5a^2$ and $5a^2$). For this example, the GCF would be $5a^2$.

6. Have the students take turns until time expires or a certain score is reached, such as 20 points.

7. At the end of the activity, have the students turn in their papers with the monomials and the GCFs.

Problem-Solving Activity

The Machine ☀

Directions:

1. Draw the machine shown below on the board.

2. Write the following values on the board, showing them on the machine diagram one set at a time:

in = 18, 30	out = 6
in = 28, 14	out = 14
in = 64, 28	out = 4

3. Ask the students what the machine is doing. Then have them find the "out" value for each of the following pairs of "in" values:

54 and 42   51 and 9   42 and 30

4. Have the students make up some inputs of their own and exchange them with a partner, who should find the "out" values. Have them check their partner's answers.

5. Now give the students the following pairs of inputs and instruct them to find the "out" values:

a^2b and ab^2 a^3b^3 and ab^2 $6ab^2$ and $12a^2b^3$

Discuss the results.

6. Have the students make up some inputs using numbers and variables. Select some of the inputs to give to the class. Include at least one example of two monomials that have a GCF of 1, so the students will see that some numbers or monomials have a GCF of 1 (NO other common factors).

9-2 *Objective:* **Use the greatest common factor and the distributive property to factor polynomials with the grouping technique, and use these techniques to solve equations.**

Sample Test: Factor the following polynomials by using the greatest common factor (GCF) and the distributive property.

1. $24x^2 - 16x$

   Solution: 8x(3x – 2)

2. $18x^2y^3 + 15x^3y^5 - 21x^4y^2$

   Solution: 3x²y²(6y + 5xy³ – 7x²)

3. Solve: $2x^2 - 4x = 0$

   Solution: x = 0, 2

4. Solve: $3x^2 + 6x = 0$

   Solution: x = 0, –2

Concept Development Activities

Using Algebra Tiles 💡

Directions:

Materials:

▶ Algebra tiles

1. Have the students use a set of algebra tiles to build rectangles with dimensions A × B, such as

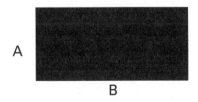

A

B

2. For example, show the class that given $x^2 + 3x$, you would build a rectangle with dimensions as follows:

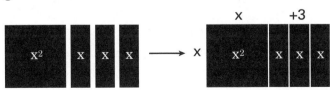

So the area of the rectangle is x(x + 3). Therefore, the factored form of $x^2 + 3x$ is x(x + 3).

3. Have the class factor the following expressions by using algebra

Answer Key for #3:
$x^2 + 4x = x(x + 4)$
$x^2 - 3x = x(x - 3)$
$x^2 + 6x = x(x + 6)$
$x^2 + x = x(x + 1)$

tiles to build the rectangles they represent:

$x^2 + 4x$ $\qquad$ $x^2 - 3x$ $\qquad$ $x^2 + 6x$ $\qquad$ $x^2 + x$

4. Ask the students to make the rectangle for $2x^2 + 6x$. Ask, "How can we find the dimensions for the length and width?" There are actually two ways:

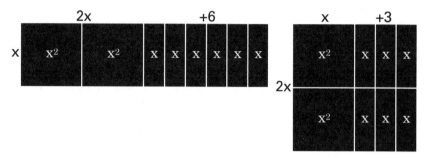

Have the students notice that $2x + 6$ can be factored with the common term of 2, resulting in $2(x + 3)$. So the completely factored expression is $2x(x + 3)$.

5. Have the class build rectangles and name the factors for the following:

$2x^2 + 4x$ $\qquad$ $x^2 - 5x$ $\qquad$ $3x^2 + 6x$ $\qquad$ $2x^2 - 6x$

6. Discuss the problems and the factors using the distributive property.

What's in Common? Part 1

Directions:

1. Divide the class into groups of four. Give one set of 48 cards to each group.

2. Have each group label the cards as follows: Twelve cards with the number 2, twelve cards with the number 3, twelve cards with the word "red," and twelve cards with the word "blue."

3. Have the students in each group select one student to shuffle and deal five cards to each person. The rest of the cards are not needed at this time, so they should be put aside.

4. The students should place their five cards face up on the table in front of them so that all students can look at everyone's hand.

5. If any student sees a card that all four group members have in

Materials:

► Blank cards or

common, he or she should place that card in a separate new stack in the middle of the table.

6. The group members should continue this process until their hands no longer have any cards that are common to those of all other members of their group.

7. Explain to the students that the cards that were placed in the center of the table represent the greatest common factor for their group.

8. Explain further that the cards remaining in their hands represent the noncommon portion of their hands (NO terms in common).

9. Have each group write its GCF next to an open parenthesis symbol on a sheet of paper, for example, "2rb(."

10. Have the group list the cards remaining in the group members' hands, one at a time, to the right of the parenthesis, with a plus sign between the entry for each student, to represent the remaining cards that need to be accounted for from the original "deal."

11. Finally, have the students place a closing parenthesis symbol on the right side of the sum of their "leftover" cards.

12. If they have completed their activity correctly, they should have a GCF factored out and the remaining terms left inside the parentheses.

13. As an example, suppose the four students were dealt the following hands:

    red, 2, red, blue, 3 or r2rb3   blue, 2, 2, 3, red or b223r

    red, red, 3, blue, 2 or rr3b2   3, blue, 2, red, 3 or 3b2r3

    The common cards would be red, blue, 2, and 3, so the GCF would be 2-3-blue-red, and the students' "leftovers" would be red, 2, red, and 3. The students have no other cards in common with all of their teammates. Their answer should therefore look like this: red blue 2 3 (red + 2 + red + 3) or 2 3 r b (r + 2 + r + 3) or 2 3 r b (2 + 3 + 2r).

14. Have the students shuffle all of the cards and repeat the activity as time allows.

15. At the end of the activity, ask the class to write the factored sentences for $3x^2y^2 + 15xy^3$ and $12a^2bc^3 + 30a^2bc$.

Materials:

▶ Blank cards or

What's in Common? Part 2

Directions:

If you had your class do the Concept Development Activity **What's in Common? Part 1** for this Objective, your students will have a set of cards that they can use for this activity and you can skip steps 1 and 2. If this is the case, explain that the cards that say "red" should be read as "r" cards and the cards that say "blue" should be read as "b" cards. You will need to give each group four additional blank cards. Then, follow steps 3–16.

1. Divide the class into groups of four. Give one set of 52 cards to each group.

2. Have each group label the cards as follows: Twelve cards with the number 2, twelve cards with the number 3, twelve cards with the word "red," and twelve cards with the word "blue." This will leave four blank cards.

3. Have the groups keep the four blank cards out of the deck for use later in the activity. Then have them select one student in each group to shuffle and deal five cards to each person. The rest of the cards are not needed at this time, so they should be put aside.

4. The students should place their five cards face up on the table in front of them so that all students can look at everyone's hand.

5. Each student should next determine the most abbreviated way to write his or her combination of cards. The students should write the numbers first, followed by the variables, using exponents for any cards that repeat within their hands. Have the students write a multiplication symbol between each element of their hands to avoid confusion later (e.g., r, r, 2, 3, 2 should be written as $2^2 \cdot 3 \cdot r^2$).

6. Each student should write his or her abbreviated "hand" on one of the four blank cards.

7. All four group members should place the card on which they have written their abbreviated "hand" face up in the center of the table so that all group members may view them.

8. As the students look at the abbreviated "hands," instruct them to

Chapter 9—Using Factoring

find any "2's" that are common to all four cards. If there are any, have them write a "2" on a blank piece of paper. Next, have them determine the lowest exponent of "2" that appears in the four hands and write it as an exponent for the "2" they have written on their paper.

9. Repeat step 8 for the number 3 and then for the letters r and b. This will take a while, and it is important that you keep the students organized so they stay on track.

10. Once the students have completed step 9, the term they have written on their paper should be the GCF for their hands.

11. Have the group write an open parenthesis symbol to the right of the GCF on their paper.

12. Ask the dealer in each group to compare his or her abbreviated hand to the GCF and determine what would be left if the GCF were removed from his or her hand. Have this student write these remaining elements inside the open parenthesis followed by a plus symbol. Repeat this step for the other three group members. The last person should place a closing parenthesis on the right side of his or her term.

13. If the students have completed the activity correctly, they will have factored out the GCF from their four original hands.

14. For example, if the four members were dealt the following cards:

2, 2, 3, r, r   2, 3, 2, r, b   b, 2, b, r, 3   2, 3, 3, r, b

their abbreviated hands would be:

$2^2 \cdot 3 \cdot r^2$ $2^2 \cdot 3 \cdot r \cdot b$ $2 \cdot 3 \cdot b^2 \cdot r$ $2 \cdot 3^2 \cdot r \cdot b$

and their GCF would be $2 \cdot 3 \cdot r$. Their final answer would therefore be $2 \cdot 3 \cdot r(2r + 2b + b^2 + 3b)$.

15. After some practice with the cards, ask the students to write a factored sentence for the following:

$2^2 \cdot r \cdot b^2$ $3 \cdot 2 \cdot r^2 \cdot b$ $3 \cdot 2 \cdot r \cdot b^2$ $2^2 \cdot r \cdot b^2$

16. Have the students write factored expressions for problems such as:
$8a^2b + 4ab^2$ and $14a^3b^2c^2 + 7a^2bc^4$.

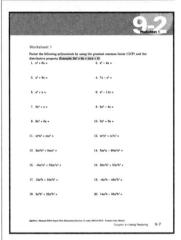
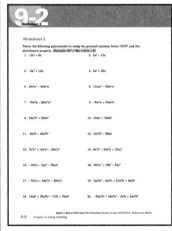

Teacher's Tip:

Worksheet 3 for this
objective, **page 9-9**,
supports this activity
with practice exercises.

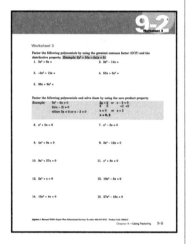

Answer Key for #7:
x = 0, 9
x = 0, –5
x = 0, 3
x = –1

Factor and Solve

Directions:

1. Write the sentence a · b = 0 on the board. Ask the students what numbers make it a true statement. If necessary, ask, "If a = 4, what must 'b' equal?" **(0)** "If b = 6, what must 'a' equal?" **(0)** Then ask, "If a = $\frac{1}{16}$, what must 'b' equal?" **(0)**

2. Help the students see that no matter what value you pick for a or b, in order for a · b = 0 to be true, one or both of the values must be equal to zero. Start to refer to this concept as the "zero product property."

3. Write 2x · y = 0 on the board. Continue discussing the concept that either x or y must be equal to zero for this equation to be a true statement. Either 2x = 0 or y = 0.

4. Next, discuss with the class what combinations work for the equation a + b = 0. Point out that many combinations work: (1, –1), (2, –2), (8, –8), and so on. Emphasize the fact that the zero product property works only for multiplication and that it does not hold for addition.

5. Write x^2 + 3x = 0 on the board. Ask the students to give you the factored form of that equation. **[x(x + 3) = 0]** Explain that by factoring the original problem, you have created an equivalent equation that involves the multiplication of two terms, which can easily be solved by using the zero product property. Explain that if x · (x + 3) = 0, then either x = 0 or (x + 3) = 0. Solving these two equation factors yields two answers, x = 0 or x = –3.

6. Solve $4x^2$ + 6x = 0 with the class. **[2x(2x + 3) = 0; x = 0 or x = $-\frac{3}{2}$]**

7. Then have the students solve the following equations independently:

   $x^2 - 9x = 0$ $5x + x^2 = 0$ $2x^2 - 6x = 0$ $2x + 2 = 0$

Practice Activities

Card Draw

Directions:

Materials:
▶ Blank cards

1. Label one side of each card with an integer starting from 1 and continuing to the number that represents the student population in your class. On the other side of each card, write a monomial that contains a random combination of a factorable integer between 1 and 60 and the variables x, y, and/or z. Any variable used can contain an exponent from 1 to 6, for example, $8x^2y^3z^2$. Include cards such as x^2 and $6x$.

2. Assign a number to each of the students so each student's number corresponds to one of the cards. Alternatively, you may have the students number off from 1 to whatever your class population is.

3. Shuffle the cards and randomly select two of them.

4. Have the two students whose numbers correspond to the numbers on the cards go up to the board. Then give them their corresponding cards.

5. Ask them to write the monomials from their cards on the board side by side with an addition or subtraction symbol between them. *Example:* $8x^2y^3z^2 + 12xy^2z^2$.

6. Have the rest of the class factor the two monomials and write the GCF on their own papers. **(Answer for example: $4xy^2z^2$)** Students should work quietly. You might want to make this a competition to see who can get the most correct.

7. Repeat this process until all cards have been used.

8. Each student should have answers for all but their own problem. Alternatively, you could give them time to get back to their seats to complete that problem as well.

Equation Solving

Directions:

1. Write the following equation on the board:
    $$x^2 \pm bx = 0$$

2. Ask the students to write on a sheet of paper an equation like the one on the board, but they should substitute a number for b and choose either "+" or "−" for their equation. *Example:* $x^2 + 10x = 0$

3. Now write the equation $ax^2 \pm bx = 0$ on the board.

4. Have the students write on their paper an equation like the one on the board, but they should substitute numbers for a and b and choose either the "+" or "−" sign. *Example:* $3x^2 + 2x = 0$. The students should now have two equations on their paper.

5. Form groups of four students. Have each student, working independently, solve all the equations (eight) for the group on a new sheet of paper. Then have the four students compare their answers. If any of the solutions differ, the group should work together to determine the correct answers.

6. Each group should then exchange the eight problems with a different group and solve the new problems. Continue the sharing of problems as time allows.

Find the Solutions

Directions:

1. Have the students form groups of four and give each group 20 cards. Ask each group to label the cards as follows:

    On six cards, they should write the following equations, one equation per card.

$x^2 + 4x = 0$	$3x + x^2 = 0$	$2x^2 - 4x = 0$
$5x - 5x^2 = 0$	$x^2 + 2x = 0$	$x^2 - 3x = 0$

    On the remaining 14 cards, they should write the following solutions, one solution per card: 0, 0, 0, 0, 0, 0, 1, −1, 2, −2, 3, −3, 4, −4.

2. Have the students in each group shuffle the equation cards and the solution cards separately and deal one equation card to each student in the group. Place the two extra equation cards off to the side. Have the students place the solution cards in a stack face down.

3. Ask the students to solve the equation they have been dealt on their own sheet of paper.

4. After all of the students in a group are finished solving their equations, have one student take the top card from the stack of solution cards and place it next to the stack, face up. He or she should take the card if it is a solution to his or her equation. Play continues clockwise with each student selecting either the face-up card and keeping it if it is a solution to his or her problem.

5. After all solution cards have been selected, each student must show the group that his or her solution cards are correct by proving that they solve the original equation and make it a true statement.

6. Have the students separate the cards into equation cards and solution cards, shuffle all of the equation cards, and redeal.

Problem-Solving Activity

Length and Width of a Rectangle 🔆

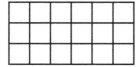

1. Present the following sample problem to the class.

   Find the length, width, and total area in square units of the following rectangle:

   Explain that the length is 6 units and the width is 3 units. Therefore, by the formula area = length × width, the total area is 18 square units. Invite the students to count the square units if they want to check your work.

2. Ask, "What do you think the dimensions of the following rectangle are if the area of the interior spaces are as labeled?"

Tell the students to think of the left rectangle as a square. Explain the procedure as follows: If it is a square, its dimensions must be equal. So, the length and width of the left rectangle would both be x units long. If the width of the left rectangle is x units, then the width of the right rectangle must also be x units since both rectangles have the same width. Now have the students look at the right rectangle. Explain that its area can also be found by using length × width. Since its width must be "x" units, the length can be determined by seeing what number multiplied by x equals 3x, the actual area. The answer for the length of the right rectangle would be 3 units, since x times 3 is 3x.

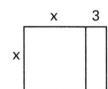

3. Explain that, therefore, the total area of the entire rectangle could be written as $x^2 + 3x$, since adding the small areas together should equal the entire large area. Finally, explain that if the entire large rectangle is thought of as one total area, it would have length "x + 3" and width "x", and the area could be written as $x(x + 3)$. This means that $x^2 + 3x = x(x + 3)$. Ask the students what they think the "x" to the left of the parentheses is. **(The GCF of x^2 and 3x)**

4. Ask the students to find the lengths and widths of the following rectangles if the areas of the interior spaces are as labeled:

   a.

   | $4x^2$ | 14x |

   b.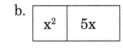

   | x^2 | 5x |

   c.

   | $9x^2$ | 15x |

   Remind the students that since the left rectangle in each problem has square units, they might want to assume that it is in fact a square. This might help them figure out its dimensions more quickly.

5. Ask the students to find the dimensions (lengths and widths) of rectangles with the following areas:

   a. $x^2 + 7x$ b. $x^2 + 40x$ c. $2x^2 + 8x$

9-3 *Objective:* **Factor quadratic trinomials of the form ax² + bx + c and solve equations by factoring.**

Sample Test:

1. Factor the following quadratic polynomial: $x^2 + 6x - 16$
   Solution: (x − 2)(x + 8)

2. Solve the following quadratic equation: $x^2 + 5x - 14 = 0$
   Solution: x = 2, −7

Concept Development Activities

Find the Product and Factors I

Directions:

1. Have the students draw the following rectangular diagram on a sheet of paper:

   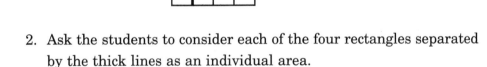

2. Ask the students to consider each of the four rectangles separated by the thick lines as an individual area.

3. Remind the students of the formula for the area of a rectangle, length × width. Then have them calculate how many square units are in each rectangle.

4. Have the students write an expression for the total area of the entire large rectangle by adding the areas of the individual rectangles together. **[(2 + 6 + 1 + 3) = 12 square units]**

5. Remind the students that the area of a square is calculated by the formula side × side, or s × s = total area of a square.

   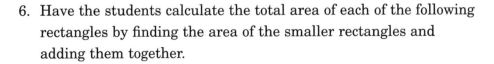

6. Have the students calculate the total area of each of the following rectangles by finding the area of the smaller rectangles and adding them together.

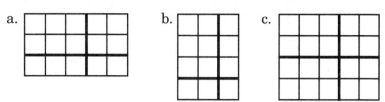

a.   b.   c.

7. Present the diagram to the right and ask the students to calculate its length and width. The students should come up with a length of x + 3 and a width of x + 1.

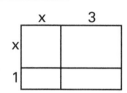

8. Discuss the fact that since "x" is a variable, it could be anything. As "x" increases, so do the sizes of the small rectangles, and therefore so does the area of the overall large rectangle.

9. Have the students write an expression for the total area of the large rectangle shown in #7 by adding the smaller areas together. They should get $x^2 + 3x + 1x + 3$, which can be simplified to $x^2 + 4x + 3$.

   Remind the students that another way to find area is length × width, or, from step 7, area equals (x + 3)(x + 1), or $x^2 + 4x + 3$. This expression represents the total area of the large rectangle, and if the students choose different values for x and substitute them into the expression and simplify it, their answers for the total area will change accordingly. Have the students try the following values for x to see what total areas they get as answers: 1, 2, 3, 4, and 5. **(8, 15, 24, 35, 48)**

10. Discuss how the expression $x^2 + 4x + 3$ is a quadratic trinomial. This would be a good time to review vocabulary.

11. Have the students construct a rectangle similar to the one in step 7 with the dimensions x + 2 by x + 4 and calculate its total area. **($x^2 + 6x + 8$)** Have the students try some other dimensions.

Find the Product and Factors II

Directions:

1. Present the rectangular figure at the right to the students and ask them to calculate the length and width of the overall large rectangle.

x^2	4x
2x	8

Materials:

▶ Algebra tiles can be used to make the figures, but their use is optional.

2. The students should get a length of (x + 4) and a width of (x + 2). Tell them to think of the upper left rectangle as a square with the area x^2, so its length and width are both x. Also, remind them that if they know the length or width of a rectangle, its other dimension will be whatever number multiplies with the dimension they know to give them the area within the rectangle.

   Explain that the overall area of the large rectangle shown in #1 is $x^2 + 4x + 2x + 8$, which simplifies to $x^2 + 6x + 8$. Be sure they see that this area should be equal to the length, (x + 4) times the width (x + 2). Show the students that, therefore, $x^2 + 6x + 8 = (x + 2)(x + 4)$.

3. Repeat the procedure from steps 1 and 2 for the rectangular figure at the right.

x^2	5x
1x	5

   The students should get a length of (x + 5) and a width of (x + 1), and the total area found by adding the small rectangles together will be equal to the total area found by multiplying the length and width of the large rectangle, or $x^2 + 6x + 5 = (x + 5)(x + 1)$.

4. Repeat the procedure from steps 1 and 2 for the rectangular figure at the right.

x^2	8x
3x	24

   This time the students should get a length of (x + 8) and a width of (x + 3), and the total area found by adding the small rectangles together will be equal to the total area found by multiplying the length and width of the large rectangle, or $x^2 + 11x + 24 = (x + 3)(x + 8)$.

5. Ask the students to practice multiplying the factors from the previous problems to prove to themselves that the length times the width of the large rectangle does in fact give them the total area obtained by adding the areas of the smaller rectangles together.

   a. $(x + 2)(x + 4) = x^2 + 6x + 8$

   b. $(x + 1)(x + 5) = x^2 + 6x + 5$

   c. $(x + 3)(x + 8) = x^2 + 11x + 5$

6. Have the students find the area and dimensions for the following rectangles:

   a.

x^2	$3x$
x	3

   b.

x^2	$3x$
$2x$	6

   c.

x^2	$3x$
$3x$	9

   d.

x^2	$4x$
x	4

7. Have the students find the dimensions for the following rectangles:

   a. $x^2 + 2x + 1x + 2 =$
      $x^2 + 3x + 2$

   b. $x^2 + 3x + 2x + 6 =$
      $x^2 + 5x + 6$

Algebra Tiles

Materials:

▶ One set of algebra tiles for every two students

Directions:

1. Review how to find the product of two binomials by using algebra tiles. For example, make a rectangle like the one to the right with $(x + 2)$ as the desired length and $(x + 1)$ as the width. Be sure the students see that $(x + 1)(x + 2) = x^2 + 3x + 2$.

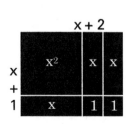

2. Next, show the students that the model to find factors of a trinomial is to **make a rectangle** out of the given trinomial.

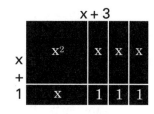

In other words, the model is to work backward from what is shown in step 1.

Use algebra tiles to factor the trinomial $x^2 + 4x + 3$ (as shown at the right), and show the students how to determine the dimensions of the overall rectangle. The dimensions are $(x + 3)(x + 1)$.

Teacher's Tip:

If the students need more practice multiplying binomials, refer to **Objective 8-5**.

3. Write the following polynomials on the board. Have the students use algebra tiles to find the factors. Call on students to give you the factors they found and write them under the appropriate polynomials.

$x^2 + 5x + 6$ $x^2 + 4x + 4$ $x^2 + x - 6$ $x^2 + 6x + 5$

Teacher's Tip:

Worksheet 1 for this objective, **page 9-12**, supports this activity with practice exercises.

4. As an example, $x^2 + 5x + 6 = (x + 2)(x + 3)$. Discuss the relationship between the numbers (5 and 6) and the factors (2 and 3). **(2 + 3 = 5 and 2 · 3 = 6)** Use the model to show why the relationship exists. Repeat for all of the polynomials on the board.

5. Ask the students to find the factors of $x^2 + 7x + 10$ and $x^2 + x + 12$. Allow the students to use the algebra tiles if they need the model to find the factors.

Making Area Rugs

Directions:

1. This activity shows that a quadratic trinomial can represent the total area of a rectangle, called an "area rug" here. The following steps are designed to help the students discover the actual lengths and widths for their area rug diagrams.

2. Draw a rectangular area rug diagram, such as those shown below, to represent a quadratic trinomial. Point out that although a trinomial has only three elements, the area rug has four rectangles. The area rug diagram is similar to the algebra tile concept in the previous activity. This concept may be difficult for many students to comprehend.

3. Note that in all of the following problems, the trinomial has no leading coefficient for the x^2 term. In other words, it is just like having the coefficient 1 in front of it.

4. Have the students draw a blank area rug made up of four rectangles, as shown in the diagram to the right.

5. Present the trinomial $x^2 + 5x + 6$ to the class. Have them place the x^2 term in the upper left rectangle and the constant number in the lowest right rectangle, as shown in the diagram to the right.

x^2	
	6

6. Now have them make a list of all combinations of factors for the constant number (+6). Point out that only one combination of factors from their list will add to equal the coefficient of the middle term in the original trinomial (+5). This combination will be the two coefficients that they must use inside the remaining two rectangles, the upper right and lower left, in their area rug. **(2x + 3x)**

7. Have the students begin to fill in the overall outside lengths and widths of the large rectangle that makes up their whole area rug by placing an x as both the length and width for the upper left rectangle. Remind them that since the upper left rectangle is a square, it has a length and width of x.

8. The diagram should now look like the one at the right.

x^2	3x
2x	6

9. The students will now have enough information to complete the overall length and width of the large rectangle. **[(x + 3)(x + 2)]**

10. Remind the students that their overall lengths and widths are the "factored" form of the original quadratic trinomial.

11. Have students make area rugs and find the lengths and widths for the following quadratic trinomials one at a time. Ask for volunteers to present their completed area rugs by drawing them on the board for all to see. Make sure that they label the overall length and width for the large rectangle. Also, ask them to prove, by multiplying the factors, that the length times the width equals the original trinomial.

    a. $x^2 + 2x + 1$ b. $x^2 + 5x + 4$

    c. $x^2 + 7x + 10$ d. $x^2 + 7x + 12$

Answer Key for #11:
a. (x + 1)(x + 1)
b. (x + 1)(x + 4)
c. (x + 5)(x + 2)
d. (x + 3)(x + 4)

More Area Rugs

Directions:

1. This is another activity that shows that a quadratic trinomial can represent the total area of a rectangle, called an "area rug" here. The following steps are designed to help the students discover the actual lengths and widths for their area rug diagrams.

2. Draw a rectangular area rug to represent a quadratic trinomial. Point out that although a trinomial has only three elements, the area rug has four small rectangles. The area rug diagram is similar to the algebra tile concept in the **Algebra Tiles** activity earlier in this Objective. This concept may be difficult for many students to comprehend.

3. Note that in all of the following problems the trinomial is of the form $ax^2 + bx + c$. In other words, it has leading coefficient a for the x^2 term and b for the x term, and the constant ("plain") term is c, where a, b, and c can equal any numbers. An example of such a quadratic trinomial is $2x^2 + 11x + 12$.

4. Have the students draw a blank area rug made up of four rectangles, as shown at the right.

5. Using $2x^2 + 11x + 12$ as an example, have the students multiply the coefficient of the x^2 term with the last constant term (a × c, or 2 × 12 = 24).

6. Have the students write a new trinomial based on the original trinomial by using x^2 without its coefficient, the middle term as it is in the problem, and the "new" constant they got from multiplying the first and last coefficients together in step 5. **($x^2 + 11x + 24$)**

7. Have the students make a list of all combinations of factors for the new constant number. **(The factors of 24 are 1 and 24, –1 and –24, 2 and 12, –2 and –12, 3 and 8, –3 and –8, 4 and 6, and –4 and –6.)**

8. Ask the students to find the one combination of factors from their list that adds to be equal to the middle term in the original trinomial. **(3 and 8)**

9. Have the students place the x^2 term in the upper left rectangle, and the constant number in the lower right rectangle, of their area rug.

Teacher's Tip:

Worksheet 2 for this objective, **page 9-13**, supports this activity with practice exercises.

10. The combination the students found in step 8 will be the two numbers they must use inside the remaining two rectangles, in the upper right and lower left of their area rugs.

11. Have the students begin to fill in the overall outside lengths and widths of the large rectangle that makes up their whole area rug by placing an "x" as both the length and width for the upper left rectangle. Remind them that because the upper left rectangle is a square it has a length and width of "x." This should help the students see that the areas of the upper right and lower left rectangles must contain both the number from the combination that they found as well as an x. **(3x and 8x)**

12. The students now have enough information to complete the overall length and width of the large rectangle. **[(x + 8) and (x + 3)]**

13. Remind the students that the overall length and width is the "factored" form of the new quadratic trinomial they constructed in step 6 when they multiplied the first and last coefficients.

14. Have the students write the lengths and widths of their rugs as two binomials that are multiplied together. **[(x + 8)(x + 3)]**

15. Now explain that because you had them multiply the first and last coefficients to make a trinomial that was easier to factor, they must now divide the numbers in their binomials by the original coefficient "a" to get back to the original problem. This will result in fractions in their two factors. **[The factors will now be $\left(x + \frac{8}{2}\right)\left(x + \frac{3}{2}\right)$.]**

16. Ask the students to reduce the fractions if possible. **[$(x + 4)\left(x + \frac{3}{2}\right)$.]**

17. Now have the students "move" the denominator out from the bottom of any fraction and place it as a leading coefficient in front of the x in the binomial. The resulting binomials will be the correct factors of the original trinomial. **[(x + 4)(2x + 3)]**

18. Have the students multiply the two binomial factors together to prove that they are, in fact, equal to the original trinomial, and therefore the lengths and widths are, in fact, the factored form of the original trinomial and the total area for the original rectangle.

19. Draw a rectangular area rug to represent a quadratic trinomial. Then, present the following example to the class:

Original trinomial: $6x^2 - 7x - 3$

Following the same procedures as above and working the problem on the board, explain the following steps for finding the factors of a quadratic trinomial. Multiply 6 times –3 and form the *new* trinomial to be factored: $x^2 - 7x - 18$. Insert the x^2 and –18 in the rectangles.

The factors of –18 are:
1 and –18, –1 and 18, 2 and –9, –2 and 9, 3 and –6, and –3 and 6.

The combination that adds to be equal to the middle coefficient, –7, is 2 and –9. No other combination will work. Therefore, the two factors are $(x - 9)$ and $(x + 2)$.

Now divide the two numbers in these factors by the original coefficient of the x^2 term, 6, to get $\left(x - \frac{9}{6}\right)\left(x + \frac{2}{6}\right)$ or, after reducing the fractions, $\left(x - \frac{3}{2}\right)\left(x + \frac{1}{3}\right)$.

By bringing the denominators out in front of the x's, the factors become $(2x - 3)(3x + 1)$. Show that $(2x - 3)(3x + 1) = 6x^2 - 7x - 3$, the original trinomial.

20. Have the students factor the following trinomials one at a time. Ask for volunteers to present the completed area rugs by drawing them on the board for all to see. Make sure that they label the overall length and width for the large rectangle. Also, ask them to prove, by multiplying the factors, that the length times the width does actually equal the original given trinomial.

Answer Key for #20:
a. $(2x + 5)(x + 4)$
b. $(3x - 1)(x - 6)$
c. $(4x + 3)(x - 1)$
d. $(3x + 2)(2x + 1)$

a. $2x^2 + 13x + 20$ b. $3x^2 - 19x + 6$

c. $4x^2 - x - 3$ d. $6x^2 + 7x + 2$

Teacher's Tip:

Worksheet 3 for this objective, **page 9-14**, supports this activity with practice exercises.

Double Factoring

Directions:

1. Explain to the students that there is another algorithm for factoring trinomials that have a leading coefficient. Since the middle term will have the leading coefficient, we cannot use the rule of finding the factors of the last term whose sum is the middle term.

   Example: $x^2 + 6x + 8 \rightarrow 4 + 2 = 6$ and $4 \cdot 2 = 8$

2. What we can do is multiply the leading coefficient times the last term to find the correct middle terms. This is because the leading coefficient is used as a factor in the middle term. Work through the following example on the board, helping students to understand the steps for factoring trinomials with a leading coefficient.

   Example 1: $2x^2 + 3x - 5$

   a. Multiply the $(2)(-5) = -10$: Find the factors of -10 whose sum is $+3$. $+5$ and -2 are the factors.

   b. Set up the middle terms so they can be factored again. **$(2x^2 - 2x + 5x - 5)$** *Note:* The $+5$ and -2 are the coefficients of the middle term.

   c. Factor the expression by pairs. **[2x(x – 1) + 5(x – 1)]**

   d. Complete the factoring. **[(2x + 5)(x – 1)]**

3. *Example 2:* $3x^2 + 11x - 4$

   Steps:

   a. Multiply the leading coefficient and the last term: **[3(–4) = –12]**

   b. Find the factors of -12 that give the middle term (11) as a sum: **(–1, +12)**

   c. Set up the middle terms for more factoring: **(3x² + 12x – x – 4)**

   d. Factor by pairs: **[3x(x + 4) – 1(x + 4)]**

   e. Complete the factoring: **[(3x – 1)(x + 4)]**

   Check: $(3x - 1)(x + 4) = 3x^2 + 12x - x - 4 = 3x^2 + 11x - 4$

Solve the Trinomial Equation

Directions:

1. Write the problem $x^2 + 5x + 4 = 0$ on the board.

2. Ask the students how they might solve this equation. Let them try various methods (subtraction, dividing by 5 or x, and so on).

3. If the students do not suggest factoring, review factoring and show that the problem can be written as $(x + 4)(x + 1) = 0$.

4. Review the zero product property:

   If $a \cdot b = 0$, then $a = 0$ or $b = 0$.

5. Solve the factors from the example:
   $(x + 4) = 0$ or $(x + 1) = 0$; therefore, $x = -4$ or $x = -1$, or $x = -4, -1$, is the solution to the problem.

6. Have the students substitute these solutions into the equation $x^2 + 5x + 4 = 0$ to show that they work:
   $(-4)^2 + 5(-4) + 4 = 0$ $(-1)^2 + 5(-1) + 4 = 0$

7. Have the students use factoring to solve the following equations:

   a. $x^2 + 6x + 8 = 0$ b. $x^2 - 2x - 15 = 0$ c. $2x^2 + 11x + 12 = 0$

Practice Activities

Sharing the Factors

Directions:

1. Present two binomials of the form $(x \pm a)$ and $(x \pm b)$, where $-10 \le a \le 10$ and $-10 \le b \le 10$.

2. With the class, multiply the binomials to get a trinomial; for example, $(x + 4)(x - 7) = x^2 - 3x - 28$.

3. Divide the class into groups of four.

4. Have each group design three similar problems with two binomials of the same form as in the example. Have them write these problems on a piece of paper.

Teacher's Tip:

Worksheets 4 and 5
for this objective,
pages 9-15 and 9-16,
support this activity
with practice exercises.

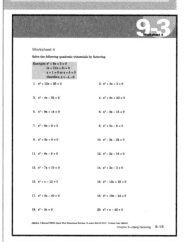

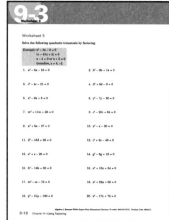

Answer Key for #7:
a. $x = -2, -4$
b. $x = 5, -3$
c. $x = -\frac{3}{2}, -4$

5. On a new sheet of paper, have the students write the three trinomials they get by multiplying their binomial pairs.

6. Have the groups exchange their trinomials with another group in the class.

7. The task for each group is to factor the three trinomials they received.

8. After the students have finished, have each group pick one problem to put onto an overhead transparency and present to the class.

9. The group should show how they found the factors to the problem. This will allow the class to see different ways to find the factors. The students need to find a method that they understand and can use.

10. Review as time allows.

11. As an extension to this activity, have each student write an explanation of how to factor a trinomial such as $x^2 + x - 6$. Review the written explanations.

12. Repeat the activity using two binomials of the form $(ax \pm b)$ and $(x \pm c)$. This will provide practice factoring trinomials with a coefficient for the x^2 term.

Materials:

▶ Blackline master for a **5 × 5 bingo card** is in the Appendix.

▶ Game markers to cover squares

Find the Solution Bingo

Directions:

1. Have the students put the numbers −3, −2, −1, 0, 1, 2, 3 at random in the squares of the 5 × 5 bingo cards, anywhere they want. They will have to repeat some numbers to fill the 25 squares.

2. Write an equation on the board, selected at random from the list below.

3. Ask the students to solve the equation and cover the squares that have the solution(s) with their markers. Have the students write the equations and solutions on a piece of paper to hand in at the end of the activity.

4. Continue with other equations. The first student to get five markers in a row should call out, "Bingo!" If the student's answers are correct, that student is the winner.

5. Alternatively, continue play until a student covers all the squares on his or her card.

List of Equations to Use	Solutions
1. $x^2 + 3x + 2 = 0$	**−2, −1**
2. $x^2 − 4x + 3 = 0$	**3, 1**
3. $x^2 − 4x + 4 = 0$	**2, 2**
4. $x^2 + x − 6 = 0$	**−3, 2**
5. $x^2 + x − 2 = 0$	**−2, 1**
6. $x^2 + 2x + 1 = 0$	**−1, −1**
7. $x^2 + 6x + 9 = 0$	**−3, −3**
8. $x^2 − x − 6 = 0$	**3, −2**
9. $x^2 − 2x = 0$	**0, 2**
10. $x^2 + 4x + 4 = 0$	**−2, −2**
11. $x^2 + x = 0$	**0, −1**
12. $x^2 − 6x + 9 = 0$	**3, 3**
13. $x^2 − 3x = 0$	**0, 3**
14. $x^2 − 2x − 3 = 0$	**−1, 3**
15. $x^2 − x − 2 = 0$	**2, −1**
16. $x^2 − 5x + 6 = 0$	**3, 2**
17. $x^2 + 2x − 3 = 0$	**−3, 1**
18. $x^2 + 4x + 3 = 0$	**−3, −1**
19. $x^2 + 5x + 6 = 0$	**−3, −2**
20. $x^2 + 2x = 0$	**−2, 0**
21. $x^2 − 4 = 0$	**−2, 2**
22. $x^2 + 3x = 0$	**0, −3**
23. $x^2 + 2x + 1 = 0$	**−1, −1**
24. $x^2 − 3x + 2 = 0$	**1, 2**
25. $x^2 − 4x + 4 = 0$	**2, 2**

Problem-Solving Activity

Paving the Yard ·☀·

Directions:

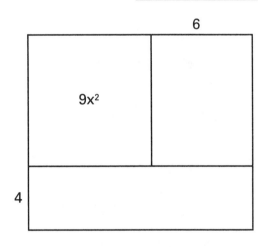

1. Read the following scenario to the students:

    A homeowner wants to pave a square area in his backyard that is $9x^2$ square feet in area. He will use square pavers that measure one foot on each side.

    Now he is considering extending the paving to two rectangular areas adjacent to the original area. The first rectangular area is to the east and is 6 feet long and as wide as the original square. The second rectangular area is to the south and is 4 feet wide and as long as his original square plus the 6-foot extension.

2. Ask the students to calculate an expression in terms of x that would indicate how many pavers the homeowner would need.

3. Ask them, "If x = 3, how large is the original square area the homeowner wanted to pave?" **(81 square feet)** "How many pavers would he need?" **(81 pavers)** "How many more pavers would he need to pave the two rectangular areas as well?" **(195 − 81 = 114 pavers)**

9 **4**

9-4 *Objective:* **Factor quadratic polynomials that are perfect squares or differences of squares and solve equations by factoring.**

Sample Test: Factor and solve the following quadratic polynomials.

1. $x^2 - 36 = 0$ **Solution: $(x + 6)(x - 6) = 0$, so $x = -6, 6$**

2. $x^2 + 6x + 9 = 0$ **Solution: $(x + 3)(x + 3) = 0$, so $x = -3$**

Concept Development Activities

Perfect Square Trinomial Area Rugs

Directions:

1. Have the students form groups of four.

2. Ask the students, working individually, to draw a square on a piece of paper, approximately 1 inch by 1 inch. Have them label its length and width as x units long. You may use algebra tiles for the model instead of drawings.

3. Have the students draw a smaller square so that its upper left corner just touches the lower right corner of the 1-inch square, as shown to the right. Ask the students to pick a number between 1 and 10 and use that number for the length and width of the smaller square. If you are using algebra tiles, use "ones" to make the small square.

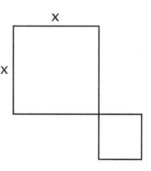

4. Have the students calculate the areas for the squares in their diagrams and put their answers inside the squares.

5. Have the students draw the borders of the upper right and lower left regions so that they are in the shape of rectangles. They should leave the lengths and widths of these two areas blank. See the example at the right, in which the sides of the smaller square were chosen to be 4.

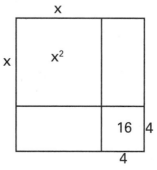

6. Have the students pass their papers to the person in their group who is on their right. Ask the students to figure out the dimensions of the upper right rectangle on the paper they have been given and write the area of the rectangle inside that rectangle. Remind them that $A = w \times h$.

7. Have the students pass their papers to the right once more. Ask the students to figure out the dimensions of the lower left rectangle on the paper they have been given and write the area of the rectangle inside that rectangle.

8. Begin a short discussion with the class concerning what appears to be true about the rectangles in the upper right and lower left regions. They should see that both have the same area. If they do not see this, point it out to them. Ask the class, "How many rectangles of this size are there in the new diagram?" If necessary, point out that there are exactly two. Ask the class, "How can you write the area for both of these rectangles as a single term?" Your goal is for them to develop a term that has a leading coefficient of "2" because there are two congruent regions. **[For the given example, this would be 2(4x) = 8x.]**

9. Have the students pass their papers to the right one more time. Ask the students to determine the overall length and width for the entire area rug now that they know the dimensions of all four smaller rectangular regions.

10. Have the students write the overall length and width as binomials in parentheses. **[For the given example, they should write (x + 4), (x + 4).]**

11. Now have the students write the two binomials next to each other, with a multiplication symbol between them. Repeat the fact that the overall length of a rectangular region times its overall width will give its area.

12. Have one student from each group come to the board and draw his or her area rug. Also, have the students write the binomial expression showing length times width of the overall rug on the board. Once this is done, ask what patterns the students see in all of the binomial expressions. If needed, point out that in each expression the two binomials are exactly the same.

13. Have all of the students multiply the binomials from each of the

rugs on the board to find the expression that represents the total area of each rug. Point out that the middle two terms from each expression can be combined in every problem to form the middle term of their final trinomial answer. Point out that all of the area rugs are perfect squares.

14. Discuss with the class that the resulting expressions are called "perfect square trinomials," and ask why they think these expresssions have that name. If needed, remind the students of what a "perfect square" is. **[For the given example, (length · width) = (x + 4)(x + 4), or (x + 4)^2 = x^2 + 4x + 4x + 16 = x^2 + 8x + 16. Both the first term, x^2, and the last term, 16, are perfect squares.]** Point out that if they are given a trinomial whose first and last terms are perfect squares, they should first attempt to break the trinomial up into two factors by using the square roots of each of these terms as the values for the first and second terms of the factors.

Student-Designed Perfect Square Trinomial Area Rugs

Directions:

Materials:

▶ Algebra tiles (optional)

1. Review with your class what perfect squares are. Give some examples if necessary. Be sure to go over examples that involve variables, such as x^2, 16a^2, and 49s^2.

2. Ask the students for six examples that you do not already have on the board.

3. Have the students choose any two perfect squares from the list to make two binomials of their own. They also need to pick either a plus symbol or a minus symbol to use for their problems. Emphasize that they must use the same symbol for both binomials. See the example at the right for the perfect squares 16a^2 and 81.

	4a	9
4a	16a^2	(36a)
9	(36a)	81

4. Have the students switch papers with someone nearby.

5. Have the students attempt to draw an area rug that would represent the particular "perfect square" for the binomials they

Teacher's Tip:

Worksheet 1 for this objective, **page 9-19**, supports this activity with practice exercises.

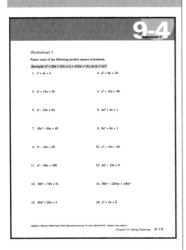

received. If needed, remind them that the area rug is a "perfect square" only if the upper right and lower left rectangles of the rug have areas that are identical. This means the students must be careful to use the same signs within both of their binomials. The area rug should make a square.

6. Once their area rugs are completed, have the students determine the overall length and width of the entire large rectangle, and label it. **[(4a + 9)(4a + 9)]**

7. Have the students multiply the overall length and width to find the overall area of their rug. After combining like terms, their answers should be in the form of a perfect square trinomial. **($16a^2 + 72a + 81$)**

8. Ask for volunteers to write their trinomial on the board.

9. After some of the students' final trinomials are on the board, begin a class discussion about what patterns hold true for all of the trinomials in the list. If the students do not state that in each case the first and last terms are perfect squares, point this out to them.

10. Ask whether anyone sees a pattern for the middle term of each trinomial in relation to the first and last terms. Help them to see that the middle term can always be found by multiplying the square roots of the first and last terms in the trinomial and doubling that result.

11. For the given example, with first term $16a^2$ and last term 81, the perfect square trinomials would have a middle term that has a coefficient of $2 \cdot 4a \cdot 9$, or $2 \cdot 4a \cdot (-9)$, so the middle term would be either 72a or −72a. The area rugs would look like the following:

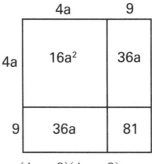

$(4a + 9)(4a + 9) =$
$16a^2 + 36a + 36a + 81 =$
$16a^2 + 72a + 81$

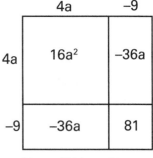

$(4a − 9)(4a − 9) =$
$16a^2 − 36a − 36a + 81 =$
$16a^2 − 72a + 81$

Both of these are perfect square trinomials.

12. Reinforce the idea that 72a (or −72a) can be calculated by taking the square roots of the first and last terms, multiplying them together, and then doubling them. Point out that the sign of the middle term is determined by the sign placed inside *both* binomials (the length and the width).

13. Emphasize that factoring can be done by doing the opposite of these steps. So, for the trinomial $16a^2 + 72a + 81$, the terms of the binomial would be the square roots of $16a^2$ and 81, and the sign would be determined by the sign of the middle term of the trinomial: $(4a + 9)(4a + 9)$.

14. Finish the exercise by giving the class three trinomials to factor individually:

    a. $9x^2 + 24x + 16$　　b. $4x^2 + 20x + 25$　　c. $25x^2 − 60x + 36$

Difference of Squares Area Rugs

Directions:

Materials:

► Algebra tiles (optional)

1. Have the students form groups of four.

2. Ask the students, working individually, to draw a square on a piece of paper, approximately 1 inch by 1 inch. Have them label its length and width as x units long.

3. Have the students draw a smaller square so that its upper left corner just touches the lower right corner of the 1-inch square, as shown to the right. Ask the students to pick a number between 1 and 10 and use that number for the length and width of the smaller square.

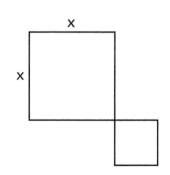

4. Have the students calculate the areas for the squares in their diagrams and put their answers inside the squares.

5. Have the students draw the borders of the upper right and lower left regions so that they are in the shape of rectangles. They should leave the lengths and widths of these two areas blank.

See the example at the right, in which the sides of the smaller square were chosen to be 3.

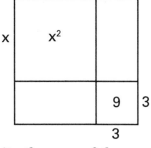

6. Have the students pass their papers to the person in their group who is on their right. Ask the students to figure out the dimensions of the upper right rectangle on the paper they have been given and write the area of the rectangle inside that rectangle. Remind them that $A = w \times h$.

7. Have the students pass their papers to the right once more. Ask the students to figure out the dimensions of the lower left rectangle on the paper they have been given and write the area of the rectangle inside that rectangle.

8. Begin a short discussion with the class concerning what appears to be true about the rectangles in the upper right and lower left regions. They should see that both have the same area. If they do not see this, point it out to them. Ask the class, "What must happen for these two areas to 'cancel' each other out?" If necessary, discuss the concept of equal terms with opposite signs canceling each other out. Use as an example $a + (-a) = 0$.

9. Ask the students to make the value for the area of either the upper right or the lower left rectangle negative. Remind them that this will also change the sign of the length or width of that region to a negative value, which will also change the area of the lower right rectangle to a negative value. Have the students fill in the four areas.

10. Have the students pass the papers to the right once more. Ask them to determine the overall length and width for the entire area rug now that they know the contents of all four smaller rectangular regions.

11. Have the students write the overall length and width as binomials in parentheses. **[For the given example, they should write (x + 3), (x − 3).]**

12. Now have the students write the two binomials next to each other, with a multiplication symbol between them. Repeat the fact that the overall length of a rectangular region times its overall width will give its area.

13. Have one student from each group come to the board and draw his or her area rug. Also, have the students write the binomial expression showing length times width of the overall rug on the board. Once this is done, ask what patterns the students see in all of the binomial expressions. If needed, point out that the two binomials differ only in the signs of the two terms.

14. Have all of the students multiply the binomials from each of the rugs on the board to find the expression that represents the total area of each rug. Point out that the middle two terms from each expression cancel each other in every problem. **[For the given example,** $(x + 3)(x - 3) = x^2 + 3x - 3x - 9 = x^2 - 9.$**]**

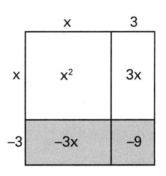

15. Discuss with the class that the resulting expression is called a "difference of squares," and ask why they think these expressions have that name. If needed, remind the students of what a "square" is and what the term "difference" means.

Student-Designed Difference of Squares Area Rugs

Directions:

1. Review with your class what perfect squares are. Give some examples if necessary. Be sure to go over examples that involve variables, such as x^2, $16a^2$, and $49s^2$.

2. Ask the students for six examples that you do not already have on the board.

3. Have the students choose any two squares from the list to make a binomial of their own that represents the difference of two squares. Be sure they place a minus symbol between them.

4. Have the students switch papers with someone nearby.

5. Have the students attempt to draw an area rug that would represent the particular "difference of squares" for the binomial they received. If needed, remind them that the area rug is a "difference of squares" only if the upper right and lower left rectangles of the rug have areas that are of identical size but

different signs. See the example at the right for the perfect squares $25a^2$ and -64.

	5a	8
5a	$25a^2$	40a
-8	-40a	-64

6. Once their area rugs are completed, have the students determine the overall length and width of the entire large rectangle and label it.
(5a + 8)(5a − 8)

7. Have the students multiply their overall length and width to see if their rug has an area equal to their original "difference of squares." **[For the given example, $25a^2 − 64 = (5a + 8)(5a − 8)$.]**

Recognize and Solve

Directions:

1. Review the concept of what a perfect square is with the students. Draw a square of length 3 on the board. Have the students calculate the area. Draw a diagram, like the one to the right, if needed.

2. Put another diagram (shown to the right) on the board and have students determine its area. **(x^2)**

3. Now ask the students what type of diagram would be required to represent a square with area $x^2 − 4$.

4. Draw the diagram to the right on the board.

	x	2
x	x^2	
2		-4

5. Ask the students what signs they would use for the 2's. (If needed, remind them that they multiply to equal −4.)

6. Discuss with the class the fact that the two unlabeled areas in the rug must cancel themselves out for the total area to be equal to $x^2 − 4$.

	x	+2
x	x^2	2x
-2	-2x	-4

7. Fill in the areas of the unlabeled rectangles and discuss how the 2's must be opposite signs for the area of this area rug to equal $x^2 − 4$.

8. Write the expression $x^2 - 9$ on the board and ask for a volunteer to try to build an area rug for it. Assist if needed.

9. Ask the students to give you additional examples of problems that would fit this pattern and go through their suggestions to determine which ones work and which ones don't, and why.

10. Put the following expressions on the board and have the students determine which ones fit a pattern of perfect squares and which fit a pattern of a difference of perfect squares.

 a. m^2 b. $a^2 + 16$ c. $b^2 - 16$

 d. $x^2 + 25$ e. c^2 f. $4x^2 - 9$

 g. $36n^2 - 49$ h. $64a^2 + 81$ i. $16 - 121x^2$

Solve Perfect Squares and Differences of Squares

Directions:

1. Review the factoring of perfect squares and differences of squares.

 Examples: $x^2 + 14x + 49$ and $x^2 - 25$

2. After the students have factored the examples, ask them, "If these were the equations $x^2 + 14x + 49 = 0$ and $x^2 - 25 = 0$, how would we solve them?"

3. Review the process of solving equations by factoring and using the zero product property.

 Examples:

$$x^2 - 25 = 0 \qquad x^2 + 14x + 49 = 0$$
$$(x + 5)(x - 5) = 0 \qquad (x + 7)^2 = 0$$
$$x + 5 = 0 \text{ or } x - 5 = 0 \qquad x + 7 = 0$$
$$x = -5 \text{ or } x = +5 \qquad x = -7$$

4. Write the following four problems on the board and have the students solve them. Discuss the problems and answer any questions.

 a. $x^2 + 8x + 16 = 0$ b. $4x^2 + 4x + 1 = 0$

 c. $x^2 - 25 = 0$ d. $9x^2 - 1 = 0$

Practice Activities

Constructing Differences of Squares

Directions:

1. Place a list of squares on the board—for example, a^2, b^2, x^2, 4, 9, 16, 25, 36, 49, 64.

2. Have the students choose one of the variable expressions and one of the numbers and them use them to construct a binomial that represents a "difference of squares." *Example:* $x^2 - 25$

3. Ask the students to sketch an area rug for their binomial to determine the overall length and width. The example to the right is for the binomial $x^2 - 25$. The overall length and width are $(x + 5)$ and $(x - 5)$.

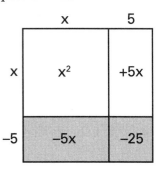

4. Discuss with the class that the overall length and width represent the factored form of the original binomial.

5. As you observe the class, select a couple of students who seem to have the correct idea and ask them to present their work on the board by writing their binomial and drawing their finished area rug. They should then prove to the class that they have found the correct length and width, or the *factors* for the binomial.

6. Repeat the process a few times for practice.

Perfect Squares Jeopardy

Directions:

1. Copy the "Jeopardy" board from the blackline master **Perfect Squares Jeopardy** onto an overhead transparency or make up your own problems to use for the game. Use the sticky notes to cover the rectangles for each problem so that they cannot be seen until they are selected.

2. If you make up the problems, make them more difficult and

Materials:

▶ Blackline master **Perfect Squares Jeopardy** is located in the *Teacher's Resource Manual*, **page 128.**

▶ Sticky notes

▶ Overhead sheet of acetate

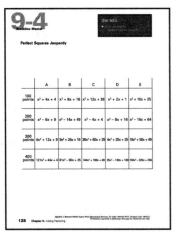

therefore worth more as you work down a column; for example, as on the blackline master, the top row of problems could be worth 100 points; the second row, 200 points; the third row, 300 points; and the bottom row, 400 points.

3. Divide the class into two or more teams.

4. Randomly select which team goes first.

5. A member of that team should name a square on the board by giving the row and column. When you remove the sticky note, the player must attempt to correctly factor the trinomial.

6. If the player is correct, his or her team receives the point value of the problem and another player from the same team repeats the process by selecting another square.

7. If, however, the first player is incorrect, a player from the next team must factor the same trinomial.

8. If that player's answer is correct, his or her team receives the point value, another player on the team selects a new trinomial, and the play continues as in steps 5 through 7.

9. If that player's answer is incorrect, the next player from the next team has a chance to factor the trinomial, and this process repeats until the trinomial has been factored correctly.

Class Competition on Differences of Squares

Directions:

1. Write a list of "differences of squares" problems on an overhead transparency. For example, use binomials such as the following:

   $x^2 - 16$ $4x^2 - 25$ $36a^2 - 49$ $144x^2 - 81y^2$

   Cover the problems with sticky notes.

2. Divide the class into two teams, and determine which team goes first.

3. Begin with the first person on that team. Remove the cover from the first binomial. The student whose turn it is should factor the binomial. All of the other class members should factor the problem on their papers individually.

Teacher's Tip:

This activity can be extended by including differences of squares problems and mixing up the problems.

Materials:

► Overhead transparency

► Sticky notes

4. If the student gives the correct answer, his or her team gets a point; if the student gives an incorrect answer, the first person from the other team has an opportunity to correctly complete the problem for a point for his or her team.

5. If neither player gives the correct answer, play moves to the next member of the first team, and the process is repeated until the binomial is factored correctly, resulting in a point being given to the appropriate team.

6. To prevent students from yelling out answers, tell them that any outbursts will result in a point for the other team.

7. As the class gets better at factoring "differences of squares," you may want to include some binomials that *appear* to be of the correct form but have a number that is not actually a perfect square or use addition instead of subtraction, just to keep the students interested. You must then explain that these binomials can be factored by another method that they will learn later. (For example, $64a^2 + 100$ is *not* a difference of squares, so it is not factorable by this method. The area rug will not work because it would produce items that are not found in the original binomial. The area rug actually produces the trinomial $64a^2 + 160a + 100$, not $64a^2 + 100$.)

Design, Share, and Solve 💡

Directions:

1. Divide the class into groups of four.

2. Have each student tear a sheet of notebook paper in half and then write a problem of the form $(x + 2)(x - 2) = 0$ or $(x + 3)^2 = 0$ on one of their half sheets of notebook paper.

3. Each student should multiply out their particular equation to form either a perfect square binomial or a perfect square trinomial.

4. Have the students write the new binomial or trinomial equations on the other half of their notebook paper. They should then exchange these papers with another person in their group by passing them to the person on their right.

5. Each student should attempt to factor the equation on the half

> **Teacher's Tip:**
>
> This activity can be extended by including perfect square trinomials or general trinomials after practice with the difference of squares is complete.

sheet of paper they were handed.

6. When the students have finished, have them compare their results with the original problem written by their group member.

7. Now have the students solve their original problems using the zero product property and check their answers by substituting the answers back into the original equations.

8. Repeat as needed for practice.

Overhead Exchange

Directions:

1. Divide the class into groups of four.

2. Have each group member write a trinomial with the first and last terms being perfect squares and the middle terms being left blank. *Example:* $36a^2$ _____ $+ 49$

3. Once all of the members of a group have their trinomials with missing middle terms, they should write all four in a list on an overhead transparency.

4. Have the groups exchange overhead transparencies.

5. The groups now must figure out what the missing middle term is for each problem on the overhead transparency they received.

6. Each group should also show what the factored form would be for the trinomial they complete. The answers should be in the form of two binomials multiplied together (like a length and width of an area rug).

7. Finally, each problem should be written as a completed perfect square trinomial. Point out that the middle terms can be either positive or negative, but that will affect the end result and what signs are used for the factors.

   For example, given $36a^2$ _____ $+ 49$, the students should be able to determine that the binomials will have the terms 6a and 7, and they have a choice to use + or − as the sign between these terms. So the choices for the factors are
   $(6a + 7)(6a + 7) = 36a^2 + 84a + 49$ and
   $(6a − 7)(6a − 7) = 36a^2 − 84a + 49$.

Materials:

► Overhead transparencies with pens

Teacher's Tip:

Worksheet 4 for this objective, **page 9-22**, supports this activity with practice exercises.

Problem-Solving Activities

Designing a Difference of Squares ⏻

Directions:

1. Present the diagram to the right to the class.

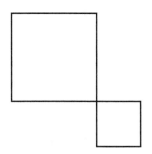

2. Ask the students to determine four different possible "differences of squares" that might be use to represent the total area of the regions above. They are to assume that both regions are in fact squares.

3. Tell the students their answers must be binomials that fit the requirements for "differences of squares," so they should be sure to think about what a square is and what "difference" stands for. They should use a variable when labeling the length and width of the original upper left square. At least two of their answers should use a numeric perfect square value for the upper-left-hand square as well (for example, $4a^2$ or $36x^2$).

How Many Perfect Square Trinomials Do You See? ⏻

Directions:

1. Give one copy of the blackline master **Perfect Square Trinomials** to each student in the class.

2. Ask the students to find as many perfect square trinomials as they can in the diagram. There are at least three.

3. Ask the students to write them in the form $ax^2 \pm bx + c$. Tell the students they might want to check the perfect square trinomials by determining what their overall lengths and widths are and simplifying them into their original trinomial forms.

Materials:

▶ Blackline master **Perfect Square Trinomials** is located in the *Teacher's Resource Manual*, **page 129.**

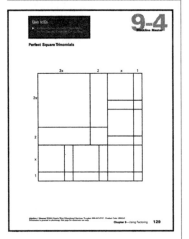

9-5 *Objective:* Solve quadratic equations by completing the square.

Note: This objective is used for the derivation of the quadratic formula. Unlike other objectives, it does not teach a technique to be used subsequently. Therefore, this objective is not required or tested in this program. The activities for this objective are teacher-directed group activities. The goal is for the students to understand how an equation of special form can be solved by completing the square. The students can work together to solve the equations that are not factorable. The introduction of completing the square will provide the students with the background necessary to follow the development of the quadratic formula, and the students will learn why the quadratic formula can be used to find solutions.

Concept Development Activities

Complete the Square

Directions:

1. Write the problem $x^2 = 25$ on the board. Ask the class how to solve it. Discuss the square root method: $x^2 = 25 \rightarrow \sqrt{x^2} = \sqrt{25}$, $x = |5|$ or $x = \pm 5$. Also discuss the factoring method: $x^2 = 25 \rightarrow$ $x^2 - 25 = 0 \rightarrow (x + 5)(x - 5) = 0 \rightarrow x = 5$ or $x = -5$.

2. Write the problem $(x + 4)^2 = 25$ on the board. Ask the class how to solve it. Discuss the square root method.

   Example: $\sqrt{(x + 4)^2} = \sqrt{25} \rightarrow x + 4 = |5|$ or $x + 4 = \pm 5$
   $$x = -4 + 5 = 1 \text{ or } x = -4 - 5 = -9$$

3. Write the problem $(x + 1)^2 = 11$ on the board. Ask the class how to solve it. Discuss the square root method.

   Example: $\sqrt{(x + 1)^2} = \sqrt{11} \rightarrow x + 1 = |\sqrt{11}| \rightarrow x + 1 = \pm\sqrt{11}$,
   $x = -1 + \sqrt{11}$ or $-1 - \sqrt{11}$. Leave this problem on the board.

4. Write the problem $x^2 + 4x - 6 = 0$ on the board. Ask the class how to solve it. Let the students discuss ideas. If no one has a way to solve it, ask if they recognize $x^2 + 4x$ as a pattern. Help them to

see that it is the start of a perfect square trinomial: $x^2 + 4x + 4$. Explain that you will write $x^2 + 4x - 6 = 0$ as:

$$\underbrace{[x^2 + 4x + 4]}_{\text{the perfect square}} - 10 = 0.$$

The 4 completes the perfect square, and $4 - 10 = -6$ (from the original equation). Explain that now you can rewrite the sentence like the problem in #3 as $(x + 2)^2 - 10 = 0 \rightarrow (x + 2)^2 = 10$.

5. Now have the students solve this equation. $\sqrt{(x + 2)^2} = \sqrt{10} \rightarrow$ $x + 2 = \left|\sqrt{10}\right| \rightarrow x + 2 = \pm\sqrt{10}, x = -2 \pm \sqrt{10}$

6. Have the class try these problems:

    a. $x^2 + 8x - 2 = 0$ b. $x^2 + 2x - 3 = 0$ c. $x^2 + 10x + 7 = 0$

Answer Key for #6:
a. $x = -4 \pm \sqrt{18}$ $\left(-4 \pm 3\sqrt{2}\right)$
b. $x = -3, 1$
c. $x = -5 \pm \sqrt{18}$ $\left(-5 \pm 3\sqrt{2}\right)$

Solving Equations by Using Square Roots

Directions:

1. Write $x^2 = 16$ on the board and ask the class to solve it. Ask, "What number squared gives you 16?" Discuss that both 4 and -4 squared equal $+16$.

2. If needed, go through the steps with the students, reminding them that they can use a square root function to remove a square since squares and square roots are inverse operations of each other.

$$x^2 = 16$$
$$\sqrt{x^2} = \pm\sqrt{16}$$
$$x = \pm 4$$

Discuss why $+4$ and -4 are both solutions of $x^2 = 16$.

Answer Key for #3:
a. $x = \pm 7$
b. $x = \pm 9$
c. $x = \pm\sqrt{13}$
d. $x = \pm 5$
e. $x = \pm\sqrt{7}$
f. $x = \pm 7$
g. $x = 4, -8$

3. Write the following equations on the board and ask the students to work in pairs to solve them in a manner similar to that in step 2. (Note that the 13 in part c is not a perfect square.)

    a. $x^2 = 49$ b. $x^2 = 81$ c. $x^2 = 13$
    d. $x^2 = 25$ e. $x^2 - 4 = 3$ f. $x^2 - 30 = 19$
    g. $(x + 2)^2 = 36$

4. Use equation g from step 3 to introduce solving equations with a

quantity $(x + 2)$ squared. Present another example, such as $(x - 6)^2 = 4$, and solve for x:

$$(x - 6)^2 = 4$$
$$\sqrt{(x - 6)^2} = \pm\sqrt{4}$$
$$x - 6 = \pm 2$$
$$x = 6 + 2 = 8, \text{ or}$$
$$x = 6 - 2 = 4$$

5. Have the pairs of students solve the following problems:

   a. $(x + 3)^2 = 100$ b. $(x - 1)^2 = 9$

   c. $(x + 4)^2 = 7$ d. $(x - 8)^2 = 17$

Using Algebra Tiles to "Complete a Square" 🔆

Directions:

1. Group the students in pairs.

2. Write the quadratic equation $x^2 + 4x + 1 = 0$ on the board.

3. Ask the students to attempt to solve this quadratic equation by any method they have learned so far: area rugs, factoring, perfect squares, difference of squares, etc.

4. After most of the pairs of students realize that they are not having any success, give a set of algebra tiles to each pair of students.

5. Ask the students to try to build a rectangle that represents $x^2 + 4x + 1 = 0$ that is as close to a square as possible. Tell them that there may appear to be a piece missing from a "perfect square," but that is okay.

6. After a reasonable amount of time, if there are any students who are confident in their answer, allow them to present the example to the class by using a set of overhead algebra tiles.

7. Say that you are going to present a solution to the class and ask for their input. Explain that you will use tiles as shown on the right to represent the units in the problem.

Materials:

► One set of algebra tiles per pair of students

1 x^2 unit

4 x units

1 unit

9.5 Concept Development

Teacher's Tip:

Worksheet 1 for this
objective, **page 9-24**,
supports this activity
with practice exercises.

9-5
Worksheet 1

Worksheet 1

Solve the following equations by using the method of completing the square. Students may
work in pairs or groups.

1. $x^2 + 12x + 8 = 0$ 2. $x^2 + 6x + 1 = 0$

3. $x^2 + 6x + 3 = 0$ 4. $x^2 + 14x + 5 = 0$

5. $x^2 - 16x + 8 = 0$

9-24   Chapter 9—Using Factoring

Answer Key for #14:

a. $x = -3 \pm \sqrt{6}$

b. $x = -5 \pm \sqrt{20}$
$\left(-5 \pm 2\sqrt{5}\right)$

c. $x = -4 \pm \sqrt{14}$

---

8. Then show that $x^2 + 4x + 1 = 0$ can be
    represented by the diagram on the right. Ask
    the students, "What is missing from this
    diagram that would complete the square?" Try
    to draw out the answer that with three more
    single unit squares, the diagram would be a
    complete square.

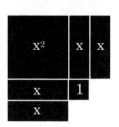

9. Discuss with the class what the dimensions of the "new complete
    square" would be. If necessary, point out that the dimensions
    would be $(x + 2)$ by $(x + 2)$.

10. Write the expression $(x + 2)(x + 2)$ on the board. Ask the class if
    they can think of another way to write this expression in a more
    concise manner. Write it as $(x + 2)^2$ on the board.

11. Remind the class that the original diagram was not a "complete
    square," so they must subtract the three missing pieces from the
    new expression. Thus, the expression changes to $(x + 2)^2 - 3$.

12. Have the pairs of students attempt to solve the equation
    $(x + 2)^2 - 3 = 0$. You may need to remind them that to "remove a
    square" they can use a "square root." If necessary, show the
    following on the board:

$$(x + 2)^2 - 3 = 0$$
$$(x + 2)^2 = 3$$
$$\sqrt{(x + 2)^2} = \pm\sqrt{3}$$
$$(x + 2) = \pm\sqrt{3}$$
$$x = -2 \pm \sqrt{3}$$

13. Discuss with the class that this expression represents two
    answers. Review how to simplify an expression containing $\pm$.
    Discuss how the answers are irrational and would have to be
    rounded off to be written without the radical sign.

14. Write the following problems on the board and have the pairs of
    students attempt to solve them by using algebra tiles and the
    concept of "completing the square."

    a. $x^2 + 6x + 3 = 0$ b. $x^2 + 10x + 5 = 0$ c. $x^2 + 8x + 2 = 0$

Practice Activities

Solving Equations by Groups

Directions:

1. Divide the class into groups of four.

2. Write the following equations on the board:

   a. $(x + 5)^2 - 9 = 0$

   b. $(x - 7)^2 - 4 = 0$

   c. $x^2 + 6x + 2 = 0$

   d. $x^2 + 14x - 5 = 0$

   e. $x^2 + 16x + 13 = 0$

   f. $x^2 + 4x - 9 = 0$

   g. $x^2 + 12x + 7 = 0$

   h. $x^2 + 8x + 11 = 0$

   i. $x^2 + 20x + 31 = 0$

3. Assign one equation to each group. Have each group solve its equation by the method of completing the square.

4. After all the groups are finished, have them trade equations with another group and verify that the work is correct.

5. Ask for a volunteer from each group to put the group's equation and the appropriate work on the board to discuss with the class as a whole.

Completing the Square Jeopardy

Directions:

1. Copy the "Jeopardy" board from the blackline master **Completing the Square Jeopardy** onto an overhead transparency or make up your own problems to use for the game. Use sticky notes to cover each problem so the problems cannot be seen until they are selected.

2. The problems in row 1 are worth 1 point, row 2 is worth 2 points, row 3 is worth 3 points, and row 4 is worth 4 points.

3. Divide the class into two or more teams.

4. Randomly select which team goes first.

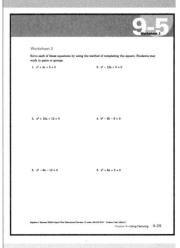

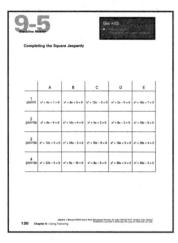

5. A member of that team names a square on the board by giving the row and column. When you remove the sticky note, the player must attempt to correctly solve the equation.

6. If the player is correct, his or her team receives the point value of the problem and another player from the same team repeats the process by selecting another square.

7. If, however, the first player is incorrect, a player from the next team must solve that same equation.

8. If that player's answer is correct, his or her team receives the point value, another player on the team selects a new equation, and the play continues as in steps 5 through 7.

9. If that player's answer is incorrect, the next player from the next team has a chance to solve the equation, and this process repeats until the problem has been solved correctly.

Problem-Solving Activity

Completing the Square With Negative Middle Terms

Directions:

1. Divide the class into groups of four.

2. Write the following equations on the board:

   a. $x^2 - 6x + 4 = 0$ b. $x^2 - 14x - 1 = 0$

   c. $x^2 - 16x + 3 = 0$ d. $x^2 - 4x - 7 = 0$

   e. $x^2 - 12x + 11 = 0$ f. $x^2 - 8x + 5 = 0$

   g. $x^2 - 20x + 21 = 0$

3. Assign one equation to each group. Have each group solve its equation by the method of completing the square.

4. After all the groups are finished, have them trade equations with another group and verify that the work is correct.

5. Ask for a volunteer from each group to put the group's equation and the appropriate work on the board to discuss with the class as a whole.

Answer Key for #2:
a. $x = 3 \pm \sqrt{5}$
b. $x = 7 \pm \sqrt{50}$ $\left(7 \pm 5\sqrt{2}\right)$
c. $x = 8 \pm \sqrt{61}$
d. $x = 2 \pm \sqrt{11}$
e. $x = 1, 11$
f. $x = 4 \pm \sqrt{11}$
g. $x = 10 \pm \sqrt{79}$

Chapter 10

Exploring Quadratic and Exponential Functions

10-1 Graph parabolas and find the coordinates of the vertex and axis of symmetry.

10-2 Estimate the roots of a quadratic equation by graphing the associated quadratic function.

10-3 Solve quadratic equations by factoring or using the quadratic formula.

10-4 Graph exponential functions and solve problems using the graphs.

10-1 *Objective:* Graph parabolas and find the coordinates of the vertex and axis of symmetry.

Sample Test: Find the coordinates of the vertex and axis of symmetry for problems 1–4 and graph problems 1 and 3 on a sheet of graph paper.

1. $y = (x - 2)^2 + 3$
   Solution: vertex (2, 3)
   axis of symmetry x = 2

2. $y = 4x^2 - 2$
   Solution: vertex (0, –2)
   axis of symmetry x = 0

3. $y = x^2 + 6x + 8$
   Solution: vertex (–3, –1)
   axis of symmetry x = –3

4. $y = 8 - 2x^2$
   Solution: vertex (0, 8)
   axis of symmetry x = 0

Solution graphs:

$y = (x - 2)^2 + 3$

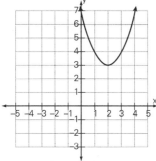

$y = x^2 + 6x + 8$

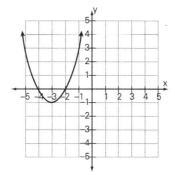

Teacher's Tip:

Worksheet 1 for this objective, **page 10-2**, supports this activity with practice exercises.

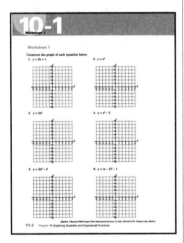

Concept Development Activities

Development of the Graph of $y = x^2$

Directions:

1. This lesson is intended to show the students:

    a. the shape of the graph $y = x^2$.

    b. that the shape is called a parabola, and that the turning point is called the vertex.

    c. that a parabola is symmetrical about the vertical line that passes through the vertex.

2. Write the equation $y = x^2$ on the board and make a table of ordered pairs for the solutions. Start by writing 1 for x and ask a student what the corresponding y value would be. **(1)** Then write 2 for x and again ask a student what the y value would be. **(4)**

3. Use the overhead projector to show the coordinate plane on the board and plot points (1, 1) and (2, 4). Ask the students if they think the graph will be the line passing through two points. Ask them for reasons for their answers. Suggest, "Let's plot another point and find out."

4. Ask the students to graph points (1, 1) and (2, 4) on their individual sheets of graph paper.

5. Then ask individual students for the values of y if x has the following values. As you plot the points on the board, the students should plot them on their paper.

    a. $x = 3$ b. $x = 4$ c. $x = \frac{1}{2}$ d. $x = 0$

6. Ask the students, "What would happen if we used negative numbers for x?"

7. Ask individual students for the values of y if x has the following values. As you plot the points on the board, the students should plot them on their paper.

    a. $x = -1$ b. $x = -2$ c. $x = -3$

    d. $x = -4$ e. $x = -\frac{1}{2}$

8. Draw a curved line through the points.

9. Ask the students whether the graph is symmetrical and, if so,

about what line. **(Yes, about the y-axis, which has the equation x = 0.)**

10. Define the shape of the graph as a parabola, and explain that the turning point is called the vertex.

11. Most students will be familiar with symmetry through art classes and earlier mathematics. Explain that if a graph is symmetric, the graph could be folded on the axis of symmetry and both halves would match up exactly.

12. In addition, discuss that the graph for $y = x^2$ is symmetric because the negative numbers squared are the same as the positive numbers squared.

13. Have the students make a graph of $y = (x + 1)^2$ by making a table and plotting points. This will help convince the students that the graph of an equation of the form $y = (x + 1)^2$ will be a parabola, not a straight line.

14. Ask the students if this graph is symmetrical. **(yes)** Then ask if it is symmetrical to the y-axis (or x = 0). **(no)** Ask what line it is symmetrical to. **(x = –1)**

Relationship of $y = x^2$ and $y = (x - b)^2$

Directions:

1. This lesson is intended to show the students:

   a. how the graph of $y = x^2$ can be shifted left and right without changing its shape.

   b. that a parabola in the form of $y = (x - b)^2$ is symmetrical about the vertical line that passes through the vertex.

   c. that the equation of the axis of symmetry is x = b, and that the vertex is (b, 0).

2. Write the equation $y = (x - 2)^2$ on the board and make a table of ordered pairs for the solutions. Start by writing 2 for x and ask a student what the corresponding y value would be. **(0)** Then write 3 for x and again ask a student what the y value would be. **(1)**

3. Use the overhead projector to show the coordinate plane on the board and plot points (2, 0) and (3, 1).

Materials:

▶ Blackline master for **graph paper** is in the Appendix.

▶ Overhead graph paper transparency

▶ Graphing calculators (if available)

Teacher's Tip:

Worksheet 2 for this objective, **pages 10-3 and 10-4**, supports this activity with practice exercises.

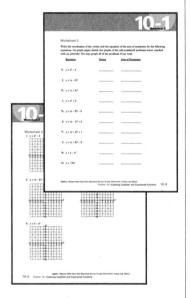

Teacher's Tip:

If you graph $y = x^2$ on another overlay, you can place it on top and move it left and right to show that the graphs are the same shape. Use the same scale.

4. Ask the students to graph points $(2, 0)$ and $(3, 1)$ on their individual sheets of graph paper.

5. Then ask individual students for the values of y if x has the following values. As you plot the points on the board, the students should plot them on their paper.

   a. $x = 4$ b. $x = 5$ c. $x = 2.5$ d. $x = 1$

   e. $x = 0$ f. $x = -1$ g. $x = -2$ h. $x = 1.5$

6. Draw a curved line through the points and ask a student to name the coordinates of the vertex. **[(2, 0)]**

7. Ask the students whether the graph is symmetrical and, if so, about what line. **(Yes, about the line x = 2.)**

8. Have the students compare the graphs of $y = (x - 2)^2$ and $y = x^2$. Be sure the students observe that the graphs are the same shape but $y = (x - 2)^2$ is moved two units to the right of $y = x^2$.

9. Discuss that the value of x that gives $y = 0$ is 2, and not 0, by showing that $(x - 2)^2 = (2 - 2)^2 = 0$.

10. Discuss what would happen for the equation $y = (x - 3)^2$. **[The graph would be three units to the right of the graph for $y = x^2$, the vertex would be (3, 0), and the axis of symmetry would be x = 3.]**

11. Discuss what would happen if the equation were $y = (x + 1)^2$. Ask, "What number would make the equation $y = 0$?" **(−1)** Ask, "What other values would be good to substitute for x?" **(0, 1, 2, and −2, −3, −4, or numbers on both sides of −1)** Ask, "How does this graph compare to the graph of $y = x^2$?" **(It is shifted one unit to the left.)** Ask, "Where is the vertex?" **[(−1, 0)]** Ask, "What is the equation of the axis of symmetry?" **(x = −1)**

12. Write the equation $y = (x - 1)^2$ on the board. Have the students describe where the graph would be in relation to the graph for $y = x^2$, where the vertex would be, and what the equation would be for the axis of symmetry. Have the students plot $y = (x - 1)^2$. Discuss their answers as a class.

Relationship of $y = x^2$ and $y = x^2 + c$

Directions:

1. This lesson is intended to show the students:

   a. how the graph of $y = x^2$ can be shifted up and down with the shape not changing.

   b. that a parabola in the form of $y = x^2 + c$ has a vertex of $(0, c)$ and the equation of the axis of symmetry is the y axis, or $x = 0$.

2. Write the equation $y = x^2 + 2$ on the board and make a table of ordered pairs for the solutions. Start by writing 0 for x and ask a student what the corresponding y value would be. **(2)** Then write 1 for x and again ask a student what the y value would be. **(3)**

3. Use the overhead projector to show the coordinate plane on the board and plot the points $(0, 2)$ and $(1, 3)$.

4. Ask the students to graph the same points on their individual sheets of graph paper.

5. Then ask individual students for the values of y if x has the following values. As you plot the points on the board, the students should plot them on their paper.

a. $x = -1$	b. $x = 2$	c. $x = -2$	d. $x = 3$
e. $x = -3$	f. $x = 4$	g. $x = -4$	

6. Draw a curved line through the points and ask a student to name the coordinates of the vertex. **[(0, 2)]**

7. Ask the students whether the graph is symmetrical and, if so, about what line. **(Yes, about the y-axis, which has the equation x = 0.)**

8. Have the students compare the graphs of $y = x^2 + 2$ and $y = x^2$. Be sure the students observe that the graphs are the same shape but $y = x^2 + 2$ is moved two units up from $y = x^2$.

9. Discuss what would happen for the equation $y = x^2 - 3$. **[The graph would be shifted down three units from the graph for $y = x^2$, the vertex would be (0, –3), and the axis of symmetry would be x = 0.]**

Materials:

- ▶ Blackline master for **graph paper** is in the Appendix.

- ▶ Overhead graph paper transparency

- ▶ Graphing calculators (if available)

Teacher's Tips:

If you graph $y = x^2$ on another overlay, you can place it on top and move it up and down to show that the graphs are the same shape. Use the same scale.

Worksheet 3 for this objective, **pages 10-5 and 10-6**, supports this activity with practice exercises.

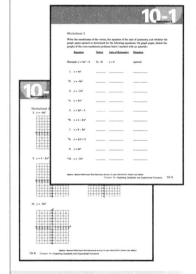

Answer Key for #5:
a. $y = 3$ b. $y = 6$ c. $y = 6$
d. $y = 11$ e. $y = 11$
f. $y = 18$ g. $y = 18$

Materials:

- Blackline master for **graph paper** is in the Appendix.
- Overhead graph paper transparency
- Graphing calculators (if available)

Teacher's Tip:

Place the graph of $y = x^2$ on an overlay so you can place it on top of the $y = (x - b)^2 + c$ graph and shift it left or right and then up and down. Be sure to use the same scale.

Answer Key for #5:
a. $y = 6$; $(-1, 6)$
b. $y = 11$; $(-2, 11)$
c. $y = 18$; $(5, 18)$

Relationship of $y = (x - b)^2 + c$ and $y = x^2$

Directions:

1. This lesson is intended to show the students:

   a. how the graph of $y = x^2$ can be shifted left or right and up or down with the shape not changing.

   b. that a parabola in the form of $y = (x - b)^2 + c$ has a vertex of (b, c), and the equation of the axis of symmetry is $x = b$.

2. Write the equation $y = (x - 1)^2 + 2$ on the board and make a table of ordered pairs for the solutions. Start by writing 1 for x and ask a student what the corresponding y value would be. **(2)** Then write 2 for x and again ask a student what the y value would be. **(3)** Ask, "What point would be symmetrical to the point (2, 3)?" **[(0, 3)]**

3. Use the overhead projector to show the coordinate plane on the board and plot the three points.

4. Ask the students to graph the points on their individual sheets of graph papers.

5. Ask individual students for the values of y if x has the following values. Have them plot the points, and ask them to determine and plot the points of symmetry.

   a. $x = 3$ b. $x = 4$ c. $x = -3$

6. Draw a curved line through the points and ask a student to name the coordinates of the vertex. **[(1, 2)]**

7. Ask the students whether the graph is symmetrical and, if so, about what line. **(Yes, about the line x = 1.)**

8. Have the students compare the graphs of $y = (x - 1)^2 + 2$ and $y = x^2$. Be sure the students observe that the graphs are the same shape but $y = (x - 1)^2 + 2$ is moved one unit to the right and two units up from $y = x^2$.

9. Discuss what would happen for the equation $y = (x + 3)^2 - 5$. **[The graph would be shifted three units to the left and five units down from the graph of $y = x^2$, the vertex would be (−3, −5), and the axis of symmetry would be x = −3.]**

Relationship of $y = ax^2$ and $y = x^2$

Directions:

Materials:

► Blackline master for **graph paper** is in the Appendix.

► Overhead graph paper transparency

► Graphing calculators (if available)

1. This lesson is intended to show the students:

   a. how the graph of $y = x^2$ changes when a coefficient is placed in front of x^2.

   b. that a parabola in the form of $y = ax^2$ has a vertex of $(0, 0)$, and the equation of the axis of symmetry is $x = 0$.

2. Write the equation $y = 2x^2$ on the board and make a table of ordered pairs for the solutions. Start by writing 0 for x and ask a student what the corresponding y value would be. **(0)** Then write 1 for x and again ask a student what the y value would be. **(2)** Ask, "What point would be symmetrical to the point $(1, 2)$?" **[(–1, 2)]**

3. Use the overhead projector to show the coordinate plane on the board and plot the three points.

4. Ask the students to graph the points on their individual sheets of graph paper.

5. Ask individual students for the values of y if x has the following values. Have them plot the points, and ask them to determine and plot the points of symmetry.

   a. $x = 2$ b. $x = 3$

Answer Key for #5:
a. $y = 8$; $(–2, 8)$
b. $y = 18$; $(–3, 18)$

6. Draw a curved line through the points and ask a student to name the coordinates of the vertex. **[(0, 0)]**

7. Have the students compare the graphs of $y = 2x^2$ and $y = x^2$. Be sure the students observe that the graph of $y = 2x^2$ is narrower than the graph of $y = x^2$.

8. Have the students compare the graph of $y = -2x^2$ with the graph of $y = 2x^2$. It may be necessary to substitute values for x, as in step 5. Be sure the students understand that the graph for $y = -2x^2$ will open downward.

9. Have the students compare the graphs of $y = -x^2$ and $y = x^2$.

10. Construct the graph of $y = x^2$ by repeating steps 2 through 5. Ask the students, "Is the graph narrower or wider than $y = x^2$?" **(wider)** Ask, "What would the graph of $y = -(x^2)$ look like?" **(Same shape, but it would open downward; all y values except the vertex would be negative.)**

Materials:

▶ Blackline master for **graph paper** is in the Appendix.

▶ Overhead graph paper transparency

Teacher's Tip:

Worksheet 4 for this objective, **pages 10-7 and 10-8**, supports this activity with practice exercises.

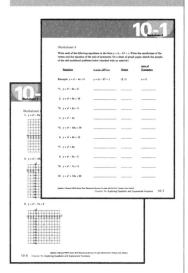

Writing a Quadratic Function of the Form $y = x^2 + bx + c$ in the Form $y = (x - b)^2 + c$

Directions:

1. Write the equation $y = x^2 + 6x + 5$ on the board.

2. Explain to the students that to graph the function it would be helpful to know the vertex and the axis of symmetry. Explain that if the equation were written in the form $y = (x - b)^2 + c$, these would be easy to determine.

3. Show the students how to use the following steps to transfer $y = x^2 + 6x + 5$ to the form $y = (x - b)^2 + c$.

   a. Subtract 5 from both sides of $y = x^2 + 6x + 5$. Write $y - 5 = x^2 + 6x$ under the original function on the board.

   b. Complete the square on the right side of the equal sign (take half of 6 and square it), and write $y - 5 + \underline{\quad} = x^2 + 6x + 9$ under the last step. Remind the students that they must add to both sides of the equation, so the blank spot on the left should be filled in with 9.

   c. Simplify the left-hand side and factor the right-hand side of the equation. Write $y + 4 = (x + 3)^2$ under the last step.

   d. Subtract the constant term on the right from both sides to get y by itself. Write $y = (x + 3)^2 - 4$ under the last step.

4. Ask a student to identify the vertex, and ask another student for the equation of the axis of symmetry. **[Vertex is (–3, –4); axis of symmetry is x = –3.]**

5. Find a few points and sketch the graph. For example, substitute –2 for x (because it is one unit from –3). Plot the points (–2, –3) and (–3, –4), and ask the students, "What point is symmetrical to (–2, –3)?" **[(–4, –3)]**

6. Point out that you may use either the original equation or the transformed function to create the graph because they are equivalent. Substitute x = –1 into both to show that they are equivalent. Plot the point (–1, 0). Ask the students to find the point symmetrical to it, and plot that point as well. **[(–5, 0)]**

7. Repeat step 6 with the values x = 0 and x = –6. **[(0, 5) and (–6, 5)]**

8. Draw the graph of the quadratic function by connecting these points and their symmetrical points.

9. Repeat step 3 with the quadratic function $y = x^2 - 8x - 9$, as follows:

   a. Add 9 to both sides: $y + 9 = x^2 - 8x$.

   b. Complete the square on the right side of the equal sign (take half of -8 and square it), and add this number (16) to both sides of the equation: $y + 9 + 16 = x^2 - 8x + 16$.

   c. Simplify the left-hand side and factor the right-hand side of the equation: $y + 25 = (x - 4)^2$.

   d. Subtract the constant term (25) from both sides to get y by itself: $y = (x - 4)^2 - 25$.

10. Identify the vertex $(4, -25)$ and axis of symmetry $(x = 4)$, find six more points, and graph the equation.

Practice Activities

Match Graph ☀

Directions:

1. Have the students work in pairs. Give one copy of the blackline master **Match Graph** to each pair of students.

2. Ask each pair of students to graph each equation and then find the graph on the blackline master that matches each equation. *Note:* There are more graphs than problems on the blackline master, so all the problems have a match but not all the graphs do.

3. Tell the students to be careful with graphing quadratics and to be sure they have the correct vertex and axis of symmetry.

4. The blackline master has two very closely related sets of problems. The answers work for both sets of problems. Be sure the students see the relationship between the graphs in problem set 1 and problem set 2.

Materials:

▶ Blackline master **Match Graph** is located in the *Teacher's Resource Manual*, **page 131**.

▶ Blackline master for **graph paper** is in the Appendix.

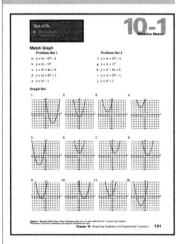

Materials:

► Blackline master **Quadratic Function Rummy** is located in the *Teacher's Resource Manual*, **page 132.**

► Blank cards or

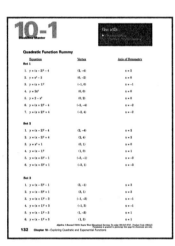

Quadratic Function Rummy

Directions:

1. The goal of this activity is to strengthen the students' skills with recognizing a quadratic function, the vertex, and the axis of symmetry.

2. Have the students work in groups of four or five. Give one copy of the blackline master **Quadratic Function Rummy** to each group.

3. Have the students make enough cards for each group. Two of the three sets will make a deck. The deck of cards will have three kinds of cards:

   a. quadratic equations

   b. vertices

   c. axis of symmetry equations

4. Directions for play:

   a. Have the students shuffle their decks of cards.

   b. Have the students select someone in each group to be dealer and to deal cards one at a time to each player until all players have six cards. The dealer then places the remaining cards face down at the center of the table, turns over the top card, and places it next to the remaining deck. The person to the left of the dealer begins play.

   c. The object of the game is to make sets consisting of a quadratic function card, a vertex card, and an axis of symmetry card that match.

   d. At each player's turn, the player may pick up the top card from the discard pile or draw the top card from the remaining cards in the deck. If that player has a set of three matching cards (or two sets of three), he or she places them face up on the table. The player finishes his or her turn by discarding one card, whether or not the player had a matching set.

   e. The first person to use all of his or her cards is the winner. Other players check that the cards played do match. If the cards do not match, the player picks them back up and discards.

f. If the deck runs out, the discard pile is shuffled and placed face down so that play can continue.

g. When a game has been completed, the winner shuffles all the cards in the deck and deals, and play starts over.

Problem-Solving Activity

Writing Quadratics

Directions:

Give each student a copy of the blackline master **Writing Quadratics**. Have the students work individually to solve the problems, which are reprinted below.

Write the quadratic equation for each of the following:

1. The graph that has the same shape as the graph of $y = x^2$, but it is shifted to the right by 3.

2. The graph that has the same shape as the graph of $y = 2x^2$, but it opens downward and is moved up by 4.

3. The graph that has the same shape as the graph of $y = x^2$, but it is moved to the left by 2.

4. The graph that has the same shape as the graph of $y = x^2$, but it is shifted to the right by 1 and down by 4.

5. The graph that has the same shape as the graph of $y = x^2$, but it is shifted up by 3.

6. The graph that has the same shape as the graph of $y = x^2$, but it is shifted to the left by 2 and up by 1.

7. The graph that has the same shape as the graph of $y = x^2$, but it is shifted to the right by 1 and opens downward.

8. The graph that is as wide as the graph of $y = \frac{1}{2}x^2$, but it is moved down by 4.

9. The graph that has the same shape as the graph of $y = x^2$, but it is shifted to the right by 100 and down by 200.

10. The graph that has the same shape as the graph of $y = x^2$, but it opens downward and is shifted up by 1.414.

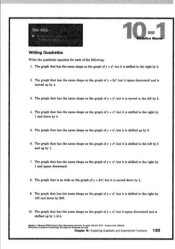

10-2 *Objective:* Estimate the roots of a quadratic equation by graphing the associated quadratic function.

Sample Test: Find the roots of the following quadratic equations by graphing the associated functions. If the roots are not exact, name the consecutive integers between which the roots lie.

1. $x^2 + 8x + 11 = 0$
   Solution: $y = x^2 + 8x + 11$
   The roots are between –1 & –2 and between –6 & –7.

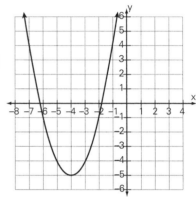

2. $x^2 + 2x + 3 = 0$
   Solution: $y = x^2 + 2x + 3$
   No real roots

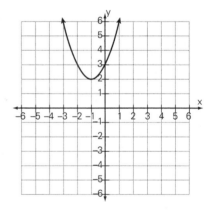

Materials:

▶ Blackline master
   Graphs of Quadratic Functions
   is located in the
   Teacher's Resource Manual, **page 134.**

▶ Overhead transparency of blackline master

Concept Development Activities

Looking at a Graph of a Quadratic Function and Finding the Zeros

Directions:

1. This lesson is intended to show the students:

   a. how to find the zeros of a quadratic function given the graph of the function.

   b. that a quadratic function might have 0, 1, or 2 zeros, or roots.

2. Give each student a copy of the blackline master **Graphs of Quadratic Functions**. Have the students construct the graph of $y = x^2 - 4x + 3$.

3. Ask a student to identify the vertex of the parabola. **[(2, –1)]** Ask another student, "Where does the graph cross the x-axis?" **[(1, 0) and (3, 0)]** Ask another student, "When we graphed straight lines, what did we call the points where the graph crossed the x-axis and the y-axis?" **(x-intercept and y-intercept)** Explain that another name for the x-intercepts of a quadratic function is the zeros of the function, because those are the points at which the value of the function, or the y value, is 0. Since $x^2 - 4x + 3 = 0$ at the points (1, 0) and (3, 0), x = 1 and x = 3 are the zeros of $y = x^2 - 4x + 3$.

4. Have the students construct the graph of $y = x^2 + 4x + 4$. Ask another student, "How many zeros does this equation appear to have?" **(1)** Ask another student, "What is the zero point?" **[(–2, 0)]** Ask another student, "Why is there only one zero?" **(Because the vertex is on the x-axis.)**

5. Have the students construct the graph of $y = x^2 - 6x + 11$. Ask, "How many zeros does this graph have?" **(None)** Ask, "Why are there no zeros?" **(Because the vertex is above the x-axis and it opens upward.)** If the students cite only that the vertex is above the x-axis, do not correct them until you show them the next problem.

6. Have the students construct the graph of $y = 4 - x^2$. Ask, "How many zeros does this graph have?" **(2)** Ask, "What are the zeros?" **[(–2, 0) and (2, 0)]** Ask, "What is the vertex?" **[(0, 4)]** Point out that this vertex is above the x-axis and the vertex of the graph in step 5 was also above the x-axis, but this graph has two zeros and the other one had none. Explain that this is because this graph opens downward and the last graph opened upward. The coefficient of x squared was positive in the equation from step 5, but it is negative in this one.

7. Have the students construct the graph of $y = x^2 + 2x - 5$. Ask, "How many zeros are there?" **(2)** Ask, "Can you tell the exact values of the zeros?" **(No)** Explain that in situations such as this one, the procedure is to state the consecutive integers between which the zeros lie. Ask, "Where are the zeros for this quadratic?"

Teacher's Tip:

Worksheet 1 for this objective, **page 10-11**, supports this activity with practice exercises.

10-2
Worksheet 1

Worksheet 1
Given the following graphs of quadratic functions, estimate the zeros. If whole number zeros cannot be found, estimate the zeros by stating the consecutive integers between which the roots lie.
Example:

Roots are –1 and 3

(One is between 1 and 2, and the other is between –3 and –4.)

8. Point out that the zeros of a quadratic are always the same distance from the axis of symmetry. If the graph is folded about the axis of symmetry, the zeros always fall on top of each other.

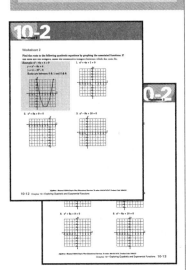

The Relationship of Roots to an Equation and Zeros of a Function

Directions:

1. This lesson is intended to show the students how to find the solutions or roots of a quadratic equation by graphing the quadratic function associated with the equation.

2. Write the quadratic equation $x^2 - 8x + 12 = 0$ on the board. Ask a student, "How can we solve this equation?" Elicit the answer that the problem can be solved by factoring and using the zero product property.

$$(x - 6)(x - 2) = 0$$
$$x - 6 = 0 \text{ or } x - 2 = 0$$
$$x = 6, 2$$

3. Ask another student, "How can we find the zeros of a quadratic function such as $y = (x - 4)^2 - 4$?" The student will probably want to graph it. Show that completing the square of the function $y = x^2 - 8x + 12$ (from step 2) gives the function $y = (x - 4)^2 - 4$. Show the students that the roots of the equation $x^2 - 8x + 12 = 0$ are the x-coordinates of the zeros of the function $y = (x - 4)^2 - 4$. Emphasize that the zeros of $y = x^2 - 8x + 12$ happen when $y = 0$, so substituting 0 for y yields the equation $x^2 - 8x + 12 = 0$.

4. Write the quadratic equation $x^2 + 6x + 4 = 0$ on the board and ask the students to solve it. Point out that it does not factor. Tell the students they can solve it by graphing the associated function $y = x^2 + 6x + 4$. Completing the square yields $y = (x + 3)^2 - 5$. Thus, the vertex is $(-3, -5)$. Now substitute $x = -2, -1$, and 0, and use the points that are symmetrical to graph the equation. Construct this graph on the overhead transparency.

5. Point out that the graph crosses the x-axis between –5 and –6 and between –1 and 0. Show that since the zeros of $y = x^2 + 6x + 4$ are

between these values, the roots of the equation $x^2 + 6x + 4 = 0$ are also between −5 and −6 and between −1 and 0.

6. Remind the students that the zeros are points with x and y coordinates because they satisfy a function with x and y. Roots, however, satisfy an equation with one variable, and therefore they are just numbers (values of x) and not ordered pairs.

7. Now write the equation $x^2 − 8x + 14 = 0$ on the board. Ask a student for the function he or she would graph to solve the equation. **($y = x^2 − 8x + 14$)**

8. Ask another student for the first step to complete the square of this function and continue asking students for steps until the square is complete.

$$y − 14 = x^2 − 8x$$
$$y − 14 + 16 = x^2 − 8x + 16$$
$$y + 2 = (x − 4)^2$$
$$y = (x − 4)^2 − 2$$

9. Ask a student to name the vertex. **[(4, −2)]** Ask another student to name some values to substitute for x and y to graph the function. Set up the table of ordered pairs and graph the function on an overhead transparency. Example points include (5, −1), (3, −1), (6, 2), (2, 2).

10. The graph crosses the x-axis between 5 and 6 and between 2 and 3, so the x-intercepts are between 5 and 6 and between 2 and 3. Reinforce the concept that another name for the x-intercepts is the zeros of the function $y = x^2 − 8x + 14$; therefore, the roots of the equation $x^2 − 8x + 14 = 0$ are values between 5 and 6 and between 2 and 3.

Practice Activities

Draw Your Own Quadratic Equation I

Directions:

1. Divide the class into groups of three or four, with as many groups of four as possible.

2. Have the students in each group mark eight cards with a "b" on

Materials:

▶ Blank cards or

one side and one of these numbers on the other side: 2, –2, 4, –4, 6, –6, 8, –8. Each number should be used once. They should then mark 13 cards with a "c" on one side and one of these numbers on the other side: 0, 1, –1, 4, –4, 9, 16, 2, –2, 3, –3, 5, –5. Each number should be used once. When the students are finished, each group will have one deck with values for b and a second deck with values for c.

3. The object is for each person in each group to form an equation in the form $x^2 + bx + c = 0$ using the b and c cards drawn, and determine the roots of that equation by graphing the associated function.

4. Have each group shuffle the two decks separately, and have each student pick one card from the b deck and one from the c deck. *Example:* b = 2 and c = –4

5. Ask each student to write a quadratic equation using the values of b and c he or she selected, for example, $x^2 + 2x – 4 = 0$. Then have the students solve their equations by graphing.

6. When the students have finished, have each student show his or her cards and solution to the rest of the group. The groups should then check the work and make corrections if needed.

7. Have the students return the cards to the appropriate decks, shuffle, and repeat the process as time allows.

Share It

Directions:

1. Have the students work in groups of four or five.

2. Ask each student to write a quadratic equation that will have exactly one root. The equation must be in the form $x^2 + bx + c = 0$; b must be an even integer (positive or negative) and c must be a nonzero integer. Note that the reason b should be an even integer is to make completing the square easier.

3. When the students are finished, have each student pass his or her problem to the student seated to his or her left (or clockwise) in the student's group, and have the students solve the new problems given to them.

4. After the student solves that problem, he or she should change the value for c so that the new equation has no roots.

5. Again, have the students pass their new problems to the left. Ask them to work the problems they receive to make sure there are no roots.

6. Now ask the students to change the value of c so that the new equation has two roots that are integers.

7. Have the students exchange problems with the same student (the student to the right now) so they can work the problems to see if there are two roots that are integers.

8. Once again, ask the students to change the value of c, this time so the new equation has two roots that are between consecutive integers.

9. Ask the students to exchange problems with the same student again (the student to the left again) so they can work the problems to see if there are two roots that are between consecutive integers.

10. Display the students' work so other students can check it.

Solve It

Directions:

1. Have each student in the class write an equation of the form $x^2 + bx + c = 0$ where $-10 \le b \le 10$ and $-5 \le c \le 5$. *Example:* $x^2 - 4x + 2 - 0$ or $x^2 - 0x + 5 = 0$

2. Quickly check the papers to see that the problems are quadratic equations and that they follow the given conditions.

3. Have the students exchange papers. Instruct them to solve the equation they received by graphing the equation. They will need to estimate the roots between two integers if the graphs do not cross at integer points.

4. Have the students exchange equations again (with a different student) and again solve the equation they received by graphing.

5. Have each two students who solved the same equation compare

Materials:

▶ Blackline master for **graph paper** is in the Appendix.

Materials:

► Blackline master
for **graph paper** is
in the Appendix.

Answer Key:
1. Answers will vary. A
good way to come up
with the equation is to
start with a perfect
square, such as
$(x - 3)^2 = 0$, and multiply
it out. A possible answer
would thus be
$x^2 - 6x + 9 = 0$.
2. Answers will vary. A
good way to come up
with the equation is to
start with a perfect
square polynomial equal
to a negative integer.
For example,
$(x + 2)^2 = -3$, which
becomes $x^2 + 4x + 7 = 0$.
3. Answers will vary. A
good way to come up
with the equation is to
start with any quadratic
equation in factored
form. For example,
$(x - 5)(x + 2) = 0$, or
$x^2 - 3x - 10 = 0$.
4. Answers will vary. A
good way to come up
with the equation is to
start with a perfect
square polynomial equal
to a positive integer that
is not a perfect square.
For example,
$(x - 1)^2 = 2$, which
becomes $x^2 - 2x + 1 = 2$,
or $x^2 - 2x - 1 = 0$.

their answers. If the answers are different, let them work out the
correct solution.

6. Look at the students' papers until you find a graph that has no
solutions. Have the students who graphed it present it to the class.

7. Then, find a graph that has two solutions and have the students
who graphed it present it to the class.

8. See if any of the graphs have one solution. If so, have it presented
to the class. If not, present one to the class. *Example:* $x^2 - 6x + 9 = 0$

Problem-Solving Activity

Writing Quadratics

Directions:

1. Ask each student to write the equation of a quadratic function of
the form $x^2 + bx + c = 0$ that has exactly one root. The values for
b and c can be positive or negative, but b must be an even
integer and not zero. Have the students exchange papers and
graph the equations they receive. Discuss the graphs.

2. Ask each student to write the equation of a quadratic function of
the form $x^2 + bx + c = 0$ that has no real roots. The values for b
and c can be positive or negative, but b must be an even integer
and not zero. Have the students exchange papers and graph the
equations they receive. Discuss the graphs.

3. Ask each student to write the equation of a quadratic function of
the form $x^2 + bx + c = 0$ that has exactly two roots. The roots
must be integers, and the values for b and c can be positive or
negative, but b must be an even integer and not zero. Have the
students exchange papers and graph the equations they receive.
Discuss the graphs.

4. Ask each student to write the equation of a quadratic function of
the form $x^2 + bx + c = 0$ that has exactly two roots. The roots
cannot be integers, and the values for b and c can be positive or
negative, but b must be an even integer and not zero. Have the
students exchange papers and graph the equations they receive.
Discuss the graphs.

10-3 *Objective:* Solve quadratic equations by factoring or using the quadratic formula.

Sample Test: Solve the following quadratic equations by factoring or using the quadratic formula $x = \dfrac{-b \pm \sqrt{b^2 - 4ac}}{2a}$. If the answer is not an integer, round the answer to the nearest hundredth.

1. $x^2 + 6x - 7 = 0$

    Solution: $(x - 1)(x + 7) = 0$
    $x = 1, -7$

2. $x^2 - 5x - 7 = 0$

    Solution:
    $a = 1, b = -5, c = -7$
    $x = \dfrac{5 \pm \sqrt{(-5)^2 - 4 \cdot 1 \cdot (-7)}}{2 \cdot 1}$
    $x = \dfrac{5 \pm \sqrt{25 + 28}}{2}$
    $x = \dfrac{5 \pm \sqrt{53}}{2}$
    $x = \dfrac{5 + 7.28}{2}$ or $x = \dfrac{5 - 7.28}{2}$
    $x = 6.14, -1.14$

Teacher's Tip:
Since students should check to see if an equation can be solved by the easiest method first, factoring is reviewed in this objective. However, if a student solves an equation correctly using the quadratic formula, he or she should receive credit even if the equation is factorable.

Concept Development Activities

Solving Equations With Perfect Squares

Directions:

1. This is a teacher-directed activity to show the students how to solve quadratic equations of the form $(x - b)^2 = c$.

2. Write $x^2 = 16$ on the board and ask a student for the solution. If the student remembers to give both solutions, ask, "Why are there two solutions?" If the student does not remember the negative solution, remind the class that two solutions exist.

3. Show that the correct method of solving equations in the form $(x - b)^2 = c$ is to take the square root of both sides, as would be done for $x^2 = 16$—that is, $\sqrt{x^2} = \sqrt{16}$. Remind the students that $\sqrt{x^2} = |x|$, so $|x| = 4$, or $x = \pm 4$.

10-3

Worksheet 1

Solve each of the following equations by taking the square root of both sides. If the answer is
not an integer, round the answer to the nearest hundredth using a calculator.

Example: $(x - 4)^2 = 7$
$\sqrt{(x-4)^2} = \sqrt{7}$
$x - 4 = \pm\sqrt{7}$
$x = 4 \pm \sqrt{7}$
$x = 6.65$ or $x = 1.35$

1. $x^2 = 81$

2. $x^2 = 45$

3. $(x - 1)^2 = 36$

4. $(x + 2)^2 = 64$

5. $(x + 5)^2 = 1$

6. $(x - 4)^2 = 49$

7. $(x - 3)^2 = 10$

8. $(x + 4)^2 = 40$

9. $(x - 7)^2 = 35$

10. $(x + 11)^2 = -5$

11. $(x + 4)^2 = 0$

10-16 Chapter 10—Exploring Quadratic and Exponential Functions

4. Now write $x^2 = 17$ on the board and work with the class to solve it:

$$\sqrt{x^2} = \sqrt{17}$$
$$|x| = \sqrt{17}$$

Have the students use a calculator to find the approximate value of $\sqrt{17}$: $x = \pm 4.123$.

5. Explain that a problem such as $(x - 3)^2 = 25$ can be solved in a very similar manner. Explain that you start by taking the square root of both sides of the equation: $\sqrt{(x-3)^2} = \sqrt{25}$.

6. Again remind the students that the square root of a variable quantity squared is its absolute value, so $|x - 3| = 5$. Explain that the absolute value means the distance from 0, which can be either positive or negative. Therefore,

$$x - 3 = \pm 5$$
$$x - 3 = 5 \text{ or } x - 3 = -5$$
$$x = 8, -2$$

7. Now write $(x + 4)^2 = 12$ on the board, and have the students help you solve the equation:

$$\sqrt{(x+4)^2} = \sqrt{12}$$
$$|x + 4| = \pm 3.464$$
$$x = -4 + 3.464 \text{ or } x = -4 - 3.464$$
$$x = -0.536, -7.464$$

8. Now write $(x - 2)^2 = -9$ on the board. Ask the students for the next step: $\sqrt{(x-2)^2} = \sqrt{-9}$. Tell the students that because there is no real number whose square is -9, there is no real solution to this equation.

Solving a Quadratic Equation of the Form $x^2 + bx + c = 0$ by Completing the Square (review)

Directions:

1. This is a teacher-directed activity to show the students how to solve quadratic equations of the form $x^2 + bx + c = 0$ by completing the square.

2. Write $x^2 + 6x + 2 = 0$ on the board and ask the students whether the problem can be factored. Explain that even though it cannot

be factored, it can be solved graphically and it can also be solved algebraically.

3. Demonstrate the solution by using the following steps:

   a. Add the opposite of the constant term to both sides of the equation: $x^2 + 6x = 0 - 2$

   b. Now complete the square on the left side and add 9 to the right side: $x^2 + 6x + 9 = -2 + 9$

   c. Factor the left side and simplify the right side: $(x + 3)^2 = 7$

   d. Take the square root of both sides: $\sqrt{(x + 3)^2} = \sqrt{7}$

   e. Simplify: $|x + 3| = 2.646$, or $x + 3 = \pm 2.646$

   f. Therefore, $x = -3 + 2.646$ or $x = -3 - 2.646$, or
      $x = -0.354, -5.646$

4. Write $x^2 - 8x + 11 = 0$ on the board. Call on students to complete
   each step:
   $$x^2 - 8x = 0 - 11$$
   $$x^2 - 8x + 16 = -11 + 16$$
   $$(x - 4)^2 = 5$$
   $$\sqrt{(x - 4)^2} = \sqrt{5}$$
   $$|x - 4| = 2.236, \text{ or } x - 4 = \pm 2.236$$
   $$x = 4 + 2.236 \text{ or } x = 4 - 2.236$$
   $$x = 6.236, 1.764$$

5. Now write $x^2 - 8x + 20 = 0$ on the board. Call on students to
   complete each step:
   $$x^2 - 8x = 0 - 20$$
   $$x^2 - 8x + 16 = -20 + 16$$
   $$(x - 4)^2 = -4$$
   $$\sqrt{(x - 4)^2} = \sqrt{-4}$$

   Since there is no real number whose square is -4, there is no real solution to this equation. Ask the students, "What does this mean for the graph of $x^2 - 8x + 20 = 0$?" **(The graph will not cross the x-axis.)**

6. Write $x^2 - 2x - 7 = 0$ on the board for the students to solve.
   (x = 3.828, -1.828)

Completing the Square of a Quadratic of the Form
$ax^2 + bx + c = 0$

Directions:

1. This activity, which demonstrates that any quadratic function can be solved by completing the square, leads up to a derivation of the quadratic formula.

2. Write $3x^2 + 6x - 8 = 0$ on the board and demonstrate how to solve the problem by using the following steps:

   a. Add the opposite of the constant term to both sides of the equation: $3x^2 + 6x = 0 + 8$

   b. Divide both sides of the equation by 3, the coefficient of x: $x^2 + 2x = \frac{8}{3}$

   c. Now complete the square on the left side and add 1 to the right side: $x^2 + 2x + 1 = \frac{8}{3} + 1$

   d. Factor the left side and simplify the right side: $(x + 1)^2 = \frac{11}{3}$

   e. Take the square root of both sides: $\sqrt{(x + 1)^2} = \sqrt{\frac{11}{3}}$

   f. Simplify: $|x + 1| = 1.915$, or $x + 1 = \pm 1.915$

   g. Therefore, $x = -1 + 1.915$ or $x = -1 - 1.915$, or $x = 0.915, -2.915$

3. Next, write $4x^2 - 7x - 9 = 0$ on the board, and explain that this equation can be solved by completing the square even though the coefficient a does not divide into b evenly. Demonstrate how to solve the problem by using the following steps:

   a. Add the opposite of the constant term to both sides of the equation: $4x^2 - 7x = 0 + 9$

   b. Divide both sides of the equation by 4, the coefficient of x: $x^2 - \frac{7}{4}x = \frac{9}{4}$

   c. Now complete the square by taking half of $\frac{7}{4}$ and squaring it and adding that number to both sides of the equation: $x^2 - \frac{7}{4}x + \left(\frac{7}{8}\right)^2 = \frac{9}{4} + \frac{49}{64}$

   d. Factor the left side and simplify the right side: $\left(x - \frac{7}{8}\right)^2 = \frac{193}{64}$

   e. Take the square root of both sides: $\sqrt{\left(x - \frac{7}{8}\right)^2} = \sqrt{\frac{193}{64}}$

   f. Simplify: $\left|x - \frac{7}{8}\right| = 1.737$, or $x - \frac{7}{8} = \pm 1.737$, or $x = .875 \pm 1.737$

   g. Therefore, $x = 2.612, -0.862$

4. Below is the derivation of the quadratic formula. You may want to write this derivation beside the solution for step 3 to have a numerical example for the students. The quadratic equation is derived in the same way that they solved $4x^2 - 7x - 9 = 0$.

Derivation of the Quadratic Formula
for $ax^2 + bx + c = 0$

$$ax^2 + bx + c = 0$$

Subtract c from both sides: $ax^2 + bx = 0 - c$

Divide both sides by a: $x^2 + \frac{b}{a}x = -\left(\frac{c}{a}\right)$

Complete the square: $x^2 + \frac{b}{a}x + \left(\frac{b}{2a}\right)^2 = -\left(\frac{c}{a}\right) + \left(\frac{b}{2a}\right)^2$

Factor the left side: $\left(x + \frac{b}{2a}\right)^2 = -\frac{c}{a} + \frac{b^2}{4a^2}$

Find common denominator for right side, and simplify: $\left(x + \frac{b}{2a}\right)^2 = \frac{-4ac}{4a^2} + \frac{b^2}{4a^2} = \frac{b^2 - 4ac}{4a^2}$

Take square root of both sides: $\sqrt{\left(x + \frac{b}{2a}\right)^2} = \sqrt{\frac{b^2 - 4ac}{4a^2}}$

Simplify square roots: $\left|x + \frac{b}{2a}\right| = \frac{\sqrt{b^2 - 4ac}}{2a}$, or

$$x + \frac{b}{2a} = \frac{\pm\sqrt{b^2 - 4ac}}{2a}$$

Subtract $\frac{b}{2a}$ from both sides: $x = -\frac{b}{2a} \pm \frac{\sqrt{b^2 - 4ac}}{2a}$

Simplify: $x = \frac{-b \pm \sqrt{b^2 - 4ac}}{2a}$

Materials:

► Calculators

► Overhead projector and transparencies (optional)

Teacher's Tip:

Worksheets 2 and 3 for this objective, **pages 10-17 to 10-20**, support this activity with practice exercises.

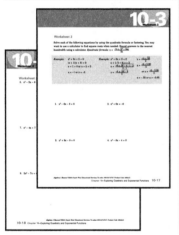

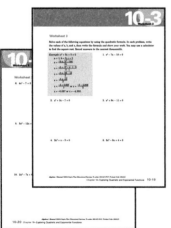

Solving a Quadratic Equation by Using the Quadratic Formula

Directions:

1. The purpose of this activity is to demonstrate how to solve a quadratic equation, written in standard form as $ax^2 + bx + c = 0$, by using the quadratic formula.

2. Tell the students their first step will be to identify the values of a, b, and c. Remind the students that if no coefficient "a" is written for x^2, it is the same as a = 1 by the identity property for multiplication ($1 \times x^2 = x^2$).

3. Write the equation $x^2 + 7x - 8 = 0$ on the board. Some students might recognize that the quadratic is factorable, and the roots are –8 and 1. Assure them that factoring, if possible, is the easier way to solve the problem, but not all quadratics are factorable.

4. Ask the students to identify the values of a, b, and c. In this case a = 1, b = 7, and c = –8.

5. Ask a student to read the quadratic formula from his or her notes:
$$x = \frac{-b \pm \sqrt{b^2 - 4ac}}{2a}$$

6. Working with the students, substitute the values for a, b, and c into the quadratic formula: $x = \dfrac{-7 \pm \sqrt{7^2 - 4 \cdot 1 \cdot (-8)}}{2 \cdot 1}$

7. Next, simplify the values inside the radical. Do the steps slowly so students can easily follow, and remind them of the order of operations as you proceed.
$$x = \frac{-7 \pm \sqrt{49 - (-32)}}{2} = \frac{-7 \pm \sqrt{49 + 32}}{2} = \frac{-7 \pm \sqrt{81}}{2}$$

8. At this point, separate the answer into two parts:
$$x = \frac{-7 + 9}{2} \text{ or } \frac{-7 - 9}{2}, \text{ or } x = \frac{2}{2}, \frac{-16}{2}, \text{ or } x = 1, -8$$

9. If the students did not recognize the roots earlier, now would be a good time to mention that the quadratic was factorable and that factoring would have been an easier way to solve it. Also mention that not all quadratics, however, are factorable, as you will now show them.

10. To demonstrate a quadratic that is not factorable, write $2x^2 - 5x - 6 = 0$ on the board.

11. Have the students identify a, b, and c. Write them on the board in an organized manner. **(a = 2, b = –5, c = –6)**

12. Next, write the quadratic formula on the board. If you consistently write the formula from the beginning, the students will become more familiar with it and better able to use it.

$$x = \frac{-b \pm \sqrt{b^2 - 4ac}}{2a}$$

13. Substitute the values for a, b, and c into the formula and simplify:

$$x = \frac{5 \pm \sqrt{(-5)^2 - 4 \cdot 2 \cdot (-6)}}{2 \cdot 2} = \frac{5 \pm \sqrt{25 + 48}}{4} = \frac{5 \pm \sqrt{73}}{4}$$

14. Separate this into two problems and use a calculator to take the square root. Round off to the nearest hundredth:
$$x = \frac{5 + 8.54}{4} \text{ or } \frac{5 - 8.54}{4}, \text{ or } x = 3.39, -0.89$$

15. Relate these answers to the answers you would get if you graphed the quadratic.

16. Now ask the students to solve the quadratic $3x^2 - 8x + 8 = 0$. This problem has no real solutions because the quantity under the square root sign is a negative number.

$$\left(x = \frac{8 \pm \sqrt{64 - 96}}{6} = \frac{5 \pm \sqrt{-32}}{6} \right)$$

Practice Activities

Draw Your Own Quadratic Equation II
(No Coefficient for x^2)

Directions:

1. You can use the cards from **Draw Your Own Quadratic Equation I** in Objective 10-2 or have the students make the cards.

2. Divide the class into groups of three or four, with as many groups of four as possible. Have the students in each group mark eight cards with a "b" on one side and one of these numbers on the other side: 2, –2, 4, –4, 6, –6, 8, –8. Each number should be used only once. Then have them mark 13 cards with a "c" on one side and one of these numbers on the other side: 0, 1, –1, 4, –4, 9, 16, 2, –2, 3, –3, 5, –5. Again, each number should be used only once.

Materials:

▶ Blank cards or 💿

When the students are finished, each group will have one deck with values for b and a second deck with values for c.

3. The object is for each person in each group to form an equation in the form $x^2 + bx + c = 0$ using the b and c cards drawn and determine the roots of that equation by completing the square.

4. Have each group shuffle the two decks separately, and have each student pick one card from the b deck and one from the c deck. *Example:* b = 2 and c = −4

5. Ask each student to write a quadratic equation using the values of b and c he or she selected. *Example:* $x^2 + 2x - 4 = 0$

6. Write the quadratic formula $x = \dfrac{-b \pm \sqrt{b^2 - 4ac}}{2a}$ on the board. Have the students solve the equation they have written by using the formula.

7. When the students have finished, have each student show his or her cards and solution to the rest of the group. The group should then check the work and make corrections if needed.

8. Have the students return the cards to the appropriate decks, shuffle, and repeat the process as time allows.

Materials:

▶ Blank cards or

Draw Your Own Quadratic Equation III (Coefficient for x^2)

Directions:

1. Divide the class into groups of three or four, with as many groups of four as possible.

2. Have the students in each group mark eight cards with an "a" on one side and one of these numbers on the other side: 1, 1, 2, 2, 3, 3, 4, 4. Each number should be used only once. Then have them mark eight cards with a "b" on one side and one of these numbers on the other side: 2, −2, 4, −4, 3, −3, 5, −5. Again, each number should be used only once. When they are done, have the students mark 13 cards with a "c" on one side and one of these numbers on the other side: 0, 1, −1, 4, −4, 9, 16, 2, −2, 3, −3, 5, −5. As before, each number should be used only once. Each group will have three decks of cards. One deck will have values for a, a second deck will have values for b, and a third deck will have values for c.

3. The object is for each person in each group to form an equation in the form $ax^2 + bx + c = 0$ using the a, b, and c cards drawn and determine the roots of that equation by using the quadratic formula.

4. Have each group shuffle the three decks separately, and have each student pick one card from the a deck, one from the b deck, and one from the c deck. *Example:* $a = 3$; $b = 4$; $c = 2$

5. Ask each student to write a quadratic equation using the values of a, b, and c he or she selected, for example, $3x^2 + 4x + 2 = 0$.

6. Write the quadratic formula $x = \dfrac{-b \pm \sqrt{b^2 - 4ac}}{2a}$ on the board. Have the students solve the equation they created by using the formula.

7. When the students have finished, have each student show his or her cards and solution to the rest of the group. The group should then check the work and make corrections if needed.

8. Have the students return the cards to the appropriate decks, shuffle, and repeat the process as time allows.

Problem-Solving Activities

Best Methods 💡

Directions:

1. Give the students the following quadratic equations.

   a. $3x^2 - 5x + (-1) = 0$
   b. $x^2 - 6x + 2 = 0$

   c. $(x - 2)^2 - 4 = 0$
   d. $(2x - 5)(3x + 4) = 0$

   Working individually, the students should decide the best method to solve each equation and then they should solve the equations. When they are finished, ask volunteers to come to the board to explain why they picked their method for that particular problem and to solve the problem by using that method. Ask for other methods for the same problems. The methods the students may use are:

   Graphing (without a graphing calculator)

   Completing the square

   Factoring and zero product property

   Quadratic formula

Answer Key for #1:
a. Use the quadratic formula because it isn't factorable, and completing the square involves fractions.

$x = \dfrac{5 \pm \sqrt{(-5)^2 - 4(3)(-1)}}{2 \cdot 3} =$

$\dfrac{5 \pm \sqrt{25 + 12}}{6} = \dfrac{5 \pm \sqrt{37}}{6}$

$= \dfrac{5 \pm 6.083}{6}$,

so $x = 1.847, -0.181$.

b. Complete the square because the value of b is even. This equation could also be graphed easily.

$x^2 - 6x + 9 = -2 + 9$
$(x - 3)^2 = 7$
$\sqrt{(x - 3)^2} = \sqrt{7}$
$|x - 3| = \pm 2.646$
$x = 3 + 2.646$ or
$x = 3 - 2.646$
$x = 5.646, 0.354$

c. Graphing is easiest. This equation can also be solved by completing the square.
The vertex is $(2, -4)$ and the roots are 0 and 4.

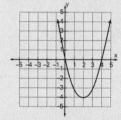

d. Factoring is easiest because it is already factored and the student only has to use the zero product property.
$2x - 5 = 0$ or $3x + 4 = 0$
$2x = 5$ or $3x = -4$
so $x = \frac{5}{2}, -\frac{4}{3}$

2. Ask the students to write a quadratic equation for which the best solution method would be completing the square.

3. Ask the students to write a quadratic equation for which the best solution method would be graphing.

4. Ask the students to write a quadratic equation for which the best solution method would be the quadratic formula.

5. Ask the students to write a quadratic equation for which the best solution method would be factoring and using the zero product property.

6. Ask the students to write a quadratic function that has a vertex of $(3, -2)$.

7. Ask the students to write a quadratic function that has an axis of symmetry of $x = -2$.

Find the Equation ☀

Directions:

1. Explain to the class that you are thinking of a quadratic equation that has the roots of $x = 2 + \sqrt{7}$ and $x = 2 - \sqrt{7}$.

2. Ask the class to find the equation that has these solutions. The students may work in groups or individually.

    Solution: $x = 2 + \sqrt{7} \rightarrow x - 2 - \sqrt{7} = 0$
    $x = 2 - \sqrt{7} \rightarrow x - 2 + \sqrt{7} = 0$

    therefore: $(x - 2 - \sqrt{7})(x - 2 + \sqrt{7}) = 0$
    $x^2 - 2x + \sqrt{7}x - 2x + 4 - 2\sqrt{7} - \sqrt{7}x + 2\sqrt{7} - 7 = 0$
    $x^2 - 4x - 3 = 0$ **is the equation.**

3. Ask the class to find the quadratic equation that has solutions of $x = \dfrac{3 + \sqrt{2}}{2}$ and $x = \dfrac{3 - \sqrt{2}}{2}$.

    Solution: $x = \dfrac{3 + \sqrt{2}}{2} \rightarrow 2x - 3 - \sqrt{2} = 0$

    $x = \dfrac{3 - \sqrt{2}}{2} \rightarrow 2x - 3 + \sqrt{2} = 0$

    therefore: $(2x - 3 - \sqrt{\sqrt{2}})(2x - 3 + \sqrt{2}) = 0$
    $4x^2 - 6x + 2\sqrt{2}x - 6x + 9 - 3\sqrt{2} - 2\sqrt{2}x + 3\sqrt{2} - 2 = 0$
    $4x^2 - 12x + 7 = 0$

10-4 *Objective:* **Graph exponential functions and solve problems using the graphs.**

Sample Test:

1. Graph: $y = 4^x$ **Solution:**

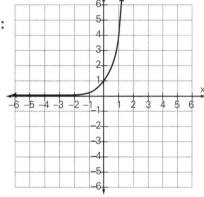

2. Using the formula $A = P\left(1 + \frac{r}{n}\right)^{nt}$, find the amount of money you would have after 20 years if you invested \$4,000 at 5% compounded quarterly.

Solution: $A = 4{,}000\left(1 + \frac{.05}{4}\right)^{4(20)} = \$10{,}805.94$

Concept Development Activities

Graphing $y = 2^x$

Directions:

1. This is a teacher-directed activity to help the students understand the shape of an exponential function.

2. Give one copy of the blackline master **Graphing** to each student.

3. Copy the table of ordered pairs for $y = 2^x$ on the board and call on students one at a time to fill in each value.

4. Review zero powers and negative powers for those students who don't remember these subjects.

5. Have the students plot the points on graph paper. Discuss the shape of the graph.

Materials:

► Blackline master **Graphing** is located in the *Teacher's Resource Manual*, **page 135.**

► Blackline Master for **graph paper** is in the Appendix.

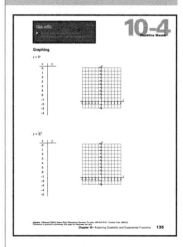

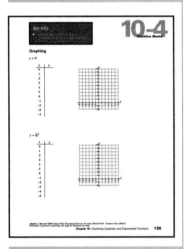

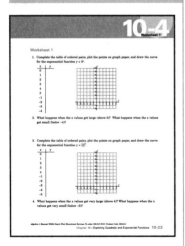

Graphing $\left(\frac{1}{2}\right)^x$

Directions:

1. This is a teacher-directed activity to help the students understand the shape of an exponential function when the base is less than 1.

2. Give one copy of the blackline master **Graphing** to each student.

3. Copy the table of ordered pairs for $y = \left(\frac{1}{2}\right)^x$ on the board and call on students one at a time to fill in each value.

4. Review zero powers and negative powers for those students who don't remember these subjects.

5. Have the students plot the points on graph paper. Discuss the shape of the graph.

6. Compare the shape of this graph to that of $y = 2^x$ from the previous activity. Discuss the similarities and differences.

7. Discuss that for an exponential function in the form $y = b^x$:

   • if $b > 1$ the graph will grow exponentially and look like the graph for $y = 2^x$.

   • if $b < 1$ the graph will decrease exponentially and look like the graph for $y = \left(\frac{1}{2}\right)^x$.

Exponential Growth and Decay

Directions:

Materials:
▶ Graphing calculator (or scientific calculator)

1. Explain that anything that increases by the same percent over a period of time will grow exponentially.

2. Present the following problem situation:

   If 1 million people lived in Denver, Colorado, in 1960, and the population grew at the rate of 3% annually, when would the population be 10 million?

3. Explain that the function would be: Population = Original Population × (1 + percentage of growth) raised to the power of (the current year – 1960). In symbolic form, this is:

   $$y = 1,000,000 \,(1 + .03)^{(x-1960)}$$

   where x represents the year and y represents the population.

4. Enter the function into the graphing menu on the calculator, or perform successive computations at 10-year intervals and then yearly by having a different student compute each different year.

5. Adjust the scale and the window until the function appears on the screen.

6. Note that a reasonable range of values for x would be from 1960 to 2010 and that a reasonable range of values for y would be from 0 to 12,000,000 with a scale of 250,000.

7. After you have the exponential function graphed, graph y = 10,000,000 on the same graph. Explain to the students that the point of intersection of these two graphs is the answer to the problem.

Materials:

► Graphing calculator (or scientific calculator)

Teacher's Tip:

Worksheet 2 for this objective, **page 10-24**, supports this activity with practice exercises.

Investments That Grow Exponentially

Directions:

1. The purpose of this lesson is to demonstrate to the students the development of the compound interest formula.

2. Present the following problem situation:

   For your sixteenth birthday you are given $1,000. It is invested at 6% compounded quarterly and will remain invested until you reach age 60.

3. Say to the students, "Let's find how much money you would have at the end of the first quarter (three months)." The interest earned would be given by $I = Prt$, where P is principal, r is the annual rate, and t is time (in years). Then $I = 1,000(.06)\left(\frac{1}{4}\right) = 15$. Since the interest is compounded, the interest is added to the principal, and the new principal is $1,015.

4. Now say, "Let's find out how much money you would have at the end of six months. Would you earn $15 in interest again over the following three months?" **(No, because the principal grew.)** Explain that the new interest would be $I = 1015(.06)\left(\frac{1}{4}\right) = 15.225$.

   Suggest that since there is not much difference (22.5 cents more than for the first three months), maybe they should forget compounding the interest and just take $15 a quarter or $60 a year times 44 years (60 − 16). Ask, "Will that be close enough?" To check, multiply 44 times $60 and add the total ($2,640) to the $1,000 to get $3,640 at age 60. Then, see if the 22.5 pennies would make much of a difference, compound the interest. As shown in step 4, at the end of six months, there would be $1,030.225 in the account.

   Now figure what the amount would be at the end of the third quarter: $I = 1,030.225(.06)\left(\frac{1}{4}\right) = 15.453$, so the new principal would be $1,045.678.

   At the end of the first year, the interest would be $1,045.678(.06)\left(\frac{1}{4}\right) = 15.685$, so the principal at the end of the first year would be $1,061.363.

   Explain that to find the total for age 60 by using this method, you would need to do this calculation for another 43 years.

At four calculations per year, this would mean another 172 calculations. Suggest that there may be a better way.

5. Review with the students the calculations performed for the first year:

   a. For the first quarter you multiplied $1,000(.06)\left(\frac{1}{4}\right)$ and then added the result to $1,000. This is equivalent to $1,000 + 1,000(.015)$ by using the distributive property. So, at the end of the first quarter, the total is $1,000(1 + .015)$.

   b. For the second quarter, you multiplied $1,000(1 + .015)$ by .015 and added this to $1,000(1 + .015)$. If you use the distributive property, you would have $1,000(1 + .015)(1 + .015)$.

   c. If you repeat this process for the third quarter, the amount of money would be represented by $1,000(1 + .015)(1 + .015)(1 + .015)$.

   d. If you continue the process for the fourth quarter, you would have $1,000(1 + .015)(1 + .015)(1 + .015)(1 + .015)$.

6. Show the students that if you enter these numbers on a calculator and use repeated multiplication, you will see the principal at the end of the first quarter, second quarter, third quarter, and at the end of one year.

7. Show the students that the expression can be written by using exponents: $1,000(1 + .015)(1 + .015)(1 + .015)(1 + .015) = 1,000(1 + .015)^4$.

8. Ask the students, "Why is the exponent 4?" **(Because the interest is compounded four times per year.)**

9. Then ask, "What exponent would you use for two years?" **(8, which is 4 times per year for 2 years.)**

10. Then ask, "What exponent would you use for 10 years? **(40, which is 4 times per year for 10 years.)**

11. Now compute how much principal there would be after 10 years: $1,000(1 + .015)^{40} = \$1,814.018$.

12. Show that at the end of 20 years the principal would be $1,000(1 + .015)^{80} = \$3,290.663$. Point out that this is almost the same as the principal at the end of 44 years if the interest is not compounded.

13. Show that at the end of 30 years, you would have a principal of $1{,}000(1 + .015)^{120} = \$5{,}969.323$; at the end of 40 years, the principal would be $1{,}000(1 + .015)^{160} = \$10{,}828.46$; and at the end of 44 years, it would be $1{,}000(1 + .015)^{176} = \$13{,}741.161$.

14. Ask the students, "How would the problem change if the interest were compounded monthly?" **(The interest would be $\frac{.06}{12} = .005$ and the exponent would be 12 times the number of years.)**

15. Show the graph of $y = 1{,}000(1.015)^{4x}$, where x represents the number of years and y represents the total amount of money.

16. Tell the students that the general compound interest formula is $A = P\left(1 + \frac{r}{n}\right)^{nt}$, where A is the amount of money you will have at the end of t years, P is the principal (or the original amount of money invested), r is the annual interest rate, n is the number of times the interest is compounded per year, and t is the time (in years) that the money is invested.

17. Present another problem and ask the students to use the compound interest formula given in step 16:

    Suppose you receive $5,000 in gifts for graduation. You decide to use half the amount for college spending money and invest half of it for retirement. You invest the money in a long-term Certificate of Deposit that earns 8% compounded monthly. How much money would you have at the end of 40 years?

    Give students time to work the problem, then review it on the board. Using the compound interest formula show that $A = P\left(1 + \frac{r}{n}\right)^{nt}$, with P = $2,500, r = .08, n = 12, and t = 40. Then $A = \$2{,}500\left(1 + \frac{.08}{12}\right)^{12 \cdot 40} = \$60{,}683.464$

18. Explain that the equation in step 16 is a general equation for exponential growth, and that the general equation for exponential decay can be obtained similarly by subtracting the interest times the principal from the principal: $A = C(1 - r)^t$. As an example of exponential decay, remind the students that many things (such as an automobile) become less valuable as they get older. The term used to describe this is depreciation.

19. Present the following problem, which involves exponential decay:

    Suppose on your sixteenth birthday you receive a car, and the price of the car is $18,000. The car depreciates at a rate of 17%

per year. How much will the car be worth on your twenty-first birthday?

20. Have the students determine the values for C, r, and t in the formula $A = C(1 - r)^t$. **[C = \$18,000; r = 17%, or .17; t = 5 (time is always in years)]** Substitute the values into the formula and compute:

$$A = 18,000(1 - .17)^5 = 18,000(.83)^5 = \$7,090 \text{ (rounded to nearest \$)}$$

Practice Activities

Match Graph

Directions:

1. Have the students work in pairs.

2. Copy the blackline master **Match Graph** onto construction paper and give one sheet to each pair of students. Have the students cut apart the squares to form 16 cards. The cards should be placed into two piles, problems and graphs.

3. Have each pair of students work together to graph each problem and match the correct graph card with the problem card.

4. Remind the students to be careful when graphing exponential functions to be sure they have the correct base.

5. **Alternative application:** The cards can be given to an individual to match for additional practice.

The Person With the Most Money Wins

Directions:

1. The purpose of this activity is to have students practice using the general equation for exponential growth: $A = P\left(1 + \frac{r}{n}\right)^{nt}$.

2. Form groups of four students.

3. Each student will prepare one of the four sets of six cards, as discussed in step 12. Each group of students will have four sets of six cards each.

Materials:

▶ Blackline master **Match Graph** is located in the *Teacher's Resource Manual*, **page 136**.

▶ Construction paper or

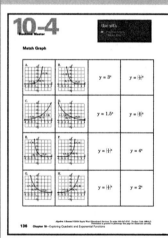

Materials:

▶ Blank cards or 💿

4. Ask the students to shuffle the four decks, and then each student should draw one card from each deck and place the cards face-up in front of himself or herself. These cards will determine the values the students will substitute in the general equation.

5. Have the students look at one another's cards and estimate which member of the group will have the most money.

6. Have each student solve his or her own problem and find the value of "A." Each student should present his or her solution to the rest of the group.

7. The group should then decide whether the student has worked the problem correctly. If the problem is correct, the student receives a point value, in dollars, that is equal to the value of A. The "dollar" amount is placed in the student's "account." If the problem is incorrect, the student receives the value of P.

8. An additional $10,000 is awarded to each person who selected the person with the "most money" in step 5.

9. After all of the students' work has been checked by the group, the students should put the cards back in the respective decks, shuffle each deck, and draw again.

10. After three rounds (time permitting), check to see which students have the most money in their accounts.

11. Award a special prize, such as bonus points, to the highest scoring student in each group.

12. Directions for cards:

   a. You will need four sets of six cards each for each group.

   b. On one side of six cards, the students should print a P. On the other side, they should write $10,000; $11,000; $12,000; $10,000; $11,000; and $12,000.

   c. On one side of six other cards, the students should print an r. On the other side, they should print 6%, 6%, 5%, 5%, 7%, and 7%.

   d. On one side of six other cards, the students should print a t. On the other side, they should write 10 years, 10 years, 12 years, 12 years, 15 years, and 15 years.

   e. On one side of six other cards, the students should print an n. On the other side, they should write 4, 4, 2, 2, 12, and 12.

Problem-Solving Activity

Which Would Amount to More Money? 🔅

Directions:

For each pair of problems below, ask the students to guess which problem would amount to more money. Then have the students work the problems to see if they were correct in their assessment.

1a. You receive an allowance of $10 the first week of every month, and the amount you receive doubles every week after that. Assume there are four weeks to a month. How much would your allowance be after one month?

1b. You receive an allowance of a penny the first day of the month, and the amount you receive doubles every day for the rest of the month. Assume the month has 30 days. How much would your allowance be after one month?

2a. You invest $1,000 at age 21 and receive 8% compounded monthly until age 65. How much money would you have at age 65?

2b. You invest $3,000 at age 40 and receive 8% compounded monthly until age 65. How much money would you have at age 65?

3a. You invest $10,000 at 10% interest compounded quarterly 10 years before you retire. How much money would you have when you retire?

3b. You invest $2,000 at 8% interest compounded quarterly 40 years before you retire. How much money would you have when you retire?

4a. You have $10,000 to put into savings. Bank I will pay 6% per year compounded quarterly. How much money will you have at the end of one year? At the end of two years?

4b. You have $10,000 to put into savings. Bank II will pay you 6.5% per year compounded annually. How much money will you have at the end of one year? At the end of two years?

Answer Key:
1. A penny doubled daily for a month (problem 1b) amounts to a lot more money than $10 doubled weekly for a month (problem 1a).
   a. Week 1: $10; Week 2: $20; Week 3: $40; Week 4: $80
      So total for the month is $150.
   b.

	Total
Day 1: 1¢	$.01
Day 2: 2¢	.03
Day 3: 4¢	.07
Day 4: 8¢	.15
Day 5: 16¢	.31
Day 6: 32¢	.63
Day 7: 64¢	1.27
Day 8: 128¢	$2^8 - 1$ cents
Day n: 2^{n-1}	$2^n - 1$ cents
Day 30: 2^{29}	$2^{30} - 1$ cents =

   $10,737,418.24 - .01
   So total for the month is $10,737,417.24

2. Investing $1,000 at age 21 (problem 2a) is better than investing $3,000 at age 40 (problem 2b). Moral: Start investing when you are young.
   a. $A = P(1 + \frac{r}{t})^{nt} =$
      $1,000(1 + \frac{.08}{12})^{12(44)} =$
      $1,000(1.0067)^{528} = \$33,392$
   b. $A = 3,000(1 + \frac{.08}{12})^{12(25)} =$
      $3,000(1.0067)^{300} = \$22,020$

3. Investing $2,000 at 8% interest for 40 years (problem 3b) is better than investing $10,000 at 8% interest for 10 years (problem 3a).
   a. $A = P(1 + \frac{r}{t})^{nt} =$
      $10,000(1 + \frac{.1}{4})^{4(10)} =$
      $10,000(1.025)^{40} = \$26,851$
   b. $A = 2,000(1 + \frac{.08}{4})^{4(40)} =$
      $2,000(1.02)^{160} = \$47,540$

4. 6.5% compounded annually (problem 4b) will yield more money than 6% compounded quarterly (problem 4a).
   a. 6% quarterly:
      Year 1: $10,613; Year 2: $11,265
   b. 6.5% annually
      Year 1: $10,650; Year 2: $11,342

Exploring Rational Expressions and Equations

11-1 Simplify rational expressions.

11-2 Multiply and divide rational expressions.

11-3 Divide a polynomial by a binomial.

11-4 Add and subtract rational expressions.

11-5 Solve rational equations.

11-1 *Objective:* Simplify rational expressions.

Sample Test: Simplify each of the following rational expressions:

1. $\dfrac{3x}{6x^2}$

   Solution: $\dfrac{1}{2x}$

2. $\dfrac{25x^2y^2}{10x^3y}$

   Solution: $\dfrac{5y}{2x}$

3. $\dfrac{x + 2}{x^2 + 3x + 2}$

   Solution: $\dfrac{1}{x + 1}$

Concept Development Activities

Simplifying Rational Expressions

Directions:

1. Tell the students that they already know a lot about rational
    expressions. Review the definition of rational expressions.
    Explain that fractions are rational expressions.

2. Write $\frac{1}{2}$ on the board. Tell the students that this number is easy
    to understand. When they divide a candy bar with a friend, for
    example, each receives $\frac{1}{2}$ of the candy bar. Ask the students,
    "What would happen if, instead, you said you wanted $\frac{16}{32}$ of the
    candy bar?" Explain that it would be more difficult to know how
    much each person would get. Write $\frac{16}{32}$ on the board and ask the
    students to help you to simplify it. When you have determined
    that $\frac{16}{32} = \frac{1}{2}$, emphasize that even though the amounts are the
    same, it is easier to use the simplified expression.

3. Write $\frac{x}{2x}$ on the board. Discuss with the students that the
    coefficient on the top (in the numerator) is actually 1, and the
    coefficient on the bottom (in the denominator) is 2, so $\frac{x}{2x}$ is
    actually the same as $\frac{1}{2}$. Show this by writing the
    following on the board:

    $$\frac{x}{2x} = \frac{1 \cdot x}{2 \cdot x} = \frac{1}{2} \cdot \frac{x}{x} = \frac{1}{2} \cdot 1 = \frac{1}{2}$$

    Tell the students that in algebra, the term "rational expression"
    is used in place of "fraction."

4. Students are usually not faced with problems with a 0
    denominator. Tell them that because division by 0 is undefined, a
    problem with zero in the denominator cannot be solved. Point out
    that if x = 0 in the expression $\frac{x}{2x}$, the fraction becomes $\frac{0}{0}$, which
    is not equal to 1, an exception to the rule that a number divided
    by itself is 1.

5. Ask the students what $\frac{3x}{9x^2}$ would be in simplified form. $\left(\frac{1}{3x}\right)$
    Discuss how they arrived at the result. Ask, "Did you strike out
    common factors or did you factor first and then reduce?" For
    example,

    $$\frac{^{1}\cancel{3}x}{_{3}\cancel{9}x^2} = \frac{1}{3x}$$

    is striking out common factors, whereas

$$\frac{3x}{9x^2} = \frac{3x}{3^2x^2} = \frac{3x}{(3x)(3x)} = \frac{1}{3x} \cdot \frac{3x}{3x} = \frac{1}{3x} \cdot 1 = \frac{1}{3x}$$

is factoring first and then reducing.

6. Now write $\frac{6a^2b^2}{3ab^4}$ on the board. Explain that you will let a = 3 and b = 2. Evaluate $\frac{6a^2b^2}{3ab^4}$ on the board by substituting the values:

$$\frac{6a^2b^2}{3ab^4} = \frac{6 \cdot 9 \cdot 4}{3 \cdot 3 \cdot 16} = \frac{216}{144} = 1.5$$

Now reduce the expression first and then substitute the values:

$$\frac{6a^2b^2}{3ab^4} = \frac{2a}{b^2} = \frac{2 \cdot 3}{4} = 1.5$$

Ask the students, "Which method seems simpler?"

7. Remind the students that expressions are reduced to make things simpler. This is especially true for complicated expressions. Write $\frac{x^2 - 4}{x^2 - 3x + 2}$ on the board. Ask the students to factor the numerator. They should obtain $(x - 2)(x + 2)$. Ask them then to factor the denominator. They should obtain $(x - 2)(x - 1)$. So now the rational expression is $\frac{(x - 2)(x + 2)}{(x - 2)(x - 1)}$. Upon simplifying, this becomes $\frac{(x + 2)}{(x - 1)}$. Point out that $x \neq 2$ and $x \neq 1$ in the original denominator because division by 0 is not allowed.

8. Now write $\frac{x^2 - 25}{x + 5}$ on the board. Ask the students to simplify the expression. $\left[\frac{(x - 5)(x + 5)}{x + 5} = x + 5; x \neq -5 \right]$

9. Now write $\frac{10x^2 - 250}{x + 5}$ on the board. Ask the students to factor the numerator. Discuss that it has a common factor and a difference of two squares as a factor: $10x^2 - 250 = 10(x^2 - 25) = 10(x - 5)(x + 5)$. Now ask the students to simplify the original expression. **[10(x – 5), or 10x – 50]**

10. Now write $\frac{x^2 + 3x + 2}{x^2 + 3x - 4}$ on the board. Ask the students to simplify the expression. They may factor it as $\frac{(x + 1)(x + 2)}{(x - 1)(x + 4)}$ but they will find no common factors. Point out that not all expressions can be simplified. For example, the rational expression $\frac{2}{3}$ cannot be simplified further either.

11. Ask the students if the expression in step 10 could be simplified if you changed it to $\frac{x^2 - 3x + 2}{x^2 + 3x - 4}$. They should see that this new expression simplifies to $\frac{x - 2}{x + 4}$.

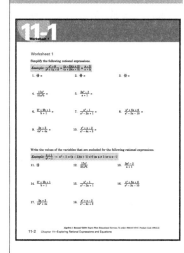

Teacher's Tip:

Worksheet 1 for this objective, **page 11-2**, supports this activity with practice exercises.

12. Now write the following rational expressions on the board and ask the students to simplify them.

    a. $\dfrac{x^2}{2x^4}$ b. $\dfrac{x^2 + 2x + 1}{x^2 - 1}$ c. $\dfrac{2x^2 + 4x + 2}{4x^2 - 4}$

    d. $\dfrac{x^2 + x - 12}{x^2 - 16}$ e. $\dfrac{x^2 + 6x + 5}{x^2 + 10x + 25}$ f. $\dfrac{3a^2b - 6ab^2}{a^2 - b^2}$

13. Discuss with the students how they obtained the results to the problems in step 12, or have different students come to the board to show how they simplified the various expressions.

14. Ask the students what values of the variable are not allowed (would make the denominator 0) in each of the expressions in step 12.

Reducing Fractions and Simplifying Rational Expressions

Directions:

1. Ask the students if they would prefer to have $\frac{1}{2}$, $\frac{32}{64}$, or $\frac{x}{2x}$ of a million dollars.

2. Discuss with the students that these fractions are all the same, so no matter which one they choose, they would get $500,000.

3. Ask the students, "What if x were equal to zero? Would the fraction still be all the same?" Discuss with the students that $\frac{0}{0}$ of a million dollars would be impossible to calculate. Maybe, then, if $x = 0$, the results are not all the same. Explain that we must assume that $x \neq 0$ because the denominator cannot be 0, and division by 0 is not possible.

4. Write the following rational expressions on the board, and ask the students to group them into sets in which all expressions are equivalent and to state what they are all equivalent to. Ask if the simplified equivalent expression is easier to understand.

$$\frac{25}{50}, \frac{7}{21}, \frac{8}{16}, \frac{5}{15}, \frac{32}{96}, \frac{145}{290}, \frac{4a}{12a}, \frac{17x}{34x}$$

5. Ask the students to write the expressions $-\frac{25}{105}$, $\frac{18}{27}$, and $\frac{-3x}{x^2 + x}$ on their papers and to simplify each of them. Then have the students exchange papers with a partner and compare their results.

6. Write $\frac{-3x}{x^2 + x}$ on the board and ask the students, "What would the result be if $x = 7$?" Discuss that if they computed $\frac{-3(7)}{7^2 + 7}$, they

would get $\frac{-21}{56} = \frac{-3}{8}$, but if they first reduced the expression to $\frac{-3}{x+1}$, they would get $\frac{-3}{8}$ right away. Stress that computation is often easier if expressions are simplified first.

7. Write the expressions $\frac{3x^2}{5x^2+3x}$, $\frac{x^2-4}{x+2}$, $\frac{x^2+2x+1}{x+1}$, $\frac{3x^2+6x+3}{2x^2-2x-4}$ on the board and ask the students to simplify each of them. Then have the students exchange papers with a partner and compare their results.

8. Ask the students to find any excluded values for the expressions from step 7. Show them as an example that for the first expression, you would let $5x^2 + 3x \neq 0$. Then $x(5x + 3) \neq 0$, or $x \neq 0$, $x \neq -\frac{3}{5}$. Point out that it is best to find the excluded values before simplifying the expression.

9. Write the expressions $\frac{7x^2y^3z^2}{21xy^5z^2}$, $\frac{15a^3b^2c}{35a^4b^3}$, $\frac{2-x}{x^2-4}$ on the board and ask the students to simplify each of them. Point out that in the second expression, there is no "c" in the denominator. Ask the students whether there would be an excluded value for the c. Point out that in the third expression the order of the numerator is incorrect, and it should be rewritten as $-x + 2 = -(x - 2)$ before simplifying it.

10. Ask the students to list the steps they would take to simplify a rational expression. They should list factoring and then removing the greatest common factor from numerators and denominators. Point out that they should also determine excluded values.

Practice Activities

Equivalent Sets 💡

Directions:

1. Have the students form groups of two.

2. Write $\frac{2}{3}$ on the board. Ask the student pairs for examples of equivalent rational expressions, such as $\frac{2x}{3x}$. Ask for another example, such as $\frac{2(x+1)}{3(x+1)} = \frac{2x+2}{3x+3}$. Tell them that $\frac{2a}{3a}$ is similar to $\frac{2x}{3x}$, so that won't count as a new expression. Discuss some of the more "interesting" student examples.

Teacher's Tip:

Worksheet 2 for this objective, **page 11-3**, supports this activity with practice exercises.

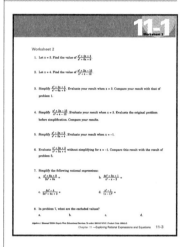

Answer Key:

7. $\frac{3x}{5x+3}$, $x - 2$, $x + 1$,

$\frac{3(x+1)}{2(x-2)}$ or $\frac{3x+3}{2x-4}$

9. $\frac{x^2}{3y^2}$, $\frac{3c}{7ab}$, $\frac{-1}{x+2}$

3. Ask the student pairs to write at least four examples of rational expressions that are equivalent to each of the following:

$$\frac{3x}{x^2 + x}, \quad \frac{x - 1}{x + 2}, \quad \frac{3x^2}{x + 1}, \quad \frac{x + 2}{x - 1}$$

4. Have the student pairs write all of the expressions they came up with for step 3 in random order on a new piece of paper. Then have them exchange this paper with another student pair, and have each pair simplify the rational expressions to find the equivalent sets.

Four in a Row Bingo

Directions:

1. Distribute a copy of the 4×4 bingo card and markers to each student.

2. Write the following rational expressions on the board or transparency, and ask the students to randomly write one of the expressions in each square on their bingo card. Each expression should be used once.

$\dfrac{x + 2}{x + 3}$	$\dfrac{2x - 1}{2x + 1}$	$\dfrac{x - 3}{x + 2}$	$\dfrac{x + 2}{x - 1}$	$\dfrac{3x}{x + 1}$	$\dfrac{5x^2}{3}$	$\dfrac{5x}{2}$	$\dfrac{x + 1}{x - 2}$
$\dfrac{x + 1}{x - 3}$	$\dfrac{x - 1}{2x}$	$\dfrac{x + 1}{2x - 1}$	$\dfrac{1}{3}$	$\dfrac{2x}{x + 3}$	$\dfrac{x^2}{2}$	$\dfrac{x - 3}{x + 3}$	$\dfrac{x - 1}{x + 3}$

3. Select one of the following expressions and write it on the board or transparency. (Alternatively, write the expressions on cards and draw one at random to write on the board.) Instruct the students to simplify the expression and to use a marker to cover the result on their bingo card. Continue selecting new expressions in this manner until a student has four in a row covered on his or her card. You may want to have students work in pairs.

$\dfrac{x^2 - x - 6}{x^2 + 5x + 6}$	$\dfrac{x^2 + 3x - 4}{x^2 + 7x + 12}$	$\dfrac{3x^2 + 6x}{x^2 + 3x + 2}$	$\dfrac{x^2 - x - 6}{x^2 - 9}$
$\dfrac{x^2 + 2x - 3}{2x^2 + 6x}$	$\dfrac{5x^2 - 5x}{2x - 2}$	$\dfrac{2x^2 + x - 1}{2x^2 + 3x + 1}$	$\dfrac{x^2 + 6x + 5}{x^2 + 3x - 10}$
$\dfrac{5x^3 + 20x^2}{3x + 12}$	$\dfrac{x^2 - 1}{3x^2 - 3}$	$\dfrac{x^2 + x - 12}{x^2 + 6x + 8}$	$\dfrac{x^2 + x}{x^2 - 3x}$
$\dfrac{x^2 + 2x + 1}{2x^2 + x - 1}$	$\dfrac{2x^2 + 8x}{x^2 + 7x + 12}$	$\dfrac{x^4 - x^2}{2x^2 - 2}$	$\dfrac{x^2 - 4}{x^2 - 3x + 2}$

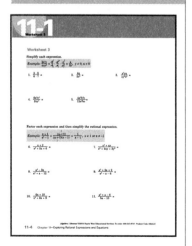

4. The first student to cover four in a row calls, "Bingo!" If his or her solutions match those that should be covered, declare the student the winner. Discuss any questions. Award prizes such as certificates, food, or points to the winning students.

5. If there is time, have the students exchange cards and play again.

Problem-Solving Activities

Missing Parts

Directions:

Give each student a copy of the blackline master **Missing Parts**. Have the students work individually to solve the problems.

Ask the students to find the missing dimensions in each of the problems on the top half of the blackline master. Have them simplify all rational expressions.

1. A rectangle has an area of $4x^3y^4$, and its length is x^2y^2. What is its width?

2. A rectangle has an area of $x^2 - 25$. The base is $x^2 + 10x + 25$. Find the height.

3. A triangle has an area of $x^2 - 9x + 8$. The base is $x^2 - 16x + 64$. Find the height. [*Hint:* $A = \frac{1}{2}bh$.]

4. A trapezoid has an area of $x^2 - 2x - 15$. It has a top base of $4x - 19$ and a bottom base of $x^2 - 5x + 7$. Find the height. [*Hint:* $A = \dfrac{h(b_1 + b_2)}{2}$.]

Can You Do It?

Directions:

Give each student a copy of the blackline master **Can You Do It?** Have the students work individually to solve the problems, which are reprinted below.

1. Simplify the following rational expressions:

   a. $\dfrac{6x^3 + 12x^2 - 18x}{2x^4 - 18x^2}$ b. $\dfrac{x^3y^2 + 3x^2y^3 + 2xy^4}{x^4y + x^3y^2 - 2x^2y^3}$

2. Evaluate problem 1a if $x = 2$.

3. Evaluate problem 1b if $x = 3$ and $y = -2$.

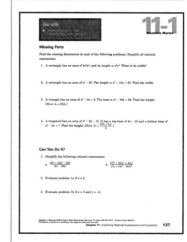

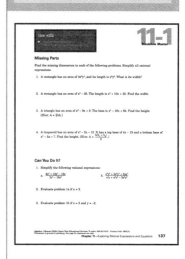

11-2 *Objective:* Multiply and divide rational expressions.

Sample Test: Perform the operation and simplify each of the following rational expressions. Indicate any excluded values of the variables.

1. $\dfrac{3x}{2x + 4} \cdot \dfrac{x + 2}{4x} =$

   Solution: $\frac{3}{8}$, x ≠ −2, 0

2. $\dfrac{3x}{2x + 4} \div \dfrac{6x}{x + 2} =$

   Solution: $\frac{1}{4}$, x ≠ −2

Concept Development Activities

Common Factors

Directions:

1. Tell the students that when we multiply $\frac{1}{2}$ by $\frac{1}{4}$, we are determining what $\frac{1}{4}$ of $\frac{1}{2}$ is. Draw a rectangle on the board and divide it in half. Then shade one half of it: ▭. Tell the students that because we want $\frac{1}{4}$ of this shaded region, we should divide the shaded region into four parts and cross-shade one of the four regions: ▭. Now divide the other half into four equal parts to show that $\frac{1}{4}$ of $\frac{1}{2}$ is $\frac{1}{8}$ of the whole rectangle: ▭. Thus, $\frac{1}{4} \times \frac{1}{2} = \frac{1}{8}$. Remind the students that $\frac{1}{4} \times \frac{1}{2} = \frac{1 \times 1}{4 \times 2} = \frac{1}{8}$.

2. Ask the students, "What does $\frac{3}{5} \times \frac{1}{3}$ equal?" Discuss the answer by using a similar rectangle model to show that $\frac{1}{5}$ is the result: ▭. Next, multiply the numerators and denominators: $\frac{3 \times 1}{5 \times 3} = \frac{3}{15}$, and reduce to obtain $\frac{1}{5}$. Ask the students if they remember a shortcut. They will probably "strike out" like factors: $\frac{\overset{1}{\cancel{3}}}{5} \times \frac{1}{\underset{1}{\cancel{3}}} = \frac{1}{5}$, which comes from the fact that $\frac{3}{5} \times \frac{1}{3} = \frac{3 \times 1}{5 \times 3} = \frac{3}{3} \times \frac{1}{5} = \frac{1}{5}$.

3. Write $\frac{4}{5} \times \frac{1}{2}$ on the board. Have the students make the rectangle model for the problem and verify it by multiplying numerators and denominators.

4. Write $\frac{14}{21} \times \frac{6}{35}$ on the board. Ask the students to find the result. Show them the factorization $\frac{2 \cdot 7}{3 \cdot 7} \cdot \frac{2 \cdot 3}{5 \cdot 7}$. Then strike out the common factors, and remind the students that a number divided by itself is 1: $\frac{2 \cdot 7}{3 \cdot 7} \times \frac{2 \cdot 3}{5 \cdot 7} = \frac{2 \cdot 2}{7 \cdot 5} = \frac{4}{35}$.

5. Write $\frac{3x^2}{y} \cdot \frac{4y^2}{2x^3}$ on the board. Ask the students if they can find any common factors in the numerators and denominators. Find the result with the students. Remind them that x and y cannot equal 0, or you cannot substitute 0 for x or y.

6. Write $\frac{x^2 - 1}{x^3} \cdot \frac{x}{x + 1}$ on the board. Ask the students if they can find any common factors in the numerators and denominators. Students often "strike out," or cancel out, terms without factoring, but remind them that only *factors* can be canceled out. Have the students factor $x^2 - 1$ so the problem now is $\frac{(x - 1)(x + 1)}{x^3} \cdot \frac{x}{(x + 1)}$. Now $\frac{x + 1}{x + 1}$ can be canceled out, as well as $\frac{x}{x}$. The result is $\frac{(x - 1)}{x^2}$. Remind the students that $x \neq 0$ and $x \neq -1$ for this problem.

7. Write $\frac{x^2 + 2x + 1}{x^2 - 1} \cdot \frac{x - 1}{x^2 - 3x - 4}$ on the board. Ask the students to find the simplified result. Ask them to check with their neighbors to verify their answers. Ask the students what factors they used, or what factors could be canceled out (remind them that $x \neq -1$, 1, or 4).

$$\frac{\cancel{(x + 1)}^2}{\cancel{(x - 1)}\cancel{(x + 1)}} \cdot \frac{\cancel{(x - 1)}}{\cancel{(x + 1)}(x - 4)} = \frac{1}{x - 4}$$

8. Ask the students to evaluate the original problem in step 7 by using $x = 2$. They should obtain $-\frac{1}{2}$. Ask them to evaluate the algebraic result they found by using $x = 2$. They can discuss that the results are the same.

9. Ask the students to evaluate the algebraic result in step 7, $\frac{1}{x - 4}$, by using $x = -1$. Ask them to evaluate the original problem by using $x = -1$. Discuss that the results differ because of the restrictions on x.

10. Write $\frac{3x^2y}{2ab} \cdot \frac{4ab^2}{3xy^2}$ and $(3x + 3) \cdot \frac{(x + 1)}{x^2 + 2x + 1}$ on the board. Ask the students to find the simplified results. $\left(\frac{2bx}{y} \text{ and } 3\right)$ Remind them that $3x + 3 = \frac{3x + 3}{1}$.

11. Write $\frac{2x + 4}{x^2 - 25} \cdot \frac{x - 5}{3x + 6}$ on the board. Have the students find the simplified result. $\left(\frac{2}{3(x + 5)}, \text{ or } \frac{2}{3x + 15}\right)$ Explain that most of the time results are written in factored form to make calculations easier.

12. Write $\frac{x + 2}{3x} \cdot \frac{12x^3}{x^2 + x - 2}$ on the board. Ask the students to find the result. $\left(\frac{4x^2}{x - 1}\right)$ Accept $\frac{4x}{x(x - 1)}$ as a correct result. Ask the students

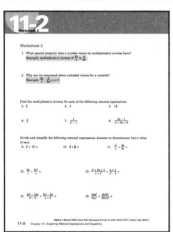

whether there are any excluded values for x. They should list the values x ≠ 0, –2, and 1, not just x ≠ 0 and 1.

Dividing Rational Expressions

Directions:

1. Ask the students, "How many 7's are there in 14?" They will quickly answer, "Two." Then ask whether $7\overline{)14}$ is the same problem written differently. Ask whether $14 \div 7$ is also the same problem.

2. Ask the students how many $\frac{1}{4}$'s are in $\frac{1}{2}$. The students may have a more difficult time coming up with the result. Help them by drawing a rectangle and dividing it in half: ☐☐. Then shade one half: ☐▨. Draw a rectangle of the same dimensions below the divided one and divide it into fourths: ☐☐▨▨. Ask the students how many of the fourths will fit into the half. They will quickly see there are two.

3. Write $\frac{1}{2} \div \frac{1}{4}$ on the board. Ask the students, "Is this the same problem we just solved [in step 2]?" Tell them you need to develop a method to find the result. Some students may offer the "invert and multiply" rule: $\frac{1}{2} \div \frac{1}{4} = \frac{1}{2} \cdot \frac{4}{1} = 2$. The results are the same.

   Ask the students why this works. They might remember that a number times its "multiplicative inverse" is 1. Ask the students, "What is the inverse of $\frac{1}{4}$?" Lead them toward the answer of 4. Tell them if you multiply $\frac{1}{4}$ by 4, or perform the multiplication $\frac{1}{4} \cdot \frac{4}{1}$, the result is 1. But if you multiply the denominator $\frac{1}{4}$ by 4, you must also multiply the numerator $\frac{1}{2}$ by 4, so you have $\left(\frac{1}{2} \cdot \frac{4}{1}\right) \div \left(\frac{1}{4} \cdot \frac{4}{1}\right)$, or $\left(\frac{1}{2} \cdot \frac{4}{1}\right) \div 1$, but any number divided by 1 is itself, so $\left(\frac{1}{2} \cdot \frac{4}{1}\right) \div 1 = \frac{1}{2} \cdot \frac{4}{1} = 2$. Other examples, such as $\frac{2}{3} \div \frac{4}{5}$ can be used.

4. Ask the students, "What is the multiplicative inverse of $\frac{2}{5}$?" $\left(\frac{5}{2}\right)$ Then ask them for the multiplicative inverses for $\frac{2}{x}$, $\frac{x+1}{x-2}$, 3, and $x + 2$. $\left(\frac{x}{2}, \frac{x-2}{x+1}, \frac{1}{3}, \frac{1}{x+2}\right)$

5. Write $\frac{2}{5} \div 2$ on the board. Ask the students to find the result. $\left(\frac{3}{5} \cdot \frac{2}{1} = \frac{4}{5}\right)$ Discuss with the students the process they used.

6. Now write $\frac{2x}{5y} \div 2y$ on the board. Ask the students what they

think the result is. Discuss how they did the problem to obtain the result of $\frac{x}{5y^2}$. You may want to discuss the restriction that $y \neq 0$.

7. Ask the students what they think $\frac{x+1}{2x} \div \frac{x^2-1}{2}$ is. If necessary, show all of the steps, such as multiplying the numerator and denominator by the multiplicative inverse $\frac{2}{x^2-1}$. Have the students evaluate the original problem as well as the simplified result when $x = 2$ and compare the values.

8. Write the following problems on the board and ask the students to find the simplified results:

   a. $\frac{2x}{3y} \div \frac{6x^2}{y}$ b. $\frac{x^2-1}{x+1} \div \frac{x-1}{x+2}$ c. $\frac{x^2-2x+1}{2x+4} \div \frac{x^2-1}{x+2}$

   Discuss the process to obtain the results.

Practice Activities

Multiplying Rational Expressions

Directions:

1. Divide the class into groups of two. Copy the expressions from the blackline master cards for **Snake to the End** onto card stock. Card set 1 has the problems and card set 2 has the answers in the corresponding squares. Be sure each problem card has its corresponding answer copied on the back.

2. Distribute one copy of the blackline master gameboard **Snake to the End**, one set of cards, one set of markers, and one blank die to each pair of students. Ask one student in each pair to write two 1's, two 2's, and two 3's on the faces of the die, one number per face. Have the other student cut the card stock into 16 cards.

3. Ask the students to shuffle the cards and place them problem-side up on the gameboard.

4. To determine who goes first in each group, have the students roll the die until one of them gets a higher number than the other. That student then has the first "turn."

5. Each student must pick the top problem card and solve the problem, working on his or her own paper. After the student is finished, the partners should check on the back of the card for the

Answer Key for #8:

a. $\frac{1}{9x}$ b. $x+2$ c. $\frac{x-1}{2(x+1)}$

Materials:

▶ Blackline master **Snake to the End** is located in the *Teacher's Resource Manual*, **pages 138–140** or ⊙.

▶ Blank die

▶ Game markers (chips, beans)

▶ Scissors

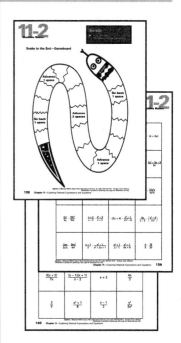

correct answer. If the student is correct, he or she should roll the die to see how many snake "scales" he or she can advance. (If the student lands on a "go back" square, he or she must follow that instruction.) If the student is incorrect, he or she should remain on the square and fail to advance. The object of the game is to get to the head of the snake first.

6. Each student keeps the cards he or she has worked, problem-side up, in front of him or her. If the players run out of cards, they can exchange the worked cards and continue until someone gets to the head of the snake.

7. A prize, such as food or bonus points, can be awarded to the winner. If time permits, the students can change groups and play again.

Division Rummy

Directions:

1. Have the students form groups of four. Give a copy of the blackline master **Division Rummy** printed on card stock to each group (there will be three pages of cards, totaling 45 cards).

2. Instruct the students to carefully cut the cards apart on the lines.

3. One student in each group should then shuffle the cards and deal six cards face down to each student in the group.

4. The students should use the usual rummy rules, making "books" of three equivalent cards. The winner will be the first person in the group to lay down all of his or her cards.

5. Prizes, such as food or bonus points, can be awarded to the winner.

6. **Variation:** Give a deck of cards to each student and have the students, working individually, find the groups of three that match.

Materials:

► Blackline master **Division Rummy** is located in the *Teacher's Resource Manual,* **pages 141–143** or ⊙.

► Scissors

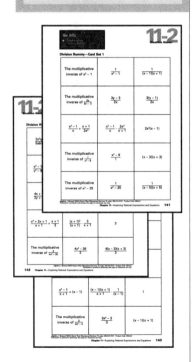

Problem-Solving Activity

You've Got the Answer 💡

Directions:

Ask the students to solve the following problems:

1. Find two different pairs of rational expressions whose product is $\dfrac{x+4}{x+2}$.

2. Find two different pairs of rational expressions whose product is $\dfrac{x^2 + 2x - 8}{2x^2 - 2}$.

3. Find two different pairs of rational expressions whose quotient is $\dfrac{x-1}{x+2}$.

4. Find two different pairs of rational expressions whose quotient is $\dfrac{x^2 + 2x - 3}{2x^2 + 7x + 6}$.

Answer Key:
Sample solutions include:

1. $\dfrac{x+4}{x} \cdot \dfrac{x}{x+2}$ and

   $\dfrac{x^2 - 16}{x - 4} \cdot \dfrac{x - 2}{x^2 - 4}$

2. $\dfrac{x+4}{2(x-1)} \cdot \dfrac{x-2}{x+1}$ and

   $\dfrac{x-2}{2(x-1)} \cdot \dfrac{x+4}{x+1}$

3. $\dfrac{x^2 - 1}{x^2 - 4} \div \dfrac{x+1}{x-2}$ and

   $\dfrac{x^2 + x - 6}{x - 2} \div \dfrac{x^2 + 5x + 6}{x - 1}$

4. $\dfrac{x+3}{2x+3} \div \dfrac{x+2}{x-1}$ and

   $\dfrac{x^2 + 6x + 9}{2x^2 + 5x + 3} \div$

   $\dfrac{x^2 + 5x + 6}{x^2 - 1}$

11-3 *Objective:* Divide a polynomial by a binomial.

Sample Test: Find each quotient:

1. $x + 3 \overline{)x^2 + 7x + 12}$

   Solution: $x + 4$

2. $x + 3 \overline{)x^2 + 7x + 15}$

   Solution: $x + 4 + \dfrac{3}{x + 3}$

Materials:

▶ Algebra tiles

▶ Product mat

Concept Development Activities

Using Algebra Tiles

Directions:

1. Ask the students what $12 \div 4$ is. **(3)** Then ask, "How can we check this answer?" Usually, the students will say we take 4×3 and see that the result is 12. In other words, $12 \div 4 = 3$ because $4 \times 3 = 12$.

2. Discuss with the students that a division problem can be made into a multiplication problem by using the multiplicative inverse. Thus, $12 \div 4 = 12 \cdot \frac{1}{4} = 3$.

3. Remind the students that
   $(x^2 + 3x + 2) \div (x + 1) = \dfrac{x^2 + 3x + 2}{1} \cdot \dfrac{1}{x + 1} = \dfrac{(x + 1)(x + 2)}{x + 1} = x + 2.$

4. Distribute a set of algebra tiles to each student.

5. Write $12 \div 4$ on the board.

6. Have the students set up the product mat with 4 on the left side and 12 units inside, as shown to the right. Show the students that because it takes 3 columns to fit the 12 units, they should write a 3 on the top of the mat. This placement looks similar to $4 \overline{)12}^{\,3}$.

7. Now write $(x^2 + 3x + 2) \div (x + 1)$ on the board. Demonstrate how to set up the product mat by using algebra tiles as shown on the right, by placing one x^2, three x's, and two 1's inside the mat.

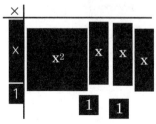

8. Now rearrange the tiles inside to form a rectangle. Start by putting the x^2 tile in the upper left corner and one of the 1's in the lower right-hand corner, as shown. Leave the remaining three x tiles and the "1" tile in random positions temporarily.

9. Ask the students to suggest placements for the three x's and the 1 to complete a rectangle under the product mat. They should come up with the arrangement on the right.

10. Ask the students, based on the arrangement in step 9, what the quotient would be. They should see that it is x + 2.

11. Now write $(x^2 - x - 6) \div (x + 2)$ on the board. Ask the students to model $x^2 - x - 6$ on the product mat (one x^2, one –x, and six –1's). Because they are dividing by x + 2, they should start with the configuration on the right.

12. Remind the students that they need to form a rectangle inside the mat. Explain that to start, they should add two x's below the x^2 tile to fill in that space. If they add two x's, they must also add two –x's, so now they will have the configuration on the right.

13. Ask the students what they can do to finish the rectangle. They should come up with the configuration shown at the right. They should then determine that the quotient is x – 3.

14. Ask the students if the inside of the mat is still $x^2 - x - 6$.

15. Remind the students that they can check the division problem

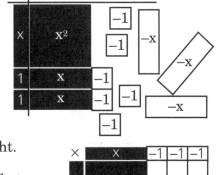

Teacher's Tip:

Worksheet 1 for this objective, **page 11-12**, supports this activity with practice exercises.

$(x^2 - x - 6) \div (x + 2)$ by multiplying by the multiplicative inverse: $\dfrac{x^2 - x - 6}{1} \cdot \dfrac{1}{x + 2} = \dfrac{(x + 2)(x - 3)}{1} \cdot \dfrac{1}{x + 2} = x - 3$. This will verify the algebra tile model results.

16. Show students the method for computing $x + 2\overline{\smash{)}x^2 - x - 6}$ and that the solution is still $x - 3$.

17. Now write $15 \div 7$ on the board. Have the students find the result. They will get 2 r1, as below. Ask if they remember that this can also be written as $2\frac{1}{7}$.

$$\begin{array}{r} 2 \text{ r1} \\ 7\overline{\smash{)}15} \\ \underline{-14} \\ 1 \end{array}$$

18. Write $(x^2 + 2x + 3) \div (x + 1)$ on the board. Have the students model $x^2 + 2x + 3$ inside the product mat, as shown on the right. The "1" is at the lower left corner of the x^2 tile because $x + 1$ is on the left of the mat.

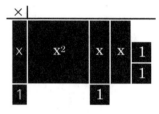

19. Show the students that the two x tiles can fit in as shown in the right, but two 1 tiles are left over. Ask the students, "Can we write the quotient as $x + 1 + \dfrac{2}{x + 1}$?" Discuss the result with the students.

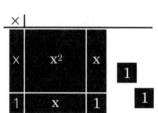

20. Show the students the method for computing $x + 1\overline{\smash{)}x^2 + 2x + 3}$ and that the solution is $x + 1 + \dfrac{2}{x + 1}$.

Dividing a Polynomial by a Binomial

Directions:

1. Write $12\overline{\smash{)}156}$ on the board. Ask the students to help find the solution. Write out each step, as on the right.

$$\begin{array}{r} 13 \\ 12\overline{\smash{)}156} \\ \underline{-12} \\ 36 \\ \underline{-36} \\ 0 \end{array}$$

2. Write out the problem as $12 = 10 + 2$ and $156 = 100 + 50 + 6$, so $12\overline{\smash{)}156} = (10 + 2)\overline{\smash{)}100 + 50 + 6}$. Now divide the 10 into the 100, and put the answer (10) in the quotient. Multiply that 10 by the

Chapter 11—Exploring Rational Expressions and Equations

10 + 2 (the divisor). Then subtract, showing the students that means adding the inverse. Then divide the 10 from the divisor into the 30 and multiply the result (3) by the divisor again. The problem on the board should look like the one below.

$$
\begin{array}{r}
10 + 3 \\
(10 + 2)\overline{)100 + 50 + 6} \\
\underline{-(100 + 20)} \\
30 + 6 \\
\underline{-(30 + 6)} \\
0
\end{array}
$$

Teacher's Tip:

Worksheet 2 for this objective, **page 11-13**, supports this activity with practice exercises.

3. Now write $11\overline{)132}$ on the board. Have the students find the quotient. Be sure to write in the subtraction signs, and go over each step in the algorithm. Then write the problem as a binomial divided into a trinomial. Find the quotient by showing each step as shown below. Be sure to include the subtraction signs (additive inverses).

$$
\begin{array}{r}
12 \\
11\overline{)132} \\
\underline{-11} \\
22 \\
\underline{-22} \\
0
\end{array}
\qquad
\begin{array}{r}
10 + 2 \\
(10 + 1)\overline{)100 + 30 + 2} \\
\underline{-(100 + 10)} \\
20 + 2 \\
\underline{-(20 + 2)} \\
0
\end{array}
$$

4. Ask the students about $(x^2 + 3x + 2) \div (x + 1)$. Ask whether they could also write the problem as $(x + 1)\overline{)x^2 + 3x + 2}$. In a manner similar to that in step 3, divide the x in the divisor into the x^2 in the dividend to get x, and place it over the x^2. Then multiply this x by $(x + 1)$, and subtract this result from the dividend. Divide the x in the divisor into this result and place the 2 in the quotient. Then multiply this 2 by $(x + 1)$ and subtract that result from the dividend, getting 0. The problem should look like the one below.

$$
\begin{array}{r}
x + 2 \\
(x + 1)\overline{)x^2 + 3x + 2} \\
\underline{-(x^2 + x)} \\
2x + 2 \\
\underline{-(2x + 2)} \\
0
\end{array}
$$

5. Have the students write $(x^2 + 3x + 2) \div (x + 1)$ and find the quotient by using rational expressions. $\left(\dfrac{x^2 + 3x + 2}{1} \div \dfrac{x + 1}{1} = \dfrac{x^2 + 3x + 2}{1} \cdot \dfrac{1}{x + 1} = \dfrac{(x + 2)(x + 1)}{1} \cdot \dfrac{1}{x + 1} = x + 2 \right)$

6. Ask the students to find the quotient of $(x^2 + 3x + 4) \div (x + 1)$ by factoring. They will discover that $x^2 + 3x + 4$ doesn't factor nicely. Point out that dividing 15 by 7, as in step 17 of the previous

activity, leaves a remainder. Similarly, doing the division for $(x + 1)\overline{)x^2 + 3x + 4}$ also leaves a remainder, and the quotient is $x + 2 + \dfrac{2}{x + 1}$.

7. Write $(x + 2)\overline{)x^2 + 7x + 10}$ on the board. Have the students perform the division by using the "new" algorithm.

8. Write $(x + 2)\overline{)x^2 + 7x + 9}$ on the board and ask the students to find the quotient.

9. Discuss with the students the process they used in step 8 and what to do with the remainder.

10. Write $(x + 1)\overline{)x^2 - 1}$ on the board. Show the students that to do the long division, you must substitute for all terms in descending order. Thus, $x^2 - 1 = x^2 + 0x - 1$, and $x - 1$ is the quotient, as shown on the right.

$$\begin{array}{r} x - 1 \\ x + 1\overline{)x^2 + 0x - 1} \\ \underline{-(x^2 + x)} \\ -x - 1 \\ \underline{-(-x - 1)} \\ 0 \end{array}$$

11. Write $(x + 1)\overline{)x^3 + 2x - 1}$ on the board. Show the students that to do the long division, you must substitute for all terms in descending order. Thus, $x^3 + 2x - 1 = x^3 + 0x^2 + 2x - 1$, and the quotient is $x^2 - x + 3 - \dfrac{4}{x + 1}$, as shown on the right.

$$\begin{array}{r} x^2 - x + 3 - \frac{4}{x+1} \\ x + 1\overline{)x^3 + 0x^2 + 2x - 1} \\ \underline{-(x^3 + x^2)} \\ -x^2 + 2x \\ \underline{-(-x^2 - x)} \\ 3x - 1 \\ \underline{-(3x + 3)} \\ -4 \end{array}$$

12. Write out all the steps with the students' help.

Practice Activities

Dividing a Polynomial by a Binomial Bingo

Directions:

1. Write one problem from the problem set (see next page) on each of the index cards (optional).

2. Hand each student a copy of the 4 × 4 bingo card.

Materials:

▶ Blackline master for a **4 × 4 bingo card** is in the Appendix.

▶ Game markers to cover squares

▶ Index cards (optional)

3. Write the following quotient set on the board:

$x + 1$ $x - 4$ $x + 2$ $x - 2$

$x - 1$ $x + 4 - \dfrac{1}{x - 1}$ $x - 3$ $x + 3$

$x + 5$ $x + 6$ $x + 3 + \dfrac{2}{x - 1}$ $x + 1 + \dfrac{3}{x - 2}$

$x + 1 - \dfrac{3}{x - 1}$ $x - 1 - \dfrac{3}{x + 1}$ $x + 1 + \dfrac{3}{x + 2}$ $x - 4 + \dfrac{5}{x + 5}$

4. Have the students write one expression from the quotient set in each of the spaces on their bingo card *randomly*. Each expression should be used only once. Then ask the students to exchange cards with another student.

5. Select a problem from the problem set by drawing an index card. Then write the problem on the board. Have the students solve the problem and place a marker over the answer on their bingo card. The first student to get four markers in a row says, "Bingo!" You should then check the student's answers. If they are correct, he or she wins the game. Prizes are at the discretion of the teacher.

6. If time permits, have the students exchange cards and play again.

PROBLEM SET (Do not write the answers **[quotients]** on the board.)

$$(x + 2)\overline{)x^2 + 3x + 2} \qquad (x + 3)\overline{)x^2 - x - 12} \qquad (x + 5)\overline{)x^2 + 7x + 10}$$

with quotients $x + 1$, $x - 4$, $x + 2$ respectively.

$$(x + 1)\overline{)x^2 - x - 2} \qquad (x + 4)\overline{)x^2 + 3x - 4} \qquad (x - 1)\overline{)x^2 + 3x - 5}$$

with quotients $x - 2$, $x - 1$, $x + 4 - \dfrac{1}{x - 1}$ respectively.

$$(x + 2)\overline{)x^2 - x - 6} \qquad (2x - 3)\overline{)2x^2 + 3x - 9} \qquad (x - 5)\overline{)x^2 - 25}$$

with quotients $x - 3$, $x + 3$, $x + 5$ respectively.

$$(x - 5)\overline{)x^2 + x - 30} \qquad (x - 1)\overline{)x^2 + 2x - 1} \qquad (x - 2)\overline{)x^2 - x + 1}$$

with quotients $x + 6$, $x + 3 + \dfrac{2}{x - 1}$, $x + 1 + \dfrac{3}{x - 2}$ respectively.

$$(x - 1)\overline{)x^2 - 4} \qquad (x + 1)\overline{)x^2 - 4} \qquad (x + 2)\overline{)x^2 + 3x + 5}$$

with quotients $x + 1 - \dfrac{3}{x - 1}$, $x - 1 - \dfrac{3}{x + 1}$, $x + 1 + \dfrac{3}{x + 2}$ respectively.

$$(x + 5)\overline{)x^2 + x - 15}$$

with quotient $x - 4 + \dfrac{5}{x + 5}$.

Materials:

▶ Blackline master **Card Match** is located in the *Teacher's Resource Manual,* **page 144** or 💿.

▶ Scissors

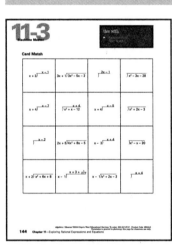

Answer Key:
1. $x^2 + 3x + 1$
2. $x - 2$
3. $2x - 4$

Card Match

Directions:

1. Have students form groups of two.

2. Give two pairs of scissors and one copy of the blackline master **Card Match** to each pair of students.

3. Instruct the students to carefully cut out the cards.

4. Have the students in each group shuffle the cards and deal them so each student has four cards. The remainder of the cards should be placed face down at the center of the table.

5. Have the students decide who goes first by some method such as the toss of a coin, the student who chooses a number closest to one you (the teacher) select, and so forth.

6. The object of the game is for the students to match division problems with their quotients. The first player draws a card from the deck. If he or she can form a "pair," the pair is put on the table and the student discards a card; if no pair can be formed, the student just discards a card. The play then goes to the other student. That student may draw a card from the deck or take the discard.

7. The first student to lay down all of his or her cards wins.

8. As an alternative activity, have the students individually match the cards.

Problem-Solving Activity

Geometry 💡

Directions:

Have the students find the missing dimension for each of the following problems:

1. A rectangle has an area of $x^3 + 4x^2 + 4x + 1$ and a width of $x + 1$. Find the length of the rectangle.

2. A rectangular shaped fish tank has a volume of $x^3 + 5x^2 - 2x - 24$. If the height is $x + 3$ and the length is $x + 4$, find the width.

3. The area of a triangle is $x^2 + 4x - 12$. If the base is $x + 6$, find the height.

11-4 *Objective:* **Add and subtract rational expressions.**

Sample Test: Find the sum or difference:

1. $\frac{3}{x} + \frac{5}{x}$

   Solution: $\frac{8}{x}$

2. $\frac{x}{x-2} - \frac{3}{x+3}$

   Solution: $\frac{x^2 + 6}{x^2 + x - 6}$

Concept Development Activities

Common Denominators and Least Common Denominators

Directions:

1. Write $\frac{1}{4}$ and $\frac{3}{4}$ on the board. Then write $\frac{1}{2}$ and $\frac{3}{4}$ on the board.

2. Remind the students that $\frac{1}{4}$ and $\frac{3}{4}$ are "like" fractions or rational expressions, whereas $\frac{1}{2}$ and $\frac{3}{4}$ are not. Ask the students whether there is a denominator that could make $\frac{1}{2}$ and $\frac{3}{4}$ like fractions. Show the students that $\frac{1}{2} \cdot \frac{2}{2} = \frac{2}{4}$, and that $\frac{2}{4}$ and $\frac{3}{4}$ are like fractions because they have the same denominator.

3. Now ask the students, "What can we do to make $\frac{1}{2}$ and $\frac{3}{8}$ into like fractions?" The students should notice that $\frac{1}{2} \cdot \frac{4}{4} = \frac{4}{8}$, and that $\frac{4}{8}$ and $\frac{3}{8}$ are like fractions.

4. Ask the students to name two unlike fractions. Use the fractions the students come up with to present an example along the following lines. Suppose they say $\frac{1}{5}$ and $\frac{2}{3}$. Demonstrate multiplying $\frac{1}{5}$ by $\frac{3}{3}$ and multiplying $\frac{2}{3}$ by $\frac{5}{5}$ to get the equivalent fractions $\frac{3}{15}$ and $\frac{10}{15}$, which are now like fractions. Some students might need to confirm that $\frac{10}{15}$ is the same as $\frac{2}{3}$. Draw a circle fraction diagram to help them see that they are equivalent.

5. Write a new number pair on the board, for example 3 and 8. Ask the students, "If these were denominators, what would be a like denominator?" Show them that it would be 24 (common multiple).

6. Now write 3 and 6 on the board and ask the same question. Some students will answer 6 and others will say 18. Accept both as

correct answers. Ask the students whether 12 or 24 or 36 or 72 would also work. Verify that they would.

7. Even if students have already mentioned 18 as a common denominator, point out that you can always find a common denominator by simply multiplying the denominators. In this example, $3 \cdot 6 = 18$, which makes 18 a common denominator. Discuss with the students that it becomes more difficult to simplify fractions when larger numbers are used. Note that 6 was the smallest common denominator we found.

8. List the denominators on the board and write their multiples in columns, such as:

3	6
$3 \cdot 1 = 3$	$6 \cdot 1 = 6$
$3 \cdot 2 = 6$	$6 \cdot 2 = 12$
$3 \cdot 3 = 9$	$6 \cdot 3 = 18$
$3 \cdot 4 = 12$	$6 \cdot 4 = 24$
$3 \cdot 5 = 15$	$6 \cdot 5 = 30$
$3 \cdot 6 = 18$	$6 \cdot 6 = 36$

Point out that in the multiples columns, 6, 12, and 18 are common. Circle these corresponding multiples. Show that 6 is the smallest common multiple, so it is called the least common multiple, and it would make the least common denominator, or LCD. Some students might want to extend the multiples columns to show that 24 and 36 are also common.

9. Now write the denominators 6 and 8 on the board and ask the students to find a common denominator. Encourage them to come up with several, such as 24, 48, and so forth. Ask them whether 96 would work. Ask them how they know whether it would work. Lead the students to discover that if both denominators divide evenly into a common number, that number would be a common denominator. Ask what number is the least common denominator for the denominators 6 and 8. Ask why it is 24. Show the students the prime factorization procedure: Since $6 = 2 \cdot 3$ and $8 = 2 \cdot 2 \cdot 2$, the 6 needs two more 2's and the 8 needs a 3 for them to have a common denominator. Thus, they each must be multiplied by their "missing" factors: $6 \cdot 2 \cdot 2 = 2 \cdot 3 \cdot 2 \cdot 2$ and $8 \cdot 3 = 2 \cdot 2 \cdot 2 \cdot 3$, which are the same, so the least common denominator is $3 \cdot 2 \cdot 2 \cdot 2 = 24$.

10. Write the following fraction pairs on the board:

$\frac{2}{5}, \frac{3}{10}$ $\qquad\qquad$ $\frac{1}{2}, \frac{1}{8}$ $\qquad\qquad$ $\frac{1}{4}, \frac{1}{3}$

Ask the students to find the least common denominator for each pair. **(10, 8, 12, respectively)**

11. Ask the students to add the pairs of fractions in step 10. $\left(\frac{7}{10}, \frac{5}{8}, \frac{7}{12}\right)$

12. Ask the students to subtract the pairs of fractions in step 10.
$\left(\frac{1}{10}, \frac{3}{8}, -\frac{1}{12}\right)$

13. Ask the students whether the prime factoring procedure for finding the LCD would be the same for more complicated denominators, such as 12 and 15. Show them the procedure: $12 = 2 \cdot 2 \cdot 3$ and $15 = 3 \cdot 5$. Next, multiply each number by the factors from the other number that it is missing. That is, multiply 12 by 5, and multiply 15 by $2 \cdot 2$:

$$12 \cdot 5 = 2 \cdot 2 \cdot 3 \cdot 5 = 60 \quad \text{and} \quad 15 \cdot 2 \cdot 2 = 3 \cdot 5 \cdot 2 \cdot 2 = 60$$

Thus, the LCD is 60.

14. Ask the students for three more pairs of numbers and write them on the board. Find the LCDs for these numbers with class participation.

15. Now ask the students, "What if you had $\frac{1}{x}$ and $\frac{1}{2x}$? Are they like fractions? What could you do to make them like fractions or rational expressions?" Suggest that they do a procedure similar to that in step 8 or 13: $x = 1 \cdot x$ and $2x = 2 \cdot x$, so you must multiply x by 2: $x \cdot 2 = 2x$, and $2x = 2x$, so the LCD is 2x.

16. Write $\frac{1}{x}$ and $\frac{1}{x+1}$ on the board. Ask the students what they think the LCD is and why. Show them that the factors of the denominators are $x = x$ and $(x + 1) = (x + 1)$, so the LCD is obtained by multiplying them together because they have no factors in common. The LCD thus is $x(x + 1)$.

17. Ask the students what the rational expressions $\frac{1}{x}$ and $\frac{1}{x+1}$ would be if they had an LCD of $x(x + 1)$. They should come up with $\frac{x+1}{x(x+1)}$ and $\frac{x}{x(x+1)}$.

18. Write $\frac{a}{3b}$ and $\frac{2}{b}$ on the board and ask the students to find the LCD. **(3b)** Discuss with the students how they got this answer.

Teacher's Tip:

Worksheet 1 for this objective, **page 11-16**, supports this activity with practice exercises.

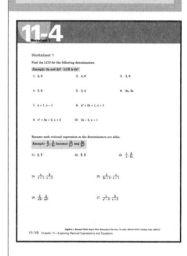

19. Write $\frac{1}{x+1}$ and $\frac{1}{x-1}$ on the board and ask the students to find the LCD. **[(x + 1)(x − 1)]** Discuss with the students how they got this answer.

Renaming Rational Expressions

Directions:

1. Tell the students that they already know how to add and subtract fractions or rational expressions. They simply have to rename the rational expressions so they have like denominators. Write $\frac{3}{8}$ and $\frac{1}{4}$ on the board. Explain that you must rename them to have the same LCD, 8. So they become $\frac{3}{8}$ and $\frac{2}{8}$.

2. Tell the students that, similarly, for the rational expressions $\frac{1}{x}$ and $\frac{3}{2x}$, you must rename them with like denominators. Ask the students what that denominator would be. Help them to see that 2x is the LCD and that the rational expressions become $\frac{2}{2x}$ and $\frac{3}{2x}$. So $\frac{1}{x} + \frac{3}{2x} = \frac{2}{2x} + \frac{3}{2x} = \frac{5}{2x}$.

3. Write the denominators $2ab^2$ and $3a^2b$ on the board. Ask the students what the factors of these expressions are. They should list the factors: $2ab^2 = 2 \cdot a \cdot b \cdot b$ and $3a^2b = 3 \cdot a \cdot a \cdot b$. Then a common denominator would need to include 2, 3, a, a, b, b, or $6a^2b^2$. Ask the students whether each of the original expressions divide evenly into $6a^2b^2$. Tell them that the renamed denominator must be evenly divisible by each of the original denominators.

4. Write the denominators 8 and 4 on the board. Ask the students to write multiples of 8 and 4:
   8 → 8, 16, 24, 32, 40, 48, 56, 64, 72
   4 → 4, 8, 12, 16, 20, 24, 28, 32, 36, 40
   Ask the students to name the common multiples: 8, 16, 24, .…
   Then ask them, "What is the least (smallest) common multiple?" **(8)** Ask, "Does 8 divide into 8 evenly? Does 4 divide into 8 evenly?" Tell them that 8 is the least common multiple, or LCM. However, because you are concerned with adding and subtracting rational expressions, the LCM of the denominators is called the least common denominator, or LCD.

5. Write the denominators x and 2x on the board. Ask the students to write multiples of each, as in step 4:

    $x \rightarrow$ x, 2x, 3x, 4x, 5x, 6x, 7x, 8x, 9x

    $2x \rightarrow$ 2x, 4x, 6x, 8x, 10x, 12x, 14x, 16x

    Ask the students to name the common multiples: 2x, 4x, 6x, 8x, ...
    Ask the students, "If x and 2x were denominators of two rational expressions, what would be the LCD?" **(2x)**

6. Now write denominators $2x^2$ and 3x and their factors on the board: $2x^2 = 2 \cdot x \cdot x$ and $3x = 3 \cdot x$. Ask, "How can we find a common denominator? Is 2 common? Is 3 common? Is x common? Is x^2 common?" The students should see that x is the only common factor, so you must multiply $2x^2$ by 3, or you must multiply 3x by $2 \cdot x$. Therefore $2x^2 \cdot 3 = 3x \cdot 2 \cdot x = 6x^2$ is the common denominator.

7. Write the denominators x – 1 and x + 1 on the board and repeat the same procedure: $x - 1 = 1 \cdot (x - 1)$ and $x + 1 = 1 \cdot (x + 1)$. Ask the students, "How can we rename a common denominator?" Since neither denominator has a common factor, we must multiply the denominators by each other to find a common denominator: (x – 1)(x + 1). Point out to the students that each of the original denominators factors evenly into the renamed denominator.

8. Do the same for the denominators 2x + 4 and 2x – 4. Show that $2x + 4 = 2 \cdot (x + 2)$ and $2x - 4 = 2 \cdot (x - 2)$. Then the common denominator must be $2 \cdot (x + 2) \cdot (x - 2)$, or $2x^2 - 8$.

9. Ask the students to find a common denominator for $x^2 + 2x + 1$ and $x^2 - 1$. Discuss with the students why $(x + 1)^2(x - 1)$ is the common denominator.

10. Write the following pairs of denominators on the board:

    x – 2 and 2x   x – 2 and 2 – x $x^2 + x - 2$ and x – 1

    Ask the students to find the common denominators. Discuss with the students why 2x(x – 2), –(x – 2), and (x + 2)(x – 1), respectively, are the common denominators.

11. Discuss with the students that rational expressions have not only denominators but also numerators. Ask the students about the $\frac{3}{8}$ and $\frac{1}{4}$ from step 1. When you renamed the $\frac{1}{4}$, you renamed both the numerator and the denominator. In other words, when the

Teacher's Tip:

Worksheet 2 for this objective, **page 11-17**, supports this activity with practice exercises.

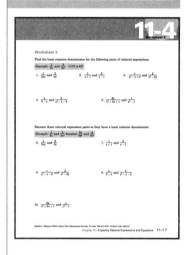

denominator was multiplied by 2 to get the common denominator of 8, the numerator also had to be multiplied by 2.

12. Write $\frac{x}{2ab^2}$ and $\frac{y}{3a^2b}$ on the board. Ask the students what the renamed rational expressions would be for them to have a common denominator. $\left(\dfrac{3ax}{6a^2b^2}\text{ and }\dfrac{2by}{6a^2b^2}\right)$

13. Write $\frac{y}{2x+4}$ and $\frac{z}{2x-4}$ on the board. Ask the students what the renamed rational expressions would be for them to have a common denominator. $\left(\dfrac{y(2x-4)}{(2x+4)(2x-4)}\text{ and }\dfrac{z(2x+4)}{(2x+4)(2x-4)}\right)$

14. Write $\frac{3}{x^2+2x+1}$ and $\frac{2}{(x-1)}$ on the board. Ask the students what the renamed rational expressions would be for them to have a common denominator. Discuss with the students that the new factors used with the denominator (to arrive at a common denominator) must also be multiplied in the numerator. $\left(\dfrac{3(x-1)}{(x+1)^2(x-1)}\text{ and }\dfrac{2(x+1)^2}{(x+1)^2(x-1)}\right)$

Adding and Subtracting Rational Expressions

Directions:

1. Tell the students that they already know how to add and subtract fractions or rational expressions. They simply have to rename the rational expressions so they have like denominators. Write $\frac{3}{8}$ and $\frac{1}{4}$ on the board. Explain that you must rename them to have the same LCD, 8. So they become $\frac{3}{8}$ and $\frac{2}{8}$.

2. Write $\frac{3}{8}$ and $\frac{2}{8}$ on the board and ask the students to add them: $\frac{3}{8}+\frac{2}{8}=\frac{5}{8}$. Then ask the students to subtract them: $\frac{3}{8}-\frac{2}{8}=\frac{1}{8}$. Discuss with the students that these are like expressions because they have the same denominators, so you can simply add or subtract the numerators and retain the denominators.

3. Write $\frac{3}{5}$ and $\frac{10}{15}$ on the board. Ask the students to add these rational expressions. Have the students discuss what they did to obtain the results. $\left(\frac{3}{5}+\frac{10}{15}=\frac{9}{15}+\frac{10}{15}=\frac{19}{15}\right)$

4. Discuss with the students that $\frac{19}{15}$ can also be written as $1\frac{4}{15}$. You decide which form is best depending on what you want to do with the result.

5. Write $\frac{2x}{x+1}$ and $\frac{3}{x-1}$ on the board. Ask the students to find the renamed rational expressions so they have an LCD. Discuss why

$\dfrac{2x(x-1)}{(x+1)(x-1)}$ and $\dfrac{3(x+1)}{(x+1)(x-1)}$ make up the desired pair.

6. Instruct the students to find the sum $\dfrac{2x}{x+1} + \dfrac{3}{x-1}$. Discuss the following steps: $\dfrac{2x}{x+1} + \dfrac{3}{x-1} = \dfrac{2x(x-1)}{(x+1)(x-1)} + \dfrac{3(x+1)}{(x+1)(x-1)} =$

$\dfrac{2x^2 - 2x + 3x + 3}{(x+1)(x-1)} = \dfrac{2x^2 + x + 3}{(x+1)(x-1)}$. Ask the students, "Can we simplify the result?" The answer is no, but remind them they should check anyway because simplified results are preferred.

7. Ask the students to find $\dfrac{2x}{x+1} - \dfrac{3}{x-1}$. Have them show the steps involved: $\dfrac{2x}{x+1} - \dfrac{3}{x-1} = \dfrac{2x(x-1)}{(x+1)(x-1)} - \dfrac{3(x+1)}{(x+1)(x-1)} =$

$\dfrac{2x^2 - 2x - 3(x+1)}{(x+1)(x-1)} = \dfrac{2x^2 - 2x - 3x - 3}{(x+1)(x-1)} = \dfrac{2x^2 - 5x - 3}{(x+1)(x-1)}$. Ask the students whether the result can be simplified.

Practice Activities

Rational Expressions to Win

Directions:

1. Have the students form pairs. Copy the expressions from the blackline master cards for **Rational Expressions to Win** onto card stock. The first page, **Cards**, has the problems, and the second page, **Card Answers**, has the solutions in the corresponding boxes. Be sure each problem card has its corresponding answer printed on the back.

2. Give one copy of the blackline masters **Rational Expressions to Win—Gameboard**, one set of cards, two game markers, and a pair of scissors to each pair of students.

3. Direct the students to carefully cut out the cards on the straight lines. Point out that the face of each card has a 1, 2, or 3 in the lower right-hand corner. Have the students shuffle the cards and place them face-side up on the gameboard. Have them place their markers on the start square of the gameboard.

4. Have each pair decide which student will go first. That player should draw a card from the top of the deck and solve the problem on his or her paper. If the student is correct, he or she advances the marker the number of squares indicated by the

Materials:

▶ Blackline master **Rational Expressions to Win** is located in the *Teacher's Resource Manual,* **pages 145–147** or ⊙.

▶ Game markers (chips, beans)

▶ Scissors

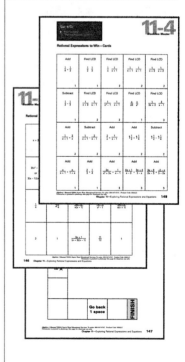

number at the lower right-hand corner of the card. The answer can be validated by looking at the back of the card. If the student is incorrect, the marker doesn't advance.

5. The students should keep the cards they draw in front of them. If they use up the deck, the students draw from the other student's pile to get a card.

6. The first student to arrive at or beyond the finish square is the winner. A prize may be awarded to the winner.

7. Have the students repeat the game as time permits with new student pairs.

My Favorite

Directions:

1. Give each student a copy of the blackline master **My Favorite— Gameboard** and **My Favorite—Markers**. Have the students carefully cut out the markers on the lines.

2. Each student should work the problems on his or her paper and find the solution to each problem on his or her gameboard. Each student should then place the marker with the corresponding answer over each problem.

3. When the students have placed all of the markers on the gameboard, they will see that "My Favorite" is "LUNCHTIME."

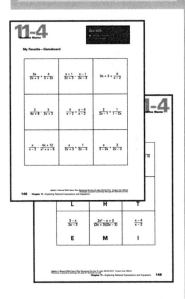

Problem-Solving Activity

Finding Rational Expressions 💡

Directions:

Give each student a copy of the blackline master **Finding Rational Expressions**. Have the students work individually to solve the problems, which are reprinted below.

1. What is the second rational expression if two rational expressions added together yield $\dfrac{3x^2 - 2x + 8}{(x + 2)(x - 2)}$ and the first rational expression is $\dfrac{3x}{x + 2}$?

2. Find at least two pairs of rational expressions whose sum is $\dfrac{3x^2 - 10x + 3}{x^2 - 1}$.

3. A rancher wants to fence a pasture into three lots. She wants to determine the lot sizes depending on the total amount of fencing used. The dimensions are shown below.

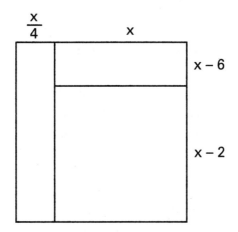

Write a formula to determine the total amount of fence (F). What are the dimensions if the rancher has 546 feet of fence? What are the dimensions if she has 926 feet of fence?

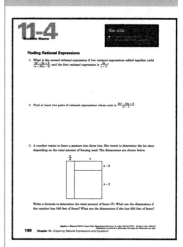

11-5 *Objective:* Solve rational equations.

Sample Test: Solve for x:

1. $\frac{1}{3} + \frac{1}{x} = \frac{4}{x}$

    Solution: x = 9

2. $\frac{2x}{x+2} + \frac{5}{x-2} = 2$

    Solution: x = –18

Concept Development Activities

Solving Rational Equations

Directions:

1. Rational equations are equations that contain rational expressions. Write $\frac{1}{x} + \frac{1}{2} = \frac{3}{4}$ on the board. Ask the students if they know a number that could be added to $\frac{1}{2}$ to get $\frac{3}{4}$. They will usually come up with $\frac{1}{4}$.

2. Ask the students, "If we looked at all of the denominators, x, 2, and 4, what would the least common denominator be?" They should say 4x. Ask the students to rename all of the rational expressions using 4x as the denominator. Write $\frac{4}{4x} + \frac{2x}{4x} = \frac{3x}{4x}$ on the board. Show the students how you multiplied the numerator and denominator in each expression by the same number.

3. Ask the students to add the expressions on the left side of the equation. Write $\frac{4 + 2x}{4x} = \frac{3x}{4x}$ on the board. Ask whether the denominators are the same. Ask, "If these are equal expressions, what can we say about the numerators?" The students should see that they also must be equal. Write $4 + 2x = 3x$ on the board and solve the equation. $x = 4$, so in step 1, $\frac{1}{x} = \frac{1}{4}$.

4. Ask the students, "What would happen if we just multiplied the equation by the least common denominator?" Remind them that *each* expression must be multiplied, so

$$\frac{1}{x} + \frac{1}{2} = \frac{3}{4} \rightarrow 4x\left(\frac{1}{x}\right) + 4x\left(\frac{1}{2}\right) + 4x\left(\frac{3}{4}\right) \rightarrow 4 + 2x = 3x$$

5. Write $\frac{2}{x} + \frac{1}{3} = 6$ on the board. Ask for suggestions for how to find x. If the students suggest multiplying by the least common

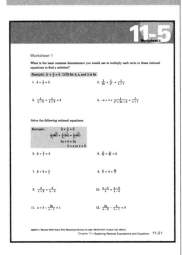

denominator, then write $\frac{2}{x}(3x) + \frac{1}{3}(3x) = 6(3x) \rightarrow 6 + x = 18x$, or $6 = 17x$, or $x = \frac{6}{17}$ on the board. Ask them whether they think they could have guessed that one!

6. Ask the students if they think this method would work for any rational equation. Ask the students to solve $\frac{4}{x-1} - \frac{1}{x} = \frac{2}{x}$. **(x = –3)**

7. Tell the students that you are going to give them a more difficult problem. Write $\frac{3}{2x} - \frac{1}{3x} = \frac{7}{2x}$ on the board. Ask the students to find the solution. **(No solution, since x ≠ 0)**

8. Now write $x + \frac{1}{x} = -2$ on the board. Ask the students what the least common denominator is. Ask, "Should we still multiply each expression by the least common denominator?" **(Yes)** Write:

$$x(x) + \frac{1}{x}(x) = -2(x) \rightarrow x^2 + 1 = -2x, \text{ or } x^2 + 2x + 1 = 0 \rightarrow$$
$$(x + 1)(x + 1) = 0 \rightarrow x + 1 = 0, \text{ so } x = -1.$$

9. Now write $\frac{2}{x+1} + \frac{1}{x-1} = 1$ on the board. Ask the students to solve the rational equation. They will get $3x - 1 = x^2 - 1 \rightarrow x^2 - 3x = x(x - 3) = 0$. Remind them that if $a \cdot b = 0$, then $a = 0$ or $b = 0$, so $x(x - 3) = 0 \rightarrow x = 0$ or $(x - 3) = 0$; $x = 0, +3$. Check the results to show the students that this works.

10. Ask the students to solve $\frac{1}{x-1} = \frac{4}{x+2}$. Use the least common denominator. Then write $\frac{1}{x} = \frac{2}{3}$ on the board. See whether the students recognize that they can use the "cross product." If not, try some more examples, such as $\frac{1}{4} = \frac{2}{x}$ and $\frac{1}{4x} = \frac{3}{5}$. If they still fail to see that they can use cross products, point this out to them.

Rational Equations and Their Solutions

Directions:

1. Ask the students, "What is a rational number?" Write a few rational numbers on the board. Ask the students, "What do you think a rational equation would be?" Write a few of their suggestions on the board.

2. Write $\frac{1}{4} + \frac{1}{8}$ on the board. Ask the students, "If we were to sum these rational numbers, how would we start?" Discuss the least common denominator with the students. Some students may

want to write the addition problem vertically and find the LCD vertically:

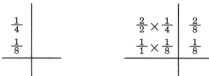

Ask the students for a couple of other rational numbers to sum. Review the steps required to find the sums.

3. Ask the students, "What if I wrote the problem $\frac{1}{4} + \frac{1}{8}$ this way: $\frac{1}{4} + \frac{1}{8} = x$? Is it still the same problem?" Explain that you solve this problem by finding the LCD "8" and multiplying each term by it: $8\left(\frac{1}{4}\right) + 8\left(\frac{1}{8}\right) = 8(x)$. Then, you solve for x: $2 + 1 = 8x \rightarrow 3 = 8x \rightarrow x = \frac{3}{8}$.

4. Ask the students, "Is $\frac{1}{4} + \frac{1}{8} = \frac{3}{8}$ true?" Then ask, "What if we wrote $\frac{1}{4} + \frac{1}{x} = \frac{3}{8}$? What should x be?" The students should say x = 8. Ask them how you might find x algebraically. Ask them for the least common denominator. Ask, "If we multiply all of the terms by 8x, will that give us x = 8?" Have the students verify that, indeed, x = 8.

5. Ask the students, "What if we write $\frac{1}{x} + \frac{1}{8} = \frac{3}{8}$? Could you find x? How?" Validate that the least common denominator is 8x, and x = 4.

6. Ask the students, "What if $\frac{1}{x} + \frac{1}{2x} = \frac{3}{8}$? Can we find x?" They should be able to find x = 4.

7. Write $\frac{2}{x-1} + \frac{x}{x-1} = 4$ on the board. Ask the students to find the least common denominator. **(x − 1)** Multiply the terms of the equation by (x − 1): $(x-1)\left(\frac{2}{x-1}\right) + (x-1)\left(\frac{x}{x-1}\right) = 4(x-1)$. Solve for x. **(x = 2)** Now have the students "check" the result: $\frac{2}{2-1} + \frac{2}{2-1} = 4 \rightarrow 2 + 2 = 4$, and 4 = 4.

8. Ask the students if they have an algorithm to solve rational equations. They should develop one that involves finding the least common denominator and distributing it through the equation.

9. Write $\frac{x}{x+2} - \frac{2}{x-1} = 1$ on the board. Ask the students, "What is the least common denominator?" Find the solution with the class. $\left(x = -\frac{1}{2}\right)$ Discuss with the class how you would check the result.

10. Write $\frac{x}{3} = \frac{2}{x+1}$ on the board and have the students find the solution. Discuss with the students that if a · b = 0, then a = 0 or

b = 0. Show them that both x = 2 and x = –3 work for this problem. More advanced students may see that the cross product is a new algorithm. Usually just finding the LCD and multiplying by it is sufficient for the majority of the class. If any of the students see the cross product algorithm, have them explain it to the class.

Practice Activities

Trade a Problem 💡

Directions:

1. Ask the students to give you two fractions to add. For example, $\frac{1}{4} + \frac{3}{8} = \frac{5}{8}$. Pick one number and replace it with x. For example, x = 1. Pick another number that you can write in terms of x. For example, if you pick 3, you can write it as 3 = 1 + 2 = x + 2 (since x = 1). Now rewrite the problem, using x: $\frac{x}{4} + \frac{x+2}{8} = \frac{5}{8}$. Ask the students to solve the problem for x.

2. Ask the students whether they could let x = 4 in the original problem and rewrite the problem. Discuss with the students the new problem and its solution. $\left(\frac{1}{x} + \frac{3}{2x} = \frac{5}{8}\right)$

3. Have the students let (x – 1) = 1 and write another equation. *Example:* $\frac{x-1}{4} + \frac{3}{8} = \frac{5(x-1)}{8}$. Solve this equation with the class.

$$8\left(\frac{x-1}{4} + \frac{3}{8}\right) = 8\left(\frac{5(x-1)}{8}\right)$$
$$(2x - 2) + 3 = 5x - 5$$
$$1 = 3x - 5$$
$$3x = 6$$
$$x = 2$$

Have the students check to see if x – 1 = 1.

4. Divide the class into groups of two. Have the students take out two sheets of paper. On one paper, they should design a problem as done in steps 1 and 2. On the second piece of paper, they should write only the resulting rational equation. Ask them to create three different rational equation problems in this manner, and to write the resulting equations on the second paper so that there is room below each equation for someone to solve it.

5. Have the students trade problems and find the solutions.

6. When the students finish finding the solutions, they can check their work. If time permits, have them create a more difficult problem to exchange with their partners.

Materials:

► Blank cards or

Problem-Solution Match

Directions:

1. Write the following equations on the board:

   $\frac{4}{x} + \frac{1}{4} = \frac{4}{x}$ $\frac{2}{x} = \frac{3}{x+2}$ $\frac{1}{2} = \frac{x}{x+1}$

   $\frac{2}{x+4} = \frac{3}{x-1}$ $x = 1$ $x = -8$

   $x = -2$ $x = -14$ $x = 4$

   $\frac{x-1}{x+1} = \frac{2x}{x-1}$ $x = 0$ $\frac{1}{2} + \frac{3}{5} = \frac{x}{10}$

   $x = 11$ $x = -4$ $\frac{1}{2} + \frac{3}{x} = \frac{1}{x}$

   $x = 3$ $x = -1$ $\frac{x-2}{x} + \frac{x-3}{x} = 7$

   $\frac{x-3}{x} = \frac{x-3}{x+2}$ $\frac{x-1}{5} = -\frac{3}{5}$

2. Divide the class into groups of four. Give each group 20 blank cards, and have them write one equation per card.

3. Have the groups choose one student to shuffle the cards and deal out all of the cards (5 cards to each student).

4. Be sure each student has paper and pencil to solve the equations.

5. The person to the left of the dealer starts. He or she puts down any matches of an equation with a solution. After all of the matches are placed on the table, the player takes a card at random from the hand of the person on his or her left (similar to Old Maid).

6. The next player on the left repeats the play—laying down any matches and taking a card from the person to his or her left.

7. Play continues until all matches have been made.

Problem-Solving Activity

Geometry With Rational Numbers

Directions:

Give each student a copy of the blackline master **Geometry With Rational Numbers**. Have the students work individually to solve the geometry problems by using rational equations. The problems are reprinted below.

1. An isosceles triangle has a base of $\dfrac{5}{2y}$ units and a side of $\dfrac{5}{3y}$ units. The perimeter is $1\frac{1}{6}$ units. What would y be? How long is each side?

2. A parallelogram has a base of $\dfrac{2x + 3}{5}$ units and a side of $\dfrac{x + 3}{x}$ units. If the perimeter is $\dfrac{42}{x}$ units, what is the length of the base and the length of a side?

3. A triangle has sides of $\dfrac{2x + 1}{2x}$, 3, and $\dfrac{2x + 1}{x}$ units. The perimeter is $\dfrac{27}{x + 2}$. What is the length of each side?

Materials:

► Blackline master **Geometry With Rational Numbers** is located in the *Teacher's Resource Manual,* **page 151.**

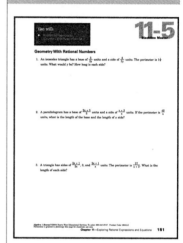

Exploring Radical Expressions and Equations

12-1 Simplify and perform operations with radical expressions.

12-2 Solve equations with radical expressions.

12-3 Use the Pythagorean theorem to solve problems.

12-4 Find the distance between two points in the coordinate plane.

12-5 Find the unknown measures of the sides of similar triangles.

12-1 *Objective:* **Simplify and perform operations with radical expressions.**

Sample Test: Simplify:

1. $\sqrt{20}$
2. $\sqrt{6} \cdot \sqrt{12}$
3. $\sqrt{25x^3y^6}$
4. $\dfrac{\sqrt{8}}{\sqrt{5}}$

Solutions: $2\sqrt{5}$ $6\sqrt{2}$ $5xy^3\sqrt{x}$ $\dfrac{2\sqrt{10}}{5}$

5. $\sqrt{2}\left(\sqrt{3} + 5\right)$
6. $\dfrac{7}{3 - \sqrt{2}}$
7. $\sqrt{\frac{5}{7}} \cdot \sqrt{\frac{7}{3}}$

Solutions: $\sqrt{6} + 5\sqrt{2}$ $3 + \sqrt{2}$ $\dfrac{\sqrt{15}}{3}$

Concept Development Activities

Materials:

▶ Blackline master for **graph paper** is in the Appendix.

▶ Paper or plastic squares (optional)

Visualizing Perfect Squares

Directions:

1. Discuss with the class that a number is a perfect square only if a geometric square can be constructed with sides of equal and integral lengths that has an area equal to the given number.

   For example, 9 is a perfect square because a square can be drawn with each side equal to 3 and an area of 9. Illustrate this by using graph paper, as shown on the right.

2. Ask if any of the students can make a square whose area is 7. Help them see that 7 is not a perfect square because you cannot draw a square with an area of 7 that has length = width = an integer. (To have an area of 7, the sides would have to be somewhere between 2 and 3 units long, because $2^2 = 4$ and $3^2 = 9$.)

3. Discuss that the relation between the area of a square and the length of a side of the square is $A = s^2$, or $\sqrt{A} = |s|$. This tells us that the length of a side of a square is the square root of the area.

4. Now have the students use graph paper to determine which of the following numbers are perfect squares by drawing squares (when possible) with the given areas:

   a. 36 b. 16 c. 12 d. 8

5. Have the students name some other perfect squares (e.g., 25, 4, 9, 49, 64).

Simplifying Radicals by Using Factor Trees

Directions:

1. Have the students make a column of perfect squares like the one shown below. Point out that every perfect square has a pair of like factors. Explain that "pairs are perfect squares."

$$1^2 = 1 \cdot 1 = 1$$
$$2^2 = 2 \cdot 2 = 4$$
$$3^2 = 3 \cdot 3 = 9$$
$$4^2 = 4 \cdot 4 = 16$$

pair of squares   perfect square

2. Now have the students reverse the process, as shown below, to "unsquare" the perfect squares. Remind them of the symbols used to indicate each operation:

$\square^2$ is the exponent of 2, to square, and
$\sqrt{}$ is the radical, to unsquare.

The columns of "unsquares" would be as follows. Discuss that the $\sqrt{9}$ is the principal root of 3 and $\sqrt{x} = |x|$ so it will be the principal root.

$$\sqrt{1} = \sqrt{1 \cdot 1} = \sqrt{1^2} = 1$$
$$\sqrt{4} = \sqrt{2 \cdot 2} = \sqrt{2^2} = 2$$
$$\sqrt{9} = \sqrt{3 \cdot 3} = \sqrt{3^2} = 3$$
$$\sqrt{16} = \sqrt{4 \cdot 4} = \sqrt{4^2} = 4$$

Point out that when factors have pairs, they can "unsquare," or they have a *square root*. For example,

$$\sqrt{49} = \sqrt{7 \cdot 7} \quad \text{so} \quad \sqrt{49} = 7$$

pair

$$\sqrt{121} = \sqrt{11 \cdot 11} \quad \text{so} \quad \sqrt{121} = 11$$

3. Ask, "What about $\sqrt{45}$?" Tell the students that since 45 is not on the list of perfect squares, it is not a perfect square.

4. Now ask, "How can we find whether 45 has any perfect square factors?" Review making a factor tree of prime factors or pairs of factors or known perfect squares, as shown to the right.

45
9 · 5
3 · 3

Teacher's Tip:

Part I of **Worksheet 1** for this objective, **page 12-2**, supports this activity with practice exercises.

Because there is a pair of 3's, $\sqrt{45}$ can be simplified as: $\sqrt{45} = \sqrt{3 \cdot 3 \cdot 5}$, and then the pair of 3's can be taken from the radical, so therefore, $\sqrt{45} = \sqrt{3 \cdot 3} \cdot \sqrt{5} = 3\sqrt{5}$.

Similarly, for $\sqrt{180}$,

so $\sqrt{180} = \sqrt{6 \cdot 6 \cdot 5} = 6\sqrt{5}$.

Answer Key for #5:
a. $7\sqrt{2}$ b. $8\sqrt{5}$
c. $42\sqrt{10}$

5. Ask the students to simplify the following numbers:

   a. $\sqrt{98}$ b. $\sqrt{320}$ c. $\sqrt{17,640}$

   Remind the students about divisibility rules (evens, divisibility by 3, 5, 9, and 10).

6. Now extend the factor tree concept to variables by considering $x^3 y^6 z^5$:

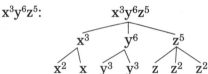

   So $\sqrt{x^3 y^6 z^5} = \sqrt{x^2 y^3 y^3 z^2 z^2 xz} = xy^3 z^2 \sqrt{xz}$.

7. Explain to the students that the absolute value is needed for y^3 because if y were negative, y^6 would be positive, but y^3 would be negative. Review that $\sqrt{x^2} = |x|$ because x^2 must always be positive, but x could be either negative or positive. The symbol $\sqrt{}$ implies the principal, or positive root, so we must include the absolute value signs to guarantee a principal root.

Finding Laws of Radical Operations

Directions:

1. Discuss with the students that binary operations can be performed on radical expressions. Ask the class to name some binary operations. (**Examples: +, −, ×, ÷**)

2. Divide the class into groups of three or four. Ask the groups to explore the following operations shown in 2a–2d below and to determine which are true for x, $y > 0$. Have them use whole numbers to determine if the operations are true or false.

(For example, $\sqrt{4} + \sqrt{16} \neq \sqrt{20}$ because $2 + 4 \neq \sqrt{20}$.) The students should be able to determine that parts a and b are false, but they should have several examples that show that parts c and d are true.

a. $\sqrt{x} + \sqrt{y} = \sqrt{x + y}$

b. $\sqrt{x} - \sqrt{y} = \sqrt{x - y}$

c. $\sqrt{x} \cdot \sqrt{y} = \sqrt{x \cdot y}$

d. $\dfrac{\sqrt{x}}{\sqrt{y}} = \sqrt{\dfrac{x}{y}}$

3. Have the students state a rule for $\sqrt{x} + \sqrt{y}$ **(can't add)**; $\sqrt{x} - \sqrt{y}$ **(can't subtract)**; and $\sqrt{x} \cdot \sqrt{y} = \sqrt{x \cdot y}$ **(can multiply)**; and $\dfrac{\sqrt{x}}{\sqrt{y}} = \sqrt{\dfrac{x}{y}}$ **(can divide)**.

4. Ask the students to simplify the following expressions as much as possible using their rules from #3:

a. $\sqrt{5} \cdot \sqrt{20}$

b. $\sqrt{3} - \sqrt{9}$

c. $\dfrac{\sqrt{52}}{\sqrt{4}}$

d. $\sqrt{12} + \sqrt{5}$

Teacher's Tip:

Part II of **Worksheet 1** for this objective, **page 12-2**, supports this activity with practice exercises.

Rationalizing Denominators

Directions:

1. Discuss with the students that expressions in mathematics are simplified to make them easier to use and easier to compute. Present the following choices and ask the class to tell you which would be easier to compute:

a. $\dfrac{\sqrt{5}}{\sqrt{3}}$ or $\dfrac{\sqrt{15}}{3}$

b. $\dfrac{\sqrt{3}}{\sqrt{5}}$ or $\dfrac{\sqrt{15}}{5}$

c. $\dfrac{\sqrt{98}}{\sqrt{2}}$ or $\sqrt{\dfrac{98}{2}}$

d. $\dfrac{\sqrt{27}}{\sqrt{3}}$ or $\sqrt{\dfrac{27}{3}}$

2. The students should indicate that it is easier to do the division when the divisor (or denominator) is a whole number and not a radical. Discuss that they should try to have no radicals in the denominator. If they cannot get rid of the denominator altogether (as in parts 1c and 1d above, where the radicals reduce to $\sqrt{49}$ and $\sqrt{9}$, respectively), ask them how they can make the denominator a rational number (no radicals). Give them time to come up with some examples.

3. Discuss that to make the denominator a rational number, the radical number must be a perfect square. For example, if we start with $\dfrac{\sqrt{5}}{\sqrt{3}}$, we must multiply the denominator by $\sqrt{3}$ to get the rational number $\sqrt{9} = 3$. But we must also multiply the numerator

Teacher's Tip:

Part I of **Worksheet 2** for this objective, **page 12-3**, supports this activity with practice exercises.

by $\sqrt{3}$, so the whole expression is multiplied by $1 \left(= \dfrac{\sqrt{3}}{\sqrt{3}}\right)$. Therefore, $\dfrac{\sqrt{5}}{\sqrt{3}} \cdot \dfrac{\sqrt{3}}{\sqrt{3}} = \dfrac{\sqrt{15}}{3}$. We can verify this is equivalent by using a calculator to calculate the original problem $\sqrt{5} \div \sqrt{3} \approx 1.3$ and the rationalized answer $\sqrt{15} \div 3 \approx 1.3$.

4. Ask the students to simplify $\dfrac{\sqrt{7}}{\sqrt{2}}. \left(\dfrac{\sqrt{14}}{2}\right)$

5. Show the students that they don't always have to multiply the denominator by itself to get a perfect square under the radical in the denominator. For example, for $\dfrac{\sqrt{7}}{\sqrt{18}}$, multiplying by $\dfrac{\sqrt{2}}{\sqrt{2}}$ will result in $\sqrt{36}$ in the denominator, and the answer will be $\dfrac{\sqrt{14}}{6}$. The students can use a factor tree to help determine the smallest number with which to multiply the numerator and denominator.

6. Ask the students to simplify $\dfrac{\sqrt{5}}{\sqrt{27}}$ and $\dfrac{6}{\sqrt{8}}. \left(\dfrac{\sqrt{15}}{9}, \dfrac{3\sqrt{2}}{2}\right)$

Rationalizing Denominators That Contain Sums or Differences

Directions:

1. Ask the students how they would rationalize (eliminate the radical in the denominator) a problem such as $\dfrac{6}{\sqrt{2}+4}$. Ask, "How do we get $\sqrt{2} + 4$ to be a rational number?"

2. Show the students that in order to eliminate the radical in a sum, they must use the "difference of perfect squares" concept [i.e., $(a + b)(a - b) = a^2 - b^2$]. So to eliminate the $\sqrt{2}$ in $\sqrt{2} + 4$, they would multiply the sum by $\sqrt{2} - 4$ to get $\left(\sqrt{2} + 4\right)\left(\sqrt{2} - 4\right) = \left(\sqrt{2}\right)^2 - 16 = 2 - 16 = -14$.

Teacher's Tip:

Part II of **Worksheet 2** for this objective, **page 12-3**, supports this activity with practice exercises.

3. Remind the students that they must multiply the numerator by the same quantity they multiply the denominator by. Therefore, for $\dfrac{6}{\sqrt{2}+4}$, both numerator and denominator must be multiplied by $\sqrt{2} - 4$ so the value of the expression is not changed. Therefore, $\dfrac{6}{\sqrt{2}+4} \cdot \dfrac{(\sqrt{2}-4)}{(\sqrt{2}-4)} = \dfrac{6(\sqrt{2}-4)}{(\sqrt{2})^2-4^2} = \dfrac{6(\sqrt{2}-4)}{-14} = \dfrac{3(\sqrt{2}-4)}{-7}$ or $\dfrac{-3\sqrt{2}+12}{7}$.

4. Ask the students to simplify $\dfrac{\sqrt{7}}{3-\sqrt{5}}$ and $\dfrac{19}{\sqrt{17}-\sqrt{2}}$. $\left(\dfrac{3\sqrt{7}+\sqrt{35}}{4}, \dfrac{19(\sqrt{17}+\sqrt{2})}{15}\right)$

Adding and Subtracting Radical Expressions

Directions:

1. Remind the students that just as 2x and 5x are "like terms," so are $\sqrt{3}$ and $5\sqrt{3}$.

2. The students already know that $\sqrt{x} + \sqrt{y} \neq \sqrt{x + y}$. Explain that radicals can be added only when they are like terms (i.e., they have the same radicand). Show the students the following examples of adding and subtracting radicals. Remind them that $\sqrt{6} = 1 \cdot \sqrt{6}$.

   a. $\sqrt{3} + 5\sqrt{3} = 1\sqrt{3} + 5\sqrt{3} = (1 + 5)\sqrt{3} = 6\sqrt{3}$

   b. $\sqrt{20} - \sqrt{45} = 2\sqrt{5} - 3\sqrt{5} = -\sqrt{5}$

   c. $2\sqrt{8} - 7\sqrt{2} + \sqrt{12} = 4\sqrt{2} - 7\sqrt{2} + 2\sqrt{3} = -3\sqrt{2} + 2\sqrt{3}$

   Students can verify that the expressions are equivalent by evaluating each using a calculator:

   a. $\sqrt{3} + 5\sqrt{3} \approx 1.73 + 8.66 \approx 10.39$
      $6\sqrt{3} \approx 10.39$

   b. $\sqrt{20} - \sqrt{45} \approx 4.47 - 6.71 \approx -2.24$
      $-\sqrt{5} \approx -2.24$

   c. $2\sqrt{8} - 7\sqrt{2} + \sqrt{12} \approx 5.66 - 9.90 + 3.46 \approx -.78$
      $-3\sqrt{2} + 2\sqrt{3} \approx -4.24 + 3.46 \approx -.78$

3. Ask the students to simplify the following expressions:
   a. $2\sqrt{5} - 4\sqrt{5} + 9\sqrt{5}$ b. $\sqrt{28} + \sqrt{63}$ c. $\sqrt{80} + \sqrt{243} + \sqrt{320}$

4. Discuss the results and answer questions.

Multiplying Expressions That Have Radicals

Directions:

1. Review the distributive property with the students:

   $2(x + 3y) = 2x + 2 \cdot 3y = 2x + 6y$

2. Ask the students to multiply a binomial by a binomial.

   $(x + 3y)(x - 2y) = x \cdot x + x \cdot (-2y) + 3y \cdot x + 3y \cdot (-2y)$
   $= x^2 - 2xy + 3xy - 6y^2$
   $= x^2 + xy - 6y^2$

12-1
Worksheet 3

Worksheet 3
Part I. Simplify.

12-1
Worksheet 3

Worksheet 3
Part I. Simplify.

3. Explain to the students that, when working with radicals, they will still use these properties but they will also use the properties of radicals. For example,

$$\sqrt{5}(3 + \sqrt{7}) = \sqrt{5} \cdot 3 + \sqrt{5} \cdot \sqrt{7}$$
$$= 3\sqrt{5} + \sqrt{5 \cdot 7}$$
$$= 3\sqrt{5} + \sqrt{35}$$

$$(5 - \sqrt{3})(2\sqrt{3} + 7) = 5 \cdot 2\sqrt{3} + 5 \cdot 7 - \sqrt{3} \cdot 2\sqrt{3} - \sqrt{3} \cdot 7$$
$$= 10\sqrt{3} + 35 - 2 \cdot 3 - 7\sqrt{3}$$
$$= 3\sqrt{3} + 29$$

4. Ask the students to simplify the following expressions:

   a. $3(\sqrt{3} - 9)$ b. $(\sqrt{2} + \sqrt{3})(2\sqrt{2} - \sqrt{3})$

5. Discuss the answers and any questions the students may have.

Practice Activities

Radical Match

Directions:

1. Have the students form groups of four. Give one copy of the blackline master **Radical Cards** to each group and ask the students to cut the cards apart.

2. Have the students shuffle the cards. Then have each group choose a dealer to deal six cards to each player. The remaining cards should be placed face down at the center of the table.

3. The game is played as follows: The student to the left of the dealer lays down (face up in front of the student) all pairs of equivalent radicals (if any) in his or her hand. That player then draws a card from the center stack, lays down any matches that card makes with the cards in his or her hand, and then discards a card face up next to the center stack.

4. Play continues to the left. Each player has the choice of picking up the former player's discard or a card from the center stack. Each player may also put a matching card from his or her hand on any face-up matches in front of any other player. Once three

---

Answer Key for #4:
a. $3\sqrt{3} - 27$
b. $1 + \sqrt{6}$

Materials:

▶ Blackline master **Radical Cards** is located in the *Teacher's Resource Manual,* **pages 152–154** or 💿.

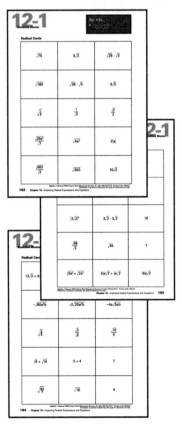

---

cards have matched, that group of cards is moved out of play. It should not be returned to the center stack.

5. The object of the game is to be the first player to discard all of the cards in your hand. That player is the winner.

6. A variation of this game is to continue play for one more round after one player has discarded all of his or her cards. The remaining players try to get rid of as many cards as they can, and the second-place winner is the one with the fewest cards in his or her hand at the end of that round.

7. Have the students reshuffle the cards and play as many games as time permits.

Radical Bingo

Directions:

1. Give a blank 5 × 5 bingo card to each student. Have the students mark the center space as a "FREE" space.

2. Place the blackline master **Radical Bingo Answers** on an overhead projector and ask the students to randomly place these answers in the lower part of each square on their bingo cards. When they are finished, they can keep their own cards or swap cards with a neighbor.

3. Make a copy of the blackline master **Radical Bingo Problems** and cut it into cards. Place the cards in a container and draw one card at a time from the container. Place the card on the overhead. Have the students work the problem and then write the problem number in a circle in the top half of the square with the matching answer. (This will help in checking their answers later.)

4. Continue drawing problem cards until a student has five matches in a row vertically, diagonally, or horizontally, or has all four corners matched. That student calls out "Bingo!"

5. Check the answers on the card with the problems you have called. If the answers are correct, declare the student the winner.

Teacher's Tip:

Worksheet 4 for this objective, **page 12-5**, supports this activity with practice exercises.

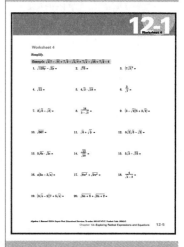

Materials:

▶ Blackline masters **Radical Bingo Problems** and **Radical Bingo Answers** are located in the *Teacher's Resource Manual*, **pages 155 and 156** or 💿.

▶ Blackline master for a **5 × 5 bingo card** is located in the Appendix.

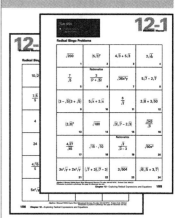

Materials:

► Blackline master **Flash Cards** is located in the *Teacher's Resource Manual*, **pages 157 and 158** or ⊘.

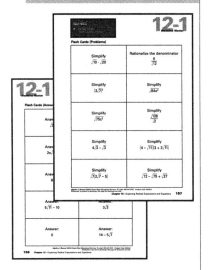

Answer Key:
1. $30\sqrt{2}$ feet
2. 72 sq. ft.

Answer Key:
1. $6ab^2c^4\sqrt{2ac}$
2. 0.5   3. 1.3   4. 0.1

Flash Cards for Practice

Directions:

1. Copy the two pages of the blackline master **Flash Cards** back-to-back. Then cut the cards apart to create a deck of cards with problems on one side and answers on the other.

2. Have the students form pairs and give each student one card.

3. Ask the students to simplify their problems, check their answers with their partners, and then check the back of the cards to see if their answers are correct.

4. Partners continue simplifying and checking until all cards have been completed.

Problem-Solving Activities

Measuring a Dog Run ⌖

Directions:

Present the following measurements to the students: A dog run is made in the shape of a rectangle. The length is $\sqrt{288}$ feet, and the width is $\sqrt{18}$ feet. Ask the students to compute the answers to the following two questions in simplified form:

1. Find the amount of fence needed to enclose the run if fencing is needed on all four sides.

2. Find the area of the dog run.

Simplifying Radicals ⌖

Directions:

Ask the students to simplify the following expressions:

1. $\sqrt{72a^3b^4c^9}$ 2. $\sqrt{0.25}$ 3. $\sqrt{1.69}$ 4. $\sqrt{0.01}$

12-2 *Objective:* **Solve equations with radical expressions.**

Sample Test: Solve the equations and check your answers.

1. $\sqrt{2x} = 6$

   Solution: x = 18

2. $\sqrt{x + 1} = 7$

   Solution: x = 48

3. $\sqrt{x - 2} - 3 = 5$

   Solution: x = 66

4. $\sqrt{4x - 3} = x$

   Solution: x = 1, 3

Concept Development Activities

Solve It 💡

Directions:

1. Write the problem $\sqrt{x + 2} = 11$ on the board. Ask the students if they can see a way to *algebraically* solve problems of this type.

2. Discuss various solutions. The students will probably reason that if $\sqrt{x + 2} = 11$, then x + 2 must equal 121. Name this solution as "squaring both sides of an equation." Show the students that $\left(\sqrt{x + 2}\right)^2 = x + 2$ and $11^2 = 121$, so $\sqrt{x + 2} = 11 \rightarrow \left(\sqrt{x + 2}\right)^2 = 11^2$ $\rightarrow x + 2 = 121 \rightarrow x = 119$.

3. Ask the students to square both sides and solve $\sqrt{x - 3} = 7$.

4. Have the students solve the following problems by squaring both sides:

   a. $\sqrt{x} = 6$ b. $\sqrt{2x + 2} = 8$ c. $\sqrt{x} + 3 = 4$

Answer Key for #3:
x = 52

Answer Key for #4:
a. x = 36
b. x = 31
c. x = 1

Concept Development

Teacher's Tip:

Worksheet 1 for this objective, **page 12-8**, supports this activity with practice exercises.

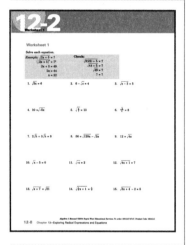

Answer Key for #4:

a. x = 25   b. x = 11
c. h = 1,521   d. x = 2
e. None   f. x = –16

Answer Key for #8:

a. x = 43   b. x = 63
c. x = 33

Squares

Directions:

1. Ask the students, "If you know that $\sqrt{9} = 3$, does $\left(\sqrt{9}\right)^2 = 3^2$?" Explain that this is the same as asking if we can square both sides.

2. Ask the students to square both sides of $13 = \sqrt{169}$. Ask, "Is the result true?" **(Yes)**

3. Ask the students to square both sides of $\sqrt{x + 1} = 6$. They will get $x + 1 = 36$. Ask them, "When is this a true statement?" **(When x = 35.)**

4. Write the following equations on the board and ask the students to find the value(s) of x that make them true statements.

   a. $\sqrt{4x} = 10$ b. $5 = \sqrt{2x + 3}$ c. $\frac{\sqrt{h}}{3} = 13$

   d. $\sqrt{x + 2} = x$ e. $\sqrt{5x} = -3$ f. $\sqrt{-9x} = 12$

5. Ask the students, "What if the equation is $\sqrt{x + 4} - 2 = 5$? How can you solve this equation?"

6. Discuss that if they square both sides of $\sqrt{x + 4} - 2 = 5$, they will get $\left(\sqrt{x + 4} - 2\right)^2 = 5^2$, and they would have to square the binomial $\left(\sqrt{x + 4} - 2\right)$. But the radical would still be part of the result: $x + 4 - 4\sqrt{x + 4} + 4 = 25$.

7. Ask whether any student can see an easier way to solve the equation. Suggest isolating the radical on one side of the equation:

$$\sqrt{x + 4} - 2 = 5$$
$$\sqrt{x + 4} = 7$$
$$\left(\sqrt{x + 4}\right)^2 = 7^2$$
$$x + 4 = 49$$
$$x = 45$$

8. Practice these examples with the students:

   a. $\sqrt{x - 7} + 12 = 18$ b. $4 = \sqrt{2x - 5} - 7$ c. $\sqrt{x + 3} + 6 = 22$

9. Point out to the students that sometimes squaring a binomial cannot be avoided, but they should first isolate the term with the radical so they are not squaring a binomial with a radical in it.

For example,
$$\sqrt{x-2} + 4 = x$$
$$\sqrt{x-2} = x - 4$$
$$\left(\sqrt{x-2}\right)^2 = (x-4)^2$$
$$x - 2 = x^2 - 8x + 16$$
$$0 = x^2 - 9x + 18$$
$$0 = (x-6)(x-3)$$
$$x = 6 \text{ or } x = 3$$

Tell the students they aren't done yet because they have to check these solutions in the original equation:

For x = 6: $\sqrt{6-2} + 4 = 6$ For x = 3: $\sqrt{3-2} + 4 = 3$
$2 + 4 = 6$ $1 + 4 \neq 3$

So the solution is x = 6. Explain that x = 3 is called an "extraneous root." Even though it is a solution to the derived equation, it is not a solution to the original equation. Emphasize to the students that they must always check their solutions in the original equation to eliminate extraneous roots.

10. Have the students try the following equations and then go over them step-by-step at the board.

    a. $\sqrt{2a-1} - a = -2$ b. $2\sqrt{w-1} + 5 = 15$ c. $4 + \sqrt{c-2} = c$

> Answer Key for #10:
> a. a = 5
> b. w = 26
> c. c = 6

Geometric Interpolation

Directions:

1. Have the students express equations with radicals on the number line for geometric interpretation. For example, for $\sqrt{t} + 2 = 11$, write the following on the number line:

Therefore, $\sqrt{t} = 9$, and thus t = 81.

2. Ask the students to make number line models of $\sqrt{c-1} + 5 = 8$, $\sqrt{x} + \sqrt{x} = 10$, and $42 = \sqrt{2x-7} + 18$. After giving them time to work, draw the following models on the board so they can check their answers.

> **Materials:**
> ▶ Blackline master for **number lines** is in the Appendix.

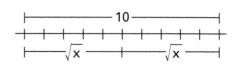

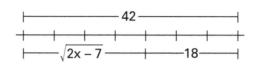

Materials:

▶ Dice (one for each group of students)

Teacher's Tip:

Worksheet 2 for this objective, **pages 12-9 and 12-10**, supports this activity with practice exercises.

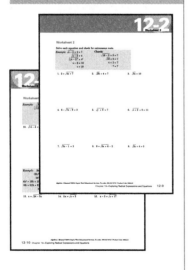

Practice Activities

Equation Roll

Directions:

1. Have the students work in pairs or groups of three. Write the following problems on the board:

   a. $\sqrt{x + \square} = 4$ b. $\sqrt{x + 1} - \square = 3$ c. $\sqrt{\square - x} + \square = 5$

2. Have each student take a turn rolling the die. For each turn, the students should put the number rolled into the boxes in each of the problems on the board. All of the students in the group should solve the problems individually and then compare answers to see if they agree. If anyone's answer is different, the students should rework the problem until they all agree on the solution. Remind the students to check their answers for extraneous roots.

   Note that equation 1c will not have an answer for a roll of 6.

Share It 💡

Directions:

1. Have the students form groups of two or three. Ask each student to make up a problem in the form $\sqrt{ax - b} = c$, where a, b, c ≠ 0.

2. Have the students pass their problem to the student on their left. Then each student should solve the new problem and pass the solution back so the student who wrote it can check it.

3. Now have the students pass their problem to the student on their right. That student is to change the original problem to one that has no solution and then pass it back for checking.

Problem-Solving Activity

Solving Radical Equations ⚡

Directions:

1. Ask the students to solve the following equations:

   a. $\sqrt{x + 2} - \sqrt{2x} = 0$

   b. $\dfrac{\sqrt{x}}{\sqrt{5}} = 7$

   c. $\sqrt{5t - 4} - 3\sqrt{t - 4} = 0$

   d. $1 + \sqrt{x} = \sqrt{x + 4}$

2. Ask the students to find two numbers such that the square root of their sum is 17 and the square root of their product is 120. (The students may use a graphing calculator to find the solution.)

   Solution:

$$\sqrt{x + y} = 17$$
$$\sqrt{xy} = 120$$
$$x + y = 289 \;\rightarrow\; y = 289 - x$$
$$\sqrt{xy} = 120 \;\rightarrow\; xy = 14{,}400$$
$$x(289 - x) = 14{,}400$$
$$289x - x^2 = 14{,}400$$
$$x^2 - 289x + 14{,}400 = 0$$
$$(x - 225)(x - 64) = 0$$
$$x = 225 \quad y = 64$$
$$\text{or}$$
$$x = 64 \quad y = 225$$

3. Ask the students to find two numbers such that the square root of their sum is 5 and the square root of their product is 12.

   Solution:

$$\sqrt{x + y} = 5$$
$$\sqrt{xy} = 12$$
$$x + y = 25$$
$$xy = 144 \;\rightarrow\; y = \frac{144}{x}$$
$$x + \frac{144}{x} = 25$$
$$x^2 + 144 = 25x$$
$$x^2 - 25x + 144 = 0$$
$$(x - 16)(x - 9) = 0$$
$$x = 16 \quad y = 9$$
$$\text{or}$$
$$x = 9 \quad y = 16$$

12-3 *Objective:* Use the Pythagorean theorem to solve problems.

Sample Test: Solve the following problems:

1. The lengths of sides of a right triangle are 4 and 7. Find the length of the hypotenuse.

   Solution: $\sqrt{65}$

2. The hypotenuse of a right triangle is 15 inches long, and one leg is 12 inches long. How long is the other leg?

   Solution: 9 inches

3. Is a triangle with sides of lengths 11, 16, and 19 a right triangle?

   Solution: No

Concept Development Activities

Pythagorean Theorem Geometrically

Directions:

1. Have the students work in pairs or groups of three. Give each group a copy of the blackline master **Pythagorean Squares** (2 pages), and an index card. Ask the students to cut out the squares.

2. Write the following triple on the board:

   3, 4, 5

3. Have the students place the squares with the lengths of the triple as sides in such a way that two vertices of each square touch a vertex of each other square, as in the diagram at the right.

4. Have them use the index card to determine whether the triangle formed by these squares has a right angle.

Materials:

▶ Blackline master **Pythagorean Squares** is located in the *Teacher's Resource Manual,* **pages 159 and 160.**

▶ Scissors

▶ Index cards

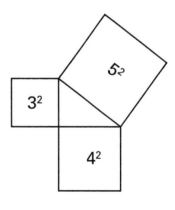

5. Ask the students to identify which sides of the triangle that is formed are the legs. Have them add the areas of those two squares and compare the sum to the area of the largest square, one side of which forms the hypotenuse.

6. Ask the students to write a mathematical sentence that describes a relation among these three squares.

7. Have the students try to find other squares on the blackline master that will make a right triangle. Suggest 6, 8, 10 if they have trouble finding more triples.

8. Ask if they see a pattern in the numbers chosen for the triples. Point out that each triple is a multiple of the original 3, 4, 5 triangle:

$$3, 4, 5 = 1 \cdot 3, 1 \cdot 4, 1 \cdot 5$$
$$6, 8, 10 = 2 \cdot 3, 2 \cdot 4, 2 \cdot 5$$
$$9, 12, 15 = 3 \cdot 3, 3 \cdot 4, 3 \cdot 5$$
$$12, 16, 20 = 4 \cdot 3, 4 \cdot 4, 4 \cdot 5$$

9. Discuss with the class that any triangle with sides that are all the same multiple of 3, 4, and 5 will be a right triangle.

Pythagorean Theorem on Graph Paper

Directions:

1. Draw a right triangle on the graph paper transparency such that each vertex is on a gridpoint and the legs are of lengths 5 and 6. Then draw a square on each leg side, as shown to the right.

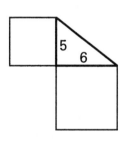

Materials:

▶ Blackline master for **graph paper** is in the Appendix.

▶ Overhead graph paper transparency

2. Have the students calculate the areas of the two squares and add them: $5^2 + 6^2 = 25 + 36 = 61$.

3. Now tell the students you are going to draw a square on the hypotenuse side that will have an area of 61. They may ask how you can do this. Explain that it is a little tricky, but they should follow what you do.

   a. Start by drawing a rectangle that has the hypotenuse as a diagonal, as shown on the right.

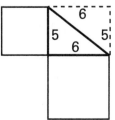

Teacher's Tip:

This activity could be adapted to a Geoboard if available.

b. Now draw right triangles that all are the same size as the original triangle (legs of 5 and 6) to form a square with the length of the diagonal (hypotenuse) as a side. Be sure the students see that each of these new triangles has the same length hypotenuse, and the four triangles form a square.

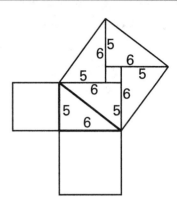

c. Calculate the area of the new square. It is composed of four right triangles, each with area $\frac{1}{2}bh = \frac{1}{2}(5)(6)$ plus one unit square in the middle, so the area is $4(15) + 1 = 61$, the same as the sum of the areas of the "leg" squares.

d. Emphasize that this illustrates the Pythagorean theorem because the sum of the areas of the "leg" squares equals the area of the "hypotenuse" square:

$$(\text{leg } 1)^2 + (\text{leg } 2)^2 = (\text{hypotenuse})^2$$

4. Have the students pick two numbers less than 10 and try this exercise on their own graph paper.

String Pythagorean Theorem

Directions:

1. Have the students take a length of string and, using a ruler as a guide, mark off 12 equal units on it with a marker pen. Then have them cut the string at the 12th unit mark. (Each unit could be 2 inches, or 6 inches, etc.)

2. Now have them bend the string into a triangle such that the sides are 3, 4, and 5 units long.

3. Ask them, "What kind of triangle did you form?" Suggest they use something that has a known right angle, such as an index card or the edge of a piece of paper, to judge whether there is a right angle in their triangle.

4. Then ask individual students how many inches each side of their triangle is. Discuss that even though the lengths of the sides may be different from student to student, the triangles are all right

triangles. Ask, "What might we be able to generalize about a triangle if the sides are in the ratio of 3k, 4k, and 5k?" **(It is a right triangle.)**

5. Explain to the students that this technique could be useful if they needed to form a right angle—for instance, in the corner of a garden plot, for a foundation for a home, and so forth. Ask for other situations where they might use the technique.

6. As an extension of this activity, ask where the vertices of a right triangle would be if the string were 36 units long.

Practice Activities

Group Answers

Directions:

1. Have the students form groups such that there are six groups in the class. Give each group a number, 1 to 6.

2. Give one copy of the blackline master **Pythagorean Theorem Problems** to each group. Have the students work with the others in their group to solve each problem on the blackline master. Each group should then write their simplified answers on a separate piece of paper with their group number at the top. Collect all of the answer papers.

3. Write the numbers 1 through 6 on the board to keep track of each group's score. Roll the die for each problem to determine which group will present their answer to the class. One of the members of that group will state the answer. If it is correct, determine if the other groups also got the correct answer by checking their papers. If so, roll the die again and go on to the next problem.

4. If any group did not get the correct answer, have someone from the group that originally stated the correct answer work the problem on the board so everyone can see how to do the problem.

5. If the group you initially call on gives an incorrect answer, roll the die again and have another group give their answer and explain how they got it at the board.

Answer Key for #6:
At 0 units, 9 units, 21 units and back at 36 units, to form the triangle

Materials:

► Blackline master **Pythagorean Theorem Problems** is located in the *Teacher's Resource Manual*, **page161**.

► Die

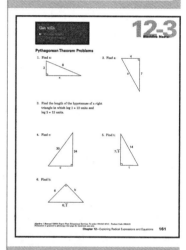

Teacher's Tip:

Worksheet 1 for this objective, **page 12-13**, supports this activity with practice exercises.

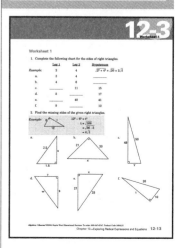

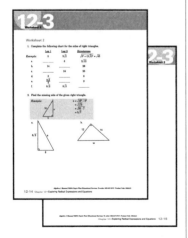

12-3
Blackline Master

Pythagorean Triples

5	6	7
8	10	11
12	12	13
16	17	20
24	25	27
36	45	60
61	144	145

162 Chapter 12—Exploring Radical Expressions and Equations

Teacher's Tip:

Worksheet 2 for this objective, **pages 12-14 and 12-15**, supports this activity with practice exercises.

6. Keep a running tally of each group's score on the board. Scoring is as follows:

   a. One point to each group that got the correct answer.

   b. A bonus point for each group chosen by the roll of the die if they got the correct answer.

Find the Pythagorean Triples

Directions:

1. Have the students form groups of three or four. Copy the blackline master **Pythagorean Triples** onto card stock and distribute one copy of the blackline master to each group. Ask the students to cut the cards apart.

2. Tell the students that the object of this activity is to group the cards into triples that could form the sides of a right triangle (i.e., they are Pythagorean triples). The students should use all the cards in the deck. As a hint, you might suggest that they start with multiples of the 3, 4, 5 Pythagorean triple.

3. Have the students make a chart that shows their results:

Leg 1	Leg 2	Hypotenuse

4. If you need to make the activity easier for the students, you can tell them which of the numbers are the hypotenuses: 10, 13, 20, 25, 45, 61, and 145.

Solutions:

Leg	Leg	Hyp.
6	8	10
11	60	61
7	24	25
17	144	145
12	16	20
27	36	45

Problem-Solving Activities

Find the Pattern 💡

Directions:

1. Have the students draw a right triangle with legs of one unit each. Have them calculate what the hypotenuse will be.

2. Have the students mark the length of the hypotenuse on the side of the index card. See diagram to the right.

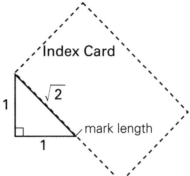

3. Tell the students to use the corner of the index card as a guide to draw a right angle and to draw a new right triangle with the two legs of this triangle equal in length to the hypotenuse of their original right triangle. See diagram to the right.

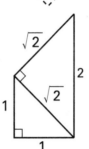

4. Ask the students to calculate the length of the hypotenuse of this new triangle. Now have them mark this length on the index card and generate another right triangle in the same manner that has two legs of this length.

5. Have the students continue this process to see if they can find a pattern for the lengths of the hypotenuses. Ask them what the length of the hypotenuse of the fifth constructed triangle would be.

Stacking Right Triangles 💡

Directions:

1. Have the students draw a right triangle with legs 1 inch long. Mark one inch on an index card and use it as a guide to form a right angle, as shown to the right.

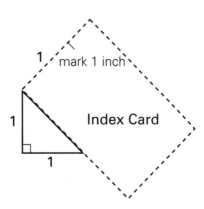

Materials:
▶ Rulers
▶ Index cards

Answer Key for #1:
$\sqrt{2}$

Answer Key for #5:
Hypotenuse of first triangle = $\sqrt{2}$; second triangle = $\sqrt{2} \cdot \sqrt{2} = 2$; third triangle = $\sqrt{2} \cdot \sqrt{2} \cdot \sqrt{2} = 2\sqrt{2}$; fourth triangle = $\sqrt{2} \cdot \sqrt{2} \cdot \sqrt{2} \cdot \sqrt{2}$ = 4; fifth triangle = $\sqrt{2} \cdot \sqrt{2} \cdot \sqrt{2} \cdot \sqrt{2} \cdot \sqrt{2} = 4\sqrt{2}$

Materials:
▶ Index cards

2. Have the students use the hypotenuse of the first triangle as one of the legs of a new triangle, with the other leg of 1 inch, as marked on the index card. Have them form that right triangle.

3. Have the students repeat step 2 at least four times. Ask them to calculate the lengths of the hypotenuses of the succeeding triangles and to look for a pattern. (See diagram to the right.)

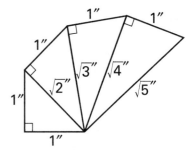

Answer Key for #4:
$\sqrt{8} = 2\sqrt{2}$

4. Ask the students what the length of the hypotenuse of the seventh triangle formed in this way would be.

Calculating Measurements

Directions:

Answer Key:
1. 13″
2. About 28.9″

Have the students calculate the measurements for these two problems:

1. Given a box with a length of 12″, a width of 3″, and a height of 4″, what would be the length of the diagonal from the top left back corner to the lower right front corner?

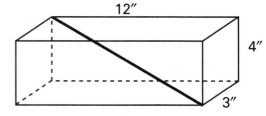

2. A new 36″ television has a screen that is 21.5″ high. How wide is the screen? (Note that a 36″ TV means the diagonal of the screen is 36″.)

3. Consider the figure to the right, in which a quadrilateral is drawn inside a square with dimensions a, b, and c as shown.

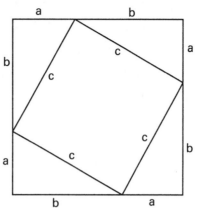

a. Explain why the quadrilateral with sides c must be a square and not just a quadrilateral.

b. Show that the area of the larger square is equal to the sum of the areas of the four triangles plus the area of the smaller square.

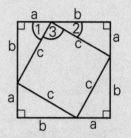

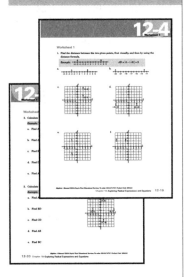

12-4 *Objective:* Find the distance between two points in the coordinate plane.

Sample Test: Find the distance between the points with the following coordinates.

1. (2, 3) and (5, 6)

2. (4, −1) and (10, 7)

Solution: $3\sqrt{2}$

Solution: 10

Concept Development Activities

Number Line Distance

Directions:

1. Review with the students how to find the distance between two points on a number line. For example,

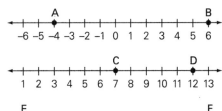

The distance from A to B is 10; $|6 - (-4)|$.
The distance from C to D is 5; $|12 - 7|$.
The distance from E to F is 12; $|-3 - (-15)|$.

2. Then move to the coordinate plane and find the distance between points. For example, draw the coordinates shown at the right on the board. Ask, "What is the distance from A to D? from C to B? from A to B? from D to C?"

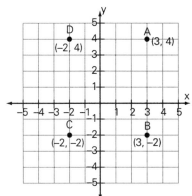

Discuss that these distances can be found by subtracting the x or y coordinates and using the absolute value of the result. For example, for the distance from A (3, 4) to D (−2, 4), you would get AD = $|3 - (-2)|$ = 5.

3. Now help the students discover how to find the distance between two points that are not aligned horizontally or vertically.

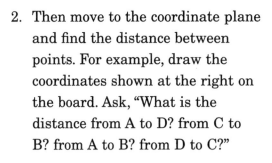

First, draw a coordinate plane with points A and B as shown to the right. Have the students find the point that would make a right triangle with A and B (the hypotenuse) and call it C.

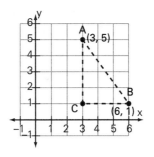

Then have the students use the technique from step 2 to find the distances from A to C and from C to B.

Ask, "How does knowing these distances help us to find the distance from A to B?" The students should recognize that the distances AC and CB are the legs of a right triangle, and the distance AB is the hypotenuse, so they can just use the Pythagorean theorem, $(AC)^2 + (CB)^2 = (AB)^2$. AC = 4 and CB = 3, so $4^2 + 3^2 = (AB)^2 = 25$, and AB = 5.

Distance Between Two Points

Directions:

1. Have students draw an x-y coordinate plane on their graph paper using a straightedge or ruler. Then have them plot points A (5, –6) and B (–4, 6).

2. Ask the students for suggestions for how to find the distance between points A and B. (They might respond "measure with the ruler," or "use a piece of string," etc.)

3. If no one comes up with the suggestion to draw a right triangle with AB as the hypotenuse, ask if that would be a possibility, and show them how to find AB by using the Pythagorean theorem. You may need to prompt them on how to algebraically find the lengths of the vertical and horizontal segments (subtract their respective coordinates).

4. Have the students work along with you to verify that AB is 15 units long. $\sqrt{[5 - (-4)]^2 + [6 - (-6)]^2} \rightarrow \sqrt{9^2 + 12^2} = \sqrt{225} = 15$

Materials:

▶ Blackline master for **graph paper** is in the Appendix.

▶ Straightedge or ruler

Teacher's Tip:

Worksheet 2 for this objective, **pages 12-21 and 12-22**, supports this activity with practice exercises.

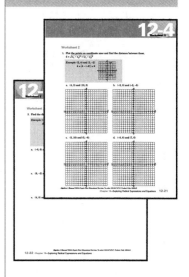

5. Now have the students use the other side of their graph paper to plot two points that are neither vertical nor horizontal to each other. Instruct them to find the distance between the points by first drawing a right triangle with their segment as the hypotenuse and then applying the Pythagorean theorem.

6. Have the students trade papers with a classmate to check each other's work.

7. Show the class how to generalize the distance formula

$$d = \sqrt{(x_1 - x_2)^2 + (y_1 - y_2)^2}$$

from the Pythagorean theorem.

Practice Activities

Find the Distance

Directions:

1. Have the students form pairs. Give each pair a paper bag that contains two red (negative) and two white (positive) dice.

2. Have one of the students reach into the bag and select two dice. That student should then roll the dice and use the numbers rolled as the coordinates of a point. [For example, if the student picks two red dice and rolls a 4 and a 1, the point would be $(-4, -1)$ or $(-1, -4)$.] Have the student plot the point on graph paper and then put the dice back in the bag.

3. The second student should now repeat step 2, plotting the point he or she rolls on the same coordinate plane as the first point. The students should then draw a line connecting the two points.

4. Then have the students, working independently, calculate the distance between the two points by using the distance formula. When they are finished, they should compare their results. Remind them that the distance formula is
$$d = \sqrt{(x_1 - x_2)^2 + (y_1 - y_2)^2}.$$

5. Now have the students, working individually, draw a right triangle and use the Pythagorean formula to find the length of the hypotenuse (their segment) of the triangle. Remind them that leg 1 $= |x_2 - x_1|$ and leg 2 $= |y_2 - y_1|$.

Materials:

► Dice (two red and two white for each group of students)

► Paper bags

► Blackline master for **graph paper** is in the Appendix.

Teacher's Tip:

Worksheet 3 for this objective, **page 12-23**, supports this activity with practice exercises.

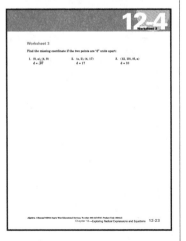

6. Repeat the steps and continue the process as long as desired.

7. *Note:* Steps 4 and 5 can be reversed.

Distance Share

Directions:

1. Have the students work in groups of three or four. Each student should have his or her own sheet of graph paper.

2. Have the students use a straightedge to place a coordinate system on their graph paper that goes from −10 to +10 on each axis.

3. Each student should then choose two points, plot them on the graph paper, and join the points by using the straightedge.

4. Then ask the students in each group to pass their paper to the student on their left.

5. The students should calculate the distance between the two points on the paper they receive.

6. Then have the students pass these papers to the student on their left for checking.

7. **Variation:** This activity can be done in three rounds. In the first round, the points should form a slanted segment; in the second round, the points should form a vertical line segment; and in the third round the points should form a horizontal line segment. The activity will illustrate that the distance formula works for any line segment.

Problem-Solving Activity

Using the Pythagorean Problem

Directions:

Ask the students to solve the following two problems:

1. A triangle has coordinates D (4, 0), E (−1, −5), and F (2, 1).

   a. Find the perimeter of this triangle.

   b. Is the triangle a right triangle? Verify your answer.

2. Suppose you live 2 miles west and 3 miles north of a park, and your friend lives 4 miles east and 5 miles south of the same park. What is the distance from your house to your friend's house?

12-5 *Objective:* **Find the unknown measures of the sides of similar triangles.**

Sample Test: Find the indicated lengths.

1. If △ABC ~ △DEF, find $\overline{AC}$ and $\overline{BC}$

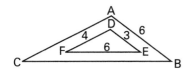

Solution: $\overline{AC} = 8, \overline{BC} = 12$

2. If △IJK ~ △MNP, find $\overline{IK}$ and $\overline{IJ}$

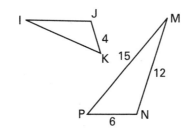

Solution: $\overline{IK} = 10, \overline{IJ} = 8$

3. Find $\overline{TS}$ and $\overline{RS}$

Solution: $\overline{TS} = 4.5, \overline{RS} = 9$

4. Find h

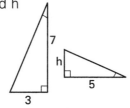

Solution: $h = \frac{15}{7}$

Concept Development Activities

Making Similar Triangles

Directions:

1. Have the students draw the diagonal across a sheet of paper and then cut the paper along this diagonal. Have them label the vertices of one of the resulting triangles with X, Y, and Z.

2. Have the students draw a line on the other triangle, that is parallel to any leg and about 2 inches from the edge. Have them cut along this line, forming a smaller triangle, and label the vertices as P, Q, and R.

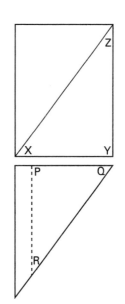

Materials:
► Rulers
► Scissors
► Protractor (optional)

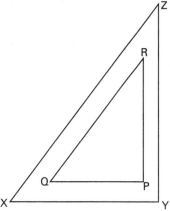

3. Have the students place the smaller triangle inside the larger triangle so that all sides of the small triangle are parallel to the sides of the larger triangle.

4. With the two triangles still "nested," have the students write the pairs of vertices that "match." (**X with Q, Z with R, and Y with P**)

5. Explain that when two triangles are similar, one will always fit inside the other with all pairs of sides parallel. The matched angles will be congruent.

6. Show the students how to list the corresponding sides and angles of the triangles. Begin by discussing how to write that the triangles are similar with matching vertices.

Have the students start by placing three slots for each triangle with the symbol for similarity, ~, between them: △___ ___ ___ ~ △___ ___ ___. Then have the students write the vertices of one triangle in the first, second, and third slot, in any order, for example, △XYZ ~ △___ ___ ___. Now point out to the students that the vertex matched with X (Q) goes in the first slot for the second triangle, the vertex matched with Y (P) goes in the middle, and the vertex matched with Z (R) goes in the third slot.

$$\triangle XYZ \sim \triangle QPR$$

Ask the students if the matching △ZXY ~ △RQP is an equivalent matching. (**Yes**)

Once the students understand how a matching is formed from paired vertices, explain that corresponding parts (angles and sides) of the triangles can be determined by looking at the positions the letters are in.

Example: △XYZ ~ △QPR gives us:
$$\frac{XY}{QP} = \frac{YZ}{PR} = \frac{XZ}{QR} \text{ (sides that are proportional)}$$
$$\angle X \cong \angle Q$$
$$\angle Y \cong \angle P$$
$$\angle Z \cong \angle R$$

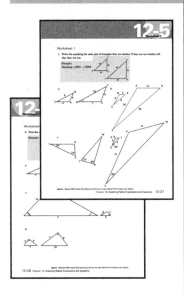

7. Have the students measure side XY and side QP to the nearest millimeter. Have them compute the ratio $\frac{QP}{XY}$ to the nearest tenth.

8. Now have them measure and compute the ratios $\frac{PR}{YZ}$ and $\frac{RQ}{XZ}$.

9. Ask, "What do you notice about the ratios?" All three ratios should be the same. Even though different students may have different ratios, all three of their individual ratios should be the same.

10. Discuss that the sides of similar triangles are in proportion, and the proportion is called the "constant of proportionality."

Cutting Similar Triangles

Directions:

1. Give one copy of the blackline master **Similar Triangles** to each student. Have the students cut the triangles apart, one pair at a time.

2. Have the students rotate, flip, and otherwise move the triangles until they can place one triangle inside the other with each pair of sides parallel.

3. Then have the students write the corresponding vertices in the form of a matching. For example, $\angle A \rightarrow \angle E$, $\angle B \rightarrow \angle F$, $\angle C \rightarrow \angle D$ and the matching is written $\triangle ABC \sim \triangle EFD$ to show which vertices match.

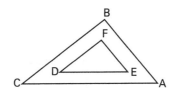

4. Next, have the students list all corresponding congruent angles and give the pairs of proportional sides as an equivalence ratio. For example, for $\triangle ABC \sim \triangle EFD$, $\angle A \cong \angle E$, $\angle B \cong \angle F$, $\angle C \cong \angle D$, and $\frac{AB}{EF} = \frac{BC}{FD} = \frac{AC}{ED}$.

5. Finally, have the students compute the constant of proportionality for each pair of triangles by measuring the lengths of the sides and finding the ratios.

   The ratios are: $\triangle ABC \sim \triangle EFD$ ratio ≈ .42 or 2.4
   $\triangle GHI \sim \triangle JKL$ ratio ≈ .72 or 1.4
   $\triangle PMN \sim \triangle TRQ$ ratio ≈ .65 or 1.5

Materials:

▶ Blackline master **Similar Triangles** is located in the *Teacher's Resource Manual*, **page 163**.

▶ Rulers

▶ Scissors

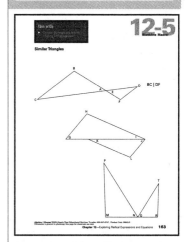

Teacher's Tip:

Worksheet 2 for this objective, **pages 12-29 and 12-30**, supports this activity with practice exercises.

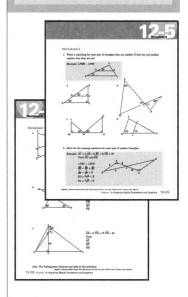

Practice Activities

Right Triangle Measures

Directions:

1. Have students count off from 1 through 8. Students with the number "1" will use an angle of 10°, those with a "2" will use an angle of 20°, and so on through 80°.

2. Using a protractor and ruler, each student should draw a right triangle with the assigned angle as the measure of one of the angles. *Example:*

3. Have the students calculate the third angle. **(90° – 10° = 80°)**

4. Have the students form groups with students that have the same angles in their triangles. For example, 10°, 80°, and 90° in one group; 20°, 70°, and 90° in the second group, etc.

5. One student (the student in the group whose last name is first alphabetically) should measure all of the sides of his or her triangle and record the measures on his or her triangle drawing.

6. The other students in the group should measure only one side of their triangle.

7. By matching the corresponding sides of their triangle to the first student's triangle, the students should compute the missing sides using proportions.

8. The students can then check their results by measuring their sides with a ruler.

9. The groups can exchange triangles with another group and repeat the process.

Triangles by Angles

Directions:

1. On a small slip of paper, write three angles that total 180° (for example, 60°, 70°, and 50°). You will need as many slips of this kind as there are students in the class. As you make the slips, follow this procedure: Make three slips with the same three measurements on them, and then change the measurements for the next group of three slips of paper, etc.

2. Distribute the slips of paper randomly as the students arrive at class.

3. Give each student a protractor and ruler. Ask each student to make a triangle that has the angles that are written on his or her slip of paper. The sides of the triangle can be of any length. Help the students draw their triangles if they need assistance.

4. Have the students with the same measurements get together in a group. There should be groups of three, and the triangles for each group should be similar.

5. Have the students in each group count off: 1, 2, 3.

   Student 1 should label his or her triangle ABC and measure all sides in centimeters. The measurements should be written on a separate paper, not on the paper with the triangle.

   Student 2 should label his or her triangle DEF and measure only one side. Again, the measurement should be written on a separate paper.

   Student 3 should label his or her triangle GHI and measure only one side. As with the other students, the measurement should be written on a separate paper.

6. Have the group then find the matching sides for the triangles. If they wish to cut out the triangles to make the matching easier, they may do so.

7. Then have the groups find the missing values of the sides by using proportions of the missing sides to the known sides of triangle 1. They can then check their results by measuring the sides.

8. The groups can exchange triangles with another group and repeat the process.

Materials:
► Protractors
► Rulers

Teacher's Tip:

Worksheet 3 for this objective, **page 12-31**, supports this activity with practice exercises.

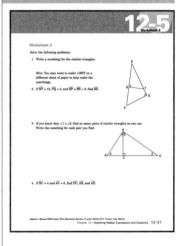

Problem-Solving Activities

Shadows

Directions:

1. Prior to starting this activity, scout out some tall objects outside, such as a flagpole or telephone poles, so that each group can work with a different object.

2. Have the students work in pairs. Have the partners measure each other's height and record the heights on paper.

3. Now take the students outside. Tell them they are going to approximate the heights of a few tall objects (such as a flagpole or telephone pole) where direct measurement is very difficult. Tell them they are going to use shadows and similar triangles.

   They should follow this example, which shows how to approximate the height of a flagpole:

   a. Students will measure the length of the shadow of the flagpole and record it on paper.

   b. Then a student will stand where his or her shadow can be measured by his or her partner. This shadow length will also be recorded on paper.

   c. The students will draw two figures, one representing the flagpole and its shadow, and the other representing the student and his or her shadow.

   d. The students will label all measurements taken and solve for the height of the flagpole by using corresponding sides of similar triangles.

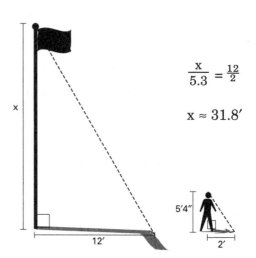

$$\frac{x}{5.3} = \frac{12}{2}$$

$$x \approx 31.8'$$

4. Have the students switch locations and repeat the activity as time permits.

Mirrors ☀

Directions:

Materials:

► Small mirrors

► Measuring tape or yardstick

1. Prior to starting this activity, scout out some tall objects outside, such as a flagpole or telephone poles, so that each group can work with a different object.

2. Have the students work in pairs. Have the partners measure each other's height and record the heights on paper.

3. Now take the students outside. Tell them they are going to approximate the heights of a few tall objects (such as a flagpole or telephone pole) where direct measurement is very difficult. Tell them they are going to use similar triangles.

   They should follow this example, which shows how to approximate the height of a two-story school:

   a. Have one of the pair of students place a mirror face up about 40′ from a corner of the building. Then have the student back away along the line of sight, looking into the mirror until the top of the building can be seen in the mirror.

   b. The other student should then measure the distance from the mirror to the student.

   c. Have the students draw a figure that represents the activity, such as the one below. Have them place the measurements found on the drawing and calculate the approximate height of the building.

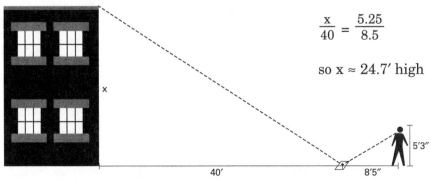

$$\frac{x}{40} = \frac{5.25}{8.5}$$

so $x \approx 24.7'$ high

4. Have the students switch locations and repeat the activity as time permits.

Materials:

▶ Tape measure or yardstick

▶ 6″ ruler

▶ Masking tape or string

Ruler ☀

Directions:

1. Have the students work in pairs.

2. Take the students outside to a large tree. Have one student from each group mark his or her eye level on the tree with tape or string. Then have that student walk approximately 40′ from the tree and turn and face the tree, holding the ruler, vertically, in front of himself or herself at eye level. Have the student move the ruler toward or away from himself or herself until it obscures the tree from the mark up. The student may have to step closer to or farther away from the tree in order to obscure the view of the tree.

3. When the tree is obscured, the partner measures the distance to the tree, the distance from the student's eye to the ruler, and the distance from the tape to the ground.

4. Have the students draw a diagram that illustrates this activity, such as that below, placing the measures on the diagram. Then have the students solve the height of the tree by using corresponding sides of similar triangles.

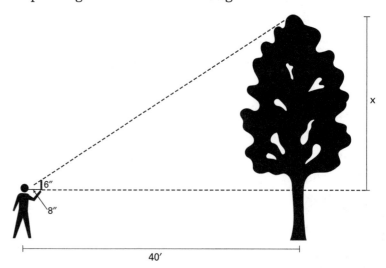

For example, $\dfrac{40'}{\left(\frac{8}{12}\right)'} = \dfrac{x}{\left(\frac{1}{2}\right)'}$, so $x \approx 30'$, or the height of the tree is 30′ plus the distance from the student's eye level to the ground.

5. Have the students find another object to measure by repeating this procedure.

Glossary

absolute value (| |)   The distance of a number from zero on the number line. Always positive. *Example:* $|{-4}| = 4$.

associative property of addition   Changing the grouping of addends does not change the sum. *Example:* $(a + b) + c = a + (b + c)$.

associative property of multiplication   Changing the grouping of factors does not change the product. *Example:* $(ab)c = a(bc)$.

axis of symmetry   A line that passes through a figure in such a way that the part of the figure on one side of the line is a mirror reflection of the part on the other side of the line.

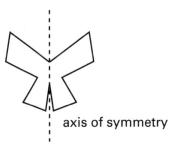

axis of symmetry

best-fit line   The line that will best connect the data or points.

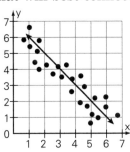

best-fit line

binary operations   Mathematical operation in which two elements are combined to yield a single result. Addition and multiplication are binary operations on the set of real numbers. *Example:* $2 + 3 = 5$.

binomial   An algebraic expression with two unlike terms. *Example:* $3x + 2y$.

coefficient   A number or quantity placed before a variable, which indicates multiplication of that variable. *Example:* 3 in the expression $3x$.

commutative property of addition	Changing the order of addends does not change the sum. *Example:* a + b = b + a.
commutative property of multiplication	Changing the order of factors does not change the product. *Example:* a(b) = b(a).
consecutive	In order. *Example:* 8, 9, and 10 are consecutive whole numbers; 2, 4, and 6 are consecutive even numbers.
constant	A quantity assumed to be unchanged throughout a given discussion.
coordinate plane	The plane determined by a horizontal number line, called the x-axis, and a vertical number line, called the y-axis, intersecting at a point called the origin. Each point in the coordinate plane can be specified by an ordered pair of numbers.

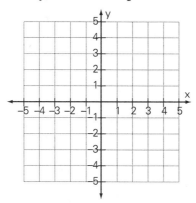

coordinate plane

dependent variables	Two variables in which the value of the first variable affects the value of the second variable.
distributive property of multiplication	For a, b, and c, a(b + c) = ab + ac.
domain	The possible values for x in a function. *Example:* the set of x coordinates in a set of ordered pairs.
equality	A statement that two quantities or mathematical expressions are equal. *Example:* m + 10 = 20 means that m + 10 must have the same value as 20.
equation	A statement that two quantities or mathematical expressions are equal. See also **equality**. *Example:* 3 + 3 = 2 · 3.

equilateral triangle	A triangle whose sides are all the same length.

 equilateral triangle

equivalent	Equal in value. *Example:* 5 + 4 is equivalent to 3 · 3.
evaluate	To ascertain the numerical value of (a function, relation, etc.). *Example:* When you evaluate the expression 3x = y for x = 2; the solution is 6.
exponential	A number written with an exponent. *Example:* 7^{-3}, a^4.
exponential function	Any function in which a variable appears as an exponent and may also appear as a base. *Example:* $y = x^{2x}$.
factor	An integer that divides evenly into another. *Example:* 1, 2, 4, and 8 are factors of 8.
finite	Capable of being completely counted. Does not include zero.
function	A special kind of relation in which every value of x has only one value of y. *Example:* The price of stamps is a function of the number of stamps you buy.
graph	A pictorial device used to show a numerical relationship among two or more things by a number of distinctive dots, lines, bars, etc.
greatest common factor	The largest number that divides into two or more numbers evenly. *Example:* 3 is the greatest common factor of 9 and 12.
horizontal	Parallel to the horizon. *Example:* In a coordinate grid, the x-axis is a horizontal line. ⟷ horizontal line
identity property of addition	A number combined with zero, equals the original number. *Example:* a + 0 = a.
identity property of multiplication	A number multiplied by one, is equal to the original number. *Example:* a · 1 = a.
image	The point or set of points in the range corresponding to a designated point in the domain of a given function.

independent variables	Two variables in which the value of the first variable does not affect the value of the second variable.
inequality	A mathematical sentence that compares two unequal expressions using one of the following symbols: <, >, ≤, or ≥. *Example:* 2 + 3 > 4.
integers	The set of whole numbers and their opposites. *Example:* –2, –1, 0, 1, 2….
integral numbers	The set of whole numbers and their opposites. See also **integers**. *Example:* –2, –1, 0, 1, 2….
inverse operations	Pairs of operations that undo each other and share an inverse relation. *Example:* Addition and subtraction are inverse operations.
isosceles triangle	A triangle that has at least two congruent sides.

isosceles triangle

line (↔)	An infinite set of points forming a straight path that extends forever in two directions.

line

line segment (—)	A part of a line defined as two endpoints and all the points on the line between them.

line segment

linear equation	A first-order equation involving two variables. Its graph is a straight line. *Example:* y = 2x + 1.
mapping	See **function**.
monomial	An algebraic expression with one term. *Example:* 5, 8x and 17mn.
multiplicative inverse	Numbers that multiply to equal one. *Example:* $2 \cdot \frac{1}{2} = 1$.

order of operations Rules describing what order to use in evaluating expressions.
PEMDAS:
1. Parentheses: evaluate within grouping symbols.
2. Exponents: do powers or roots.
3. Multiplication/Division: multiply or divide left to right.
4. Addition/Subtraction: add or subtract left to right.

ordered pair A pair of numbers that gives the coordinates of a point on a grid in this order: (horizontal coordinate, vertical coordinate).
Example: (2, 3).

origin The intersection of the x- and y-axes in the coordinate plane at (0, 0).

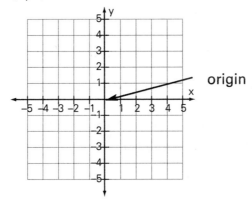

parabola The graph of a quadratic or second-degree equation. *Example:* The shape resembles the letter ∪ and can face either up, down, left, or right.

parabola

parallel (∥) Lines that do not intersect; they are always the same distance apart.

parallel lines

perpendicular (⊥)   Lines that intersect at right angles.

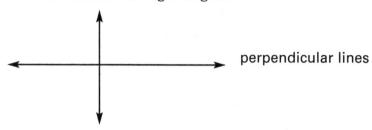

perpendicular lines

point   An exact position in space with no length, width, or thickness.

polynomial   An algebraic expression with two or more unlike terms. *Example:* 2x + y.

prime number   A number that is divisible only by itself and the number one. *Example:* 2, 13.

product   The result of multiplication. *Example:* The product of 2 and 3 is 6.

proportion   An equation that states that two ratios are equal. *Example:* $\frac{3}{8} = \frac{9}{24}$.

quadrants   The four regions on a coordinate plane formed by the intersection of the x-axis and the y-axis.

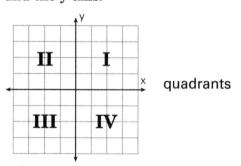

quadrants

quotient   The result of division of one quantity by another. *Example:* When 12 is divided by 3, the quotient is 4.

radical ($\sqrt{}$)   A symbol that indicates that one is to determine the square root.

radical expression   The number (radicand) and the symbol (radical) placed over the number that indicates that one is to determine the square root. *Example:* $2\sqrt{9}$.

range   The possible values for y in a function. *Example:* the y-coordinates of a set of ordered pairs.

ratio	A comparison of two numbers, using division. *Example:* $\frac{5\ \text{boys}}{8\ \text{girls}}$.
rational expression	Rational expressions are represented as the quotient of two algebraic expressions. *Example:* $\frac{3x}{6x^2}$.
rational numbers	A number that can be expressed as the ratio of two integers. *Example:* $-\frac{1}{2}, \frac{6}{5}, 0.125$.
reciprocal	Two numbers that have a product of one. *Example:* 6 and $\frac{1}{6}$ are reciprocals because $6 \cdot \frac{1}{6} = 1$.
relation	A set of ordered pairs. *Example:* They can be pairs of things (like gloves), or people (like tennis players), or numbers (like 3 and 6).
scalene triangle	A triangle that has no congruent sides.

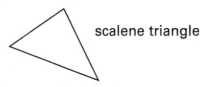

scalene triangle

scatter plot	A graph consisting of points, one for each item being measured. The two coordinates of a point represent the measures of two attributes of each item.

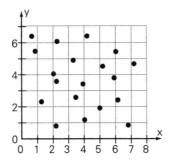

scatter plot

scientific notation	A form of writing numbers as a product of a power of ten and a decimal number greater than or equal to one and less than ten. *Example:* 2,600 is written as 2.6×10^3.
simplify	Combine like terms and apply properties to an expression to make computation easier. *Example:* When you simplify the expression $3x + 4 + 2x + 6 = 40$, you get $5x + 10 = 40$.

slope	The steepness of a line as you look at it from left to right. A line that slants upward has a positive slope, whereas a line that slopes downward has a negative slope. A numerical value for slope is found using two points on the line, where the change in y-value is divided by the change in x-value.
square root ($\sqrt{}$)	One of two equal factors of a given number. *Example:* 5 is a square root of 25 because $5 \cdot 5 = 25$.
sum	The result of addition. *Example:* The sum of 10 and 5 is 15.
symmetrical	Noting two points in a plane such that the line segment joining the points is bisected by an axis. *Example:* Points (1, 1) and (1, –1) are symmetrical with respect to the x-axis.
trinomial	An algebraic expression with three unlike terms. *Example:* $3 + t + r^2$.
variable	A letter or symbol used to represent a number. *Example:* In the expression $5y + 2 = 12$, y is a variable that represents 2.
vertex	The point at which two line segments, lines, or rays meet to form an angle. *Example:* $\angle$

vertical	At right angles to the horizon. *Example:* In a coordinate grid, the y-axis is a vertical line.

vertical line

whole numbers	Any of the numbers 0, 1, 2, 3, 4, 5, and so on.

x-axis	The horizontal axis.
x-coordinate	In an ordered pair, the value that is always written first. *Example:* In (3, 4), 3 is the x-coordinate.
x-intercept	The point where a line intersects the x-axis. *Example:* (3, 0).
y-axis	The vertical axis.
y-coordinate	In an ordered pair, the value that is always written second. *Example:* In (3, 4), 4 is the y-coordinate.
y-intercept	The point where a line intersects the y-axis. *Example:* (0, 4).
zero property of multiplication	When you multiply a number by zero, the result is zero. *Example:* $a \cdot 0 = 0$.

Index

A

Absolute value, 6-29, 6-30, 6-32, 6-34, 6-35

Addition property, 3-2 through 3-4

  of equality, 3-2 through 3-4

Additive identity property, 1-21, 1-22, 2-8

Additive inverse, 8-22 through 8-25

Associative property, 1-21, 1-24

Axes, 4-2, 4-3, 4-16, 5-5, 5-7, 5-8, 5-10, 5-37, 7-8, 7-12, 7-14

Axis, 5-6, 5-24, 5-25, 5-27, 10-1, 10-3 through 10-10, 10-13 through 10-15, 10-21, 10-28, 12-27

  of symmetry, 10-1, 10-3 through 10-10, 10-14, 10-28

B

Best-fit lines, 5-1, 5-19, 5-20, 5-21, 5-23

Binomials, 8-27, 8-28, 8-30, 8-34 through 8-36, 8-38, 8-40, 8-43, 9-22, 9-26, 9-29, 9-30, 9-34 through 9-39, 9-42 through 9-46, 11-1, 11-14, 11-16 through 11-18

  defined, 8-30

  difference of squares, 9-39, 9-42 through 9-44, 9-46

  factoring, 9-26, 9-42 through 9-44

  multiplying, 8-27, 8-34, 8-35, 8-38, 8-40, 8-43, 9-26, 9-29, 9-30, 9-34, 9-38, 9-39, 9-45

C

Coefficient, 6-19, 6-21, 8-4, 8-5, 8-20, 8-21, 8-23, 9-23 through 9-28, 9-30, 9-34, 9-36, 10-7, 10-13, 10-22, 10-24 through 10-26, 11-2

  leading, 9-23, 9-25, 9-26, 9-28, 9-34

Commutative property, 1-21, 1-23, 2-21

Completing the square, 9-1, 9-47, 9-50 through 9-52, 10-14, 10-16, 10-20, 10-22, 10-26 through 10-28

Coordinate(s), 4-3 through 4-8, 7-5, 7-6, 7-10, 7-40, 7-41, 10-1, 10-4 through 10-7, 10-14, 10-15, 12-24 through 12-28

  x-, 4-5 through 4-8, 10-14

  y-, 4-5 through 4-8

Coordinate plane, 4-2, 4-5, 6-1, 6-36, 6-37, 7-2 through 7-6, 7-11, 7-12, 7-45, 10-2, 10-3, 10-5 through 10-7, 12-1, 12-24, 12-25

D

Decimals, 2-19, 2-20, 2-32, 3-36, 3-43, 8-8, 8-9, 8-11 through 8-15

Differences of squares, 9-1, 9-39, 9-41 through 9-44, 9-46

  factoring, 9-1, 9-41, 9-44

Distributive property, 1-21, 1-23, 1-25, 8-37, 9-1, 9-6, 9-9, 9-10, 10-33, 12-7

Division, 1-10, 2-23, 2-24, 2-26 through 2-28, 3-1, 3-10, 3-11, 3-13, 3-14, 3-21, 3-22, 3-34, 6-1, 6-10, 6-14, 6-17, 6-18, 8-5, 8-7, 8-12, 8-13, 11-2 through 11-4, 11-12, 11-14, 11-15, 11-18, 11-20, 12-5

  by monomials, 8-7, 8-13

  of rational numbers, 2-24

  solving inequalities with, 6-10, 6-14, 6-17, 6-18

Division property, 3-36

  of equality, 3-36

Domain, 4-1, 4-6, 4-10, 4-11 through 4-15, 4-17, 4-27, 4-28, 4-30

E

Equality, properties of, 3-2 through 3-4, 3-12, 3-19, 3-20, 3-28, 3-36, 6-30

Equation(s),

  equivalent, 3-29, 3-36, 4-24, 5-15

  solving by factoring, 9-1, 9-14, 9-19, 9-29, 9-33, 9-41, 9-44

  solving with addition, 3-1

  solving with multiplication, 3-1, 3-14

Equation mat, 3-5, 3-6, 3-10, 3-13, 3-22, 3-23

Exponent(s), 8-2, 8-3, 8-5, 8-11, 8-12, 8-14, 8-15, 9-12, 9-13, 9-15, 10-1, 10-29 through 10-35, 12-3

  in scientific notation, 8-12, 8-14

  negative, 8-11, 8-12, 8-14

Expressions,

  algebraic, 8-4, 8-5

  equivalent, 1-2, 1-6, 1-10, 3-6, 3-22, 8-7, 11-4, 11-5, 11-6, 12-6, 12-7

  evaluating, 1-1, 1-10, 1-11, 8-21, 12-7

  quadratic, 9-20

  radical, 12-1, 12-4, 12-7

  rational, 11-1 through 11-7, 11-10, 11-11, 11-13, 11-17, 11-21, 11-23 through 11-27, 11-29, 11-30

Additional Teacher's Resources
in Algebra and Math

You Can Be Algebra Ready

Ken Andrews MA and Diane Johnson MA
Grades 6-10

When it's time for algebra, students will hit the ground running!

This comprehensive algebra readiness program combines direct instruction with guided learning, independent practice, and multi-sensory activities that provide a solid foundation for algebra success! Includes a unique problem-solving checklist for word problems, Try This sections to familiarize students with algebraic concepts, and more. Complete with 36 sequential lessons, the program includes: teacher books, consumable student workbooks, colorful vocabulary cards, poster sets, and bookmarks.

185CLASS1 Classroom Set Part 1	$185.00
185CLASS 2 Classroom Set Part 2	$185.00
185KIT Classroom Sets Part 1 and Part 2	$350.00

Algebra One-Minute Fluency Builders CD-ROM

Ray Beck EdD; Peggy Anderson PhD; Denise Conrad EdD
Grades 8-12

These fluency-building drills enable you to increase practice, set clear expectations, provide immediate feedback, and measure learning—factors that research has shown increase proficiency levels. Use separately or as a kit component in *Algebra 1 Rescue!*.

Available summer 2003

Algebra Readiness Assessment

Joseph C. Witt PhD
Grades 6-12

Accurately diagnose your students' basic math, pre-algebra, and algebra skills with this quick assessment. Can be used separately or as a kit component in *Algebra 1 Rescue!*.

Available summer 2003

Classroom Management for Algebra

Joseph C. Witt PhD
Grades 8-12

With these helpful hints, you can provide a more positive learning environment, select and teach classroom rules and procedures, and create smooth transitions. An entire section discusses instructional strategies for the student who "won't do the work" vs. the one who "can't do the work." Also includes tips on how to address such common issues as cheating, disrespect, and avoiding work. Use separately or as a kit component in *Algebra 1 Rescue!*.

Available summer 2003

The Math Rescue Series: Resources for Computation

Larry Bradsby MS and Shirley Bradsby MA
Grades K-6

Math Rescue utilizes more than 600 mutisensory activities, coded to skill level, to help students master computation. The program uses standards-based criteria and an approach that builds on individual success to assure math "computes" for all students.

106COMP (620 pages) $75.00

Simple Ways to Make Teaching Math More Fun

Bob Algozzine PhD and James Ysseldyke PhD
Grades 1-5

Use these innovative ideas and tactics to make teaching math fun for you and your students. This resource is filled with novel techniques students will enjoy, such as palindromes, lotteries, mind teasers, in-class "field trips," bingo and card games for content practice, and problem-solving activities that stress exploration and encourage curiosity.

50MATH (94 pages) $16.95